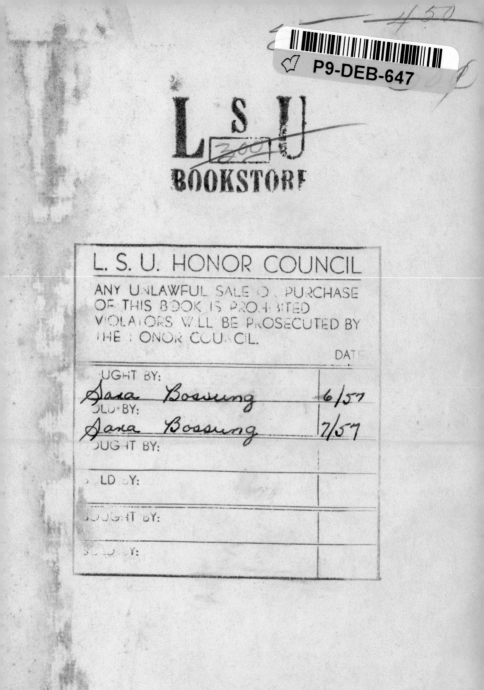

450

P9-DEB-647

L S U
BOOKSTORE

THE LIVING BODY

A TEXT IN HUMAN PHYSIOLOGY

REVISED EDITION

BY

CHARLES HERBERT BEST, M.A., M.D., D.Sc. (Lond.),
F.R.S., F.R.C.P. (Canada)

*Professor and Head of Department of Physiology, Associate Director
of the Connaught Laboratories, Research Associate in the
Banting-Best Department of Medical Research, University
of Toronto*

AND

NORMAN BURKE TAYLOR, M.D., F.R.S. (Canada), F.R.C.S.
(Edin.), F.R.C.P. (Canada), M.R.C.S. (Eng.), L.R.C.P. (Lond.)

Professor of Physiology, University of Toronto

NEW YORK
HENRY HOLT AND COMPANY

To

OUR WIVES

PREFACE TO THE REVISED EDITION

In a book such as this which has been written as an introduction to the study of physiology, the subject has been dealt with in a broad and general fashion. For the most part only material that has been generally accepted and incorporated into the body of physiological knowledge has been included. Controversial matter and the results of experimental work which perhaps will not stand the test of time have been omitted. For this reason the frequent revisions demanded of more advanced texts are not required. However, great strides have been taken by the Medical Sciences since the first edition of this book and though much of the authors' time has been devoted to work connected with the war they feel that a revision can no longer be put off. An effort has been made to bring the book thoroughly up to date. The latest findings have been incorporated in the treatment of the hemoglobin molecule, transfusions, the clotting mechanism, arterial hypertension, the control of respiration, the vitamins, and other topics. Minor corrections and clarifications have been made where possible. Several new figures have been added and others altered.

We again wish to thank Miss Mabel Cory for the preparation of the Index.

C. H. B.
N. B. T.

March 27, 1944

PREFACE TO FIRST EDITION

This book is addressed to those seeking an elementary knowledge of the actions and reactions, physical and chemical, occurring in the human body. The bodily functions of the different species of mammals are essentially the same, and data gained from experiments upon animals can in most instances be taken to apply to man. It is fortunate that this is so, for experimentation — the most fruitful method of gaining information of physiological processes — can be carried out only to a limited extent upon the human subject. In a physiological text one must always be prepared to cite experimental authority for almost every statement; yet it is not within the scope of a book of this kind to enter into any detailed discussion of the research data upon which our physiological concepts are founded. Experimental detail and intricate argument would prove wearisome to those for whom the book has been written, and would confuse rather than aid them in understanding the basic principles of the subject. A less scientific and more dogmatic method of instruction than that customary in more advanced texts must be adopted. For the beginner the picture must be drawn with a broad brush, the finer strokes being omitted lest they detract from the boldness of the outline.

It has been assumed that the reader has had some instruction in physics and chemistry, but only a very elementary knowledge of these subjects will be found necessary in order to understand the text. No such assumption has been made with regard to anatomy and histology, and, since some understanding of the construction of even the simplest machine must be had before one can understand how it works, the description of the function of the particular organ or tissue under discussion has been preceded by an outline of its anatomy and minute structure.

Though this book has been written primarily for the usual college course in human physiology, we have also had in mind its use as a text in nursing schools as well as in the physiological instruction of dental and agricultural students. Students of medicine may find it serviceable in gaining a bird's-eye view of the subject before reading more detailed texts.

A large proportion of the illustrations are original; the remainder have been borrowed from various sources and in most instances have been redrawn or modified in some way to make them more suitable for the present book.

The following is a list of figures with the sources from which they were obtained. Others not mentioned here are acknowledged in the legends. These figures are copyrighted, and reproduced in this book by permission. Figs. 22, 96 and 97, from Barcroft's *The Respiratory Function of the Blood*, Cambridge University Press; Fig. 60, from *Halliburton's Physiology*, 16th Ed., John Murray, London; Figs. 68, 69 and #4 of 72, from Lewis' *The Graphic Registration of the Heart Beat*, Shaw and Sons, London; Fig. 75, from Macleod's *Physiology in Modern Medicine*, Mosby and Co., St. Louis; Fig. 80, from Lewis' *The Blood Vessels of the Human Skin and Their Responses*, Shaw and Son, London; Fig. 120 (upper cut), from Pavlov's *The Work of the Digestive Glands*, Charles Griffin and Co., London; Fig. 121, from Carlson's *The Control of Hunger in Health and Disease*, University of Chicago Press; Fig. 132, from Cannon's *The Mechanical Factors of Digestion*, Edward Arnold, London; Figs. 135 and 138, from Du Bois' *Metabolism in Health and Disease*, Lea and Febiger, Philadelphia; Figs. 140 (upper cut), 143 and 144 from London County Council, Medical Department; Figs. 150, 152 and 157, from Falta and Meyer's *Endocrine Diseases*, Blakiston, Son and Co., Philadelphia; Figs. 151 and 153, from Joll's, *Diseases of the Thyroid Gland*, Heinemann, London; Fig. 154, from Crotti's *The Thyroid and Thymus*, Lea and Febiger, Philadelphia; Fig. 160, from Jackson's *Experimental Pharmacology*, Mosby and Co., St. Louis; Figs. 165 (lower cut), 166, 167, 177, 182 and 183, from Van Dyke's *The Physiology and Pharmacology of the Pituitary Body*, University of Chicago Press; Figs. 173 and 175, from Cushing's *The Pituitary Body and its Disorders*, Lippincott and Co., Philadelphia; Fig. 176, from Zondek's *Diseases of the Endocrine Glands*, Edward Arnold, London; Fig. 202 (upper cut) from *Howell's Physiology*, Saunders and Co., Philadelphia; Fig. 213, from Sherrington's *The Integrative Action of the Nervous System*, Yale University Press; Figs. 218, 230, 280 and 281, from *Quain's*

Anatomy, Longmans, London; Fig. 221, from Economo's *The Cytoarchitectonics of the Human Cerebral Cortex*, Oxford University Press; Fig. 232 (upper cut), from Pavlov's *Lectures on Conditioned Reflexes*, International Publishers, New York; Fig. 233, from Pavlov's *Conditioned Reflexes*, Oxford University Press, London and New York; Fig. 282, from *Gray's Anatomy*, Longmans, London.

A number of the illustrations have been taken from original articles appearing in the following publications: *The Journal of Physiology* (Figs. 33, 34 and 161); *The American Journal of Physiology* (Figs. 181 and 195); *The Quarterly Journal of Experimental Physiology* (Fig. 74); *The Journal of the American Medical Association* (Fig. 186); *The Lancet* (Figs. 136 and 137); *Brain* (Fig. 109); *The Quarterly Journal of Medicine* (Fig. 163); *Medicine* (Figs. 178 and 179); *Endocrinology* (Fig. 174); *The American Journal of Anatomy* (Fig. 168). In each instance the author of the article from which the figure was borrowed has been mentioned in the legend.

We wish to thank Dr. R. E. Haist for his careful reading of the manuscript and for the benefit which the book has derived from his critical discussion of the subject matter. We owe a large debt to Miss Mabel Cory for her painstaking work in preparing the manuscript for the press and in compiling the index.

C. H. B.
N. B. T.

University of Toronto
Toronto, Canada

CONTENTS

heart; heart sounds; valvular disease. Electrical changes
in the heart. The venous pulse. Disorders of the heart
beat. The regulation of the heart's action; cardiac
nerves; cardiac reflexes; chemical (humoral) transmission
of the vagus and accelerator effects. Control of the blood
vessels; vasoconstrictor and vasodilator nerves; aortic
and sinus nerves. The capillary circulation. The coronary circulation. The pulmonary circulation. The hepatic circulation. The cerebral circulation.

CHAPTER IV

Introductory. The air passages. The lungs. The me-
chanics of respiration; artificial respiration. The lung
air. The chemistry of respiration; the kinetic theory;
gaseous exchanges; transport of the respiratory gases in
the blood. The control of respiration; chemical and
nervous factors. Physiological modifications of respiration. Abnormal types of respiration. Dyspnea. Oxygen
want — anoxia; carbon monoxide and cyanide poisoning.
Cyanosis. The voice.

CHAPTER V

The structure of the kidney; blood and nerve supply.
The composition and formation of urine. Renal disease.
Micturition. Innervation and movements of the bladder.

CHAPTER VI

Introductory. Ferments or enzymes. The physiological
properties of smooth muscle. Digestion in the mouth;
salivary glands; composition and functions of saliva.
Mastication. Swallowing. Digestion in the stomach; the
gastric glands; composition and secretion of gastric juice.
Movements and emptying of the stomach; vomiting.
Digestion in the intestine; pancreatic juice; intestinal
juice. The bile, composition, secretion. Evacuation of
the gall-bladder. Jaundice. Movements of the small
intestine. Movements of the large intestine. Absorption
from the intestinal tract; formation of the feces.

CHAPTER VII

Introductory. General metabolism. Calorimetry. The respiratory quotient; basal metabolic rate. The metabolism of protein; nutritive value of different proteins. Purine metabolism. Carbohydrate metabolism; classification of the carbohydrates; history of carbohydrate in the body; insulin. Fat metabolism; the neutral fats; sterols and phospholipids; liver and fat metabolism; oxidation of fats. The regulation of body temperature; heat balance; heat-controlling centers. The vitamins. The principles of dietetics; the caloric requirement; the protein requirement; the mineral requirement.

CHAPTER VIII

The thyroid; goiter; hypothyroidism; hyperthyroidism. The parathyroids. Hypo- and hyperparathyroidism. The adrenals; adrenaline. Sympathin. The adrenal cortex. The pituitary body; disorders of the pituitary in man; giantism, acromegaly and dwarfism; diabetes insipidus. The sex glands; ovarian hormones; the male hormone. Gonadotropic hormones of the pituitary. The placenta. The thymus. The pineal body.

CHAPTER IX

The structure of the nerve fiber; degeneration and regeneration of nerve; physiological properties of the nerve fiber; anelectrotonus and catelectrotonus. The qualities of a stimulus; chronaxie; accommodation. Electrical changes in nerve. The nature of the nerve impulse; the "all or none" principle; refractory periods of nerve; the velocity and frequency of nerve impulses. Chemical changes in nerve; the physiology of muscular contraction; the muscle twitch; summation and tetanus; contracture; treppe; fatigue. Oxygen debt. Muscular exercise.

CHAPTER X

Structure of nervous tissue. Receptors. The reflex arc; reflex action. Reciprocal inhibition; limb reflexes; muscle tone. The spinal cord; structure; descending and ascending tracts of. The brain; the cerebrum; the cerebral cortex; the optic thalamus, corpus striatum and internal capsule; the mid-brain; the pons and medulla oblongata. Summary of sensory pathways in the brain. The cranial nerves. The cerebellum. The autonomic nervous system; anatomy; function. Chemical transmission of autonomic effects. Conditioned reflexes.

CHAPTER XI

The physiology of vision; structure of the eye; accommodation; stereoscopic vision; color vision; optical illusions; eye movements; optical defects. The ear. The physiology of hearing. The non-auditory labyrinth; semicircular canals; utricle. Postural reflexes. The sensations of taste and smell. Skin sensations.

CHAPTER XII

The female reproductive organs. The male reproductive organs. The processes of reproduction. The fetal circulation. Pregnancy and parturition.

LIST OF ILLUSTRATIONS

LIST OF ILLUSTRATIONS

COLORED PLATES

THE LIVING BODY

CHAPTER I

PROTOPLASM. THE CELL. THE TISSUES

PROTOPLASM is the material basis of all forms of life. The substance of the animal body — muscles, brain, kidney, liver, etc. — is composed largely of this "life stuff." Yet the exact chemical constitution of living protoplasm is unknown, for any of the means which might be employed to analyze it cause its death. Irreversible physical and chemical changes then occur, and we are no longer dealing with the substance whose composition we had set out to determine. The most that can be said with regard to the chemistry of protoplasm is that it consists of a watery solution of proteins, together with smaller amounts of carbohydrates (glycogen and glucose), lipids (fat-like materials) and inorganic salts (of potassium, calcium, sodium, magnesium, etc.). The word protoplasm (*literally*, the first thing formed) is itself no more than a generic term, for there are innumerable types of this material, its constitution varying in the different forms of life as well as in the different tissues of any one species. Furthermore, it is the seat of innumerable chemical reactions, oxidations and reductions, decompositions and syntheses. Its chemical nature is therefore changing ceaselessly. Upon these changes the varied phenomena of life depend.

THE PHYSIOLOGICAL PROPERTIES OF PROTOPLASM

The various physical and chemical processes of plant and animal life are simply the manifestations of the properties of protoplasm. It is these properties which we recognize as distinguishing the living from the non-living world.

The protoplasm of animals possesses four fundamental

1

properties: (1) irritability or excitability; (2) conductivity; (3) the power to convert the potential energy of food material into other forms of energy — thermal, mechanical, chemical or electrical; and (4) growth.

Irritability or excitability is the ability to respond to a stimulus. A stimulus may be defined as some change in the environment occurring at a sufficiently rapid rate. The ameba, for example, when stimulated, as by the touch of a stiff hair or by heating the water in which it is immersed, shows that it is alive by a movement and a change in form of its minute body (Fig. 1). Also, the excised muscle of the frog shows its irritability, so long as it remains alive, by shortening (contracting) when stimulated in one or other of several ways (mechanically, thermally, chemically or electrically).

Conductivity. The effect caused by a stimulus is not confined to the region in the immediate neighborhood of the stimulated point, but spreads throughout the mass of protoplasm. Thus, when one end of a muscle is stimulated the contractile process travels to the other end. When the stimulus ceases, the part of the muscle to which the stimulus was applied is the first to resume the resting state; the opposite end of the muscle is the last to become inactive. This phenomenon of the stimulated muscle illustrates the property of conductivity. Conductivity reaches its highest development in nervous tissue. The disturbance set up in a nerve fiber by a stimulus is transmitted to the farthest end of the fiber, which in some instances is several feet long. In a warm-blooded animal the disturbance or impulse, as it is called, is transmitted at the rate of some 300 feet per second, i.e., at about the velocity of a revolver bullet.

Metabolism. The ability which protoplasm possesses to liberate and convert to its own uses the energy stored in food material is referred to as metabolism (see also p. 279). The term embraces all those chemical reactions occurring in the tissues and from which energy is derived for the performance of muscular work or for sustaining the vital processes, e.g., the contractions of the heart, the activity of the nerve centers, the generation of body heat, and the manufacture of the digestive and other essential secretions (e.g., those of the ductless glands). Upon chemical reactions also depends the *growth* of the young animal. In the digestive tract the food materials are broken down into simpler compounds which are absorbed by the blood and rebuilt to form body tissue.

THE CELL

In very simple forms of life, e.g., the ameba (Fig. 1), a single small mass of protoplasm, called a cell, composes the

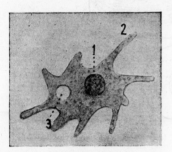

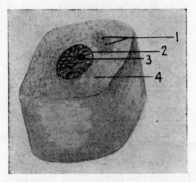

Fig. 1. An ameba. 1, nucleus; 2, a protruded portion of its cytoplasm (pseudopodium); 3, contractile vacuole.

Fig. 2. The cell. 1, centrioles; 2, nucleus; 3, nucleolus; 4, cytoplasm.

organism's entire body. Such organisms are called *unicellular*. Other forms of life whose bodies are constituted of many such microscopic blocks of protoplasm are called *multicellular*. Higher animals are constructed of immense multitudes of cells grouped together into various patterns to form the different tissues of the body.

Though, as we shall soon see (p. 6), cells vary greatly in size and shape, the majority possess certain characteristics in common. Each possesses a smaller ovoid or globular body called the *nucleus* which in a typical cell lies near its center

(Fig. 2). The substance surrounding the nucleus and constituting, in most instances, the main bulk of the cell is
called the _cytoplasm._ The nucleus like the rest of the cell
consists of protoplasm (karyoplasm), but differs from the
cytoplasm in containing irregular masses or strands of a
substance which stains strongly with basic dyes (e.g., hema-
toxylin). This dark staining material is called _chromatin._

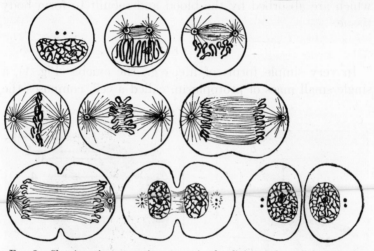

Fig. 3. Showing nine successive stages in the division of a cell by mitosis.

Unlike the cytoplasm it is rich in _nucleic acid_ (p. 294). The
nucleus of almost all types of cell contains one or more small
bodies called _nucleoli._ These bodies stain with acid dyes
(e.g., eosin).

The cytoplasm usually shows a fine granulation due to
the presence of small round or rod-shaped structures or fine
filaments called _mitochondria._ Small clear spaces called
vacuoles are seen in the cytoplasm of some cells. In others,
e.g., salivary and gastric glands, the cytoplasm contains
coarse granules from which the secretion of the gland is
derived.

The cytoplasm at the circumference of the cell is condensed to form what is usually referred to as the _cell mem-_

brane. This acts as a semipermeable membrane (p. 27), and also serves to stiffen the contour of the cell and to give it definite shape. The view is widely held that the cell membrane is composed mainly of lipid (fat-like) material. The cytoplasm also shows an area of condensation near the nucleus; this is called the *cell center*. In cells which have retained their ability to multiply, the cell center shows a small dot-like body called the *centriole*. During cell division the centriole divides into two. The two centrioles thus formed then separate, and migrate to opposite poles of the cell. From each centriole a series of fine fibers radiate

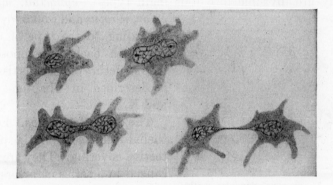

Fig. 4. Showing the reproduction of a primitive organism (e.g., an ameba) by fission.

and elongate in the direction of the nucleus which at this time is undergoing changes preparatory to division (see Fig. 3). This type of cell division is called *mitosis*.

In certain very primitive forms of life the cells multiply by a simple separation into two parts without any preliminary changes appearing in the nucleus. This type of cell reproduction is called *direct* or *amitotic* division or *fission* (Fig. 4).

THE TISSUES

Each of the various parts and organs of the body of a higher animal is highly specialized for the particular function which it is called upon to perform. Since any organ is a mass of cells, its specialization must depend upon the character of the cells of which it is composed. The ameba performs all the fundamental functions — respiration, digestion, excretion, etc., within the compass of a single cell. Like a solitary pioneer it must do all those things which are necessary for its existence. In the multicellular animal, the cells have undergone *differentiation* into various types and, like the classes of individuals making up the population of a civilized community, each type, though highly proficient in the execution of one or other particular function, has lost the versatility of the primitive organism. The tissues of the body are divisible into four main types — *epithelial, muscular, nervous* and *connective* — according to the type of cell of which each is composed. The structure of nervous tissue is described in Chapters IX and X.

Fig. 5.   Showing glandular epithelium (section of salivary gland).

The epithelial tissues. Epithelial cells serve as a protective covering. They are arranged in a series of layers or strata to form the outer part of the skin (epidermis); they also line the digestive, respiratory and urinary tracts. The various external secretory glands (digestive, mammary, sweat, etc.), as well as some of the glands of internal secretion (thyroid, parathyroid, anterior pituitary), are composed of epithelial cells arranged, in most instances, around a central cavity called an *acinus* or *alveolus* (Fig. 5). Epithelial cells are of several varieties. Some, the *columnar* type, are relatively long and narrow, appearing under the microscope as slender columns set side by side like the stakes in a palisade (Fig. 6). In some situations, as in the linings of the nose, trachea (windpipe) and bronchi, the columnar cells are surmounted by fine hair-like structures called *cilia*

(Fig. 7). Ciliated epithelium also lines the Fallopian tubes, epididymus, Eustachian tubes and middle ear. The cilia,

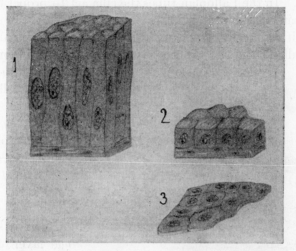

FIG. 6. Showing columnar (1), cuboidal (2) and simple squamous (3) epithelium.

which are some 3 or 4 microns [1] in length, show an incessant motion. They bend quickly in one direction and then more slowly recover their original position. The movement is repeated at the rate of ten or more per second. The rate is slowed by cold and accelerated by warmth. Carbon dioxide, ether, chloroform or alcohol vapor causes cessation of the movements. In the case of the respiratory passages the quick movement is toward the exterior, that is, toward the larynx or the nostrils. The cilia do not beat in unison; on the contrary, each beats a little time before its neighbor placed nearer the exterior. Thus

FIG. 7. Ciliated epithelium.

waves or ripples appear to pass over a ciliated surface like a field of standing wheat stirred by a breeze. The advan-

---

[1] A micron μ is $\frac{1}{1000}$ millimeter; a millimeter is about $\frac{1}{25}$ inch.

tage of such a motion is obvious; it serves to sweep mucus and dust, or other small particles, from the respiratory passages. In the Fallopian tubes the cilia act to propel the ova to their destination (p. 528).

Epithelial cells, which are about as broad as they are long, are called *cuboidal*. Another type of epithelium is composed of thin plate-like or scale-like cells, and is, therefore, termed *squamous* (*squama* = *scale*). In some situations, as on the inner surface of the tympanic membrane, the epithelium consists of a *single* layer of squamous cells lying edge to edge as in a pavement. In other places, as in the skin,

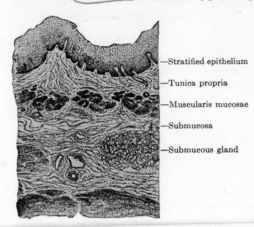

—Stratified epithelium

—Tunica propria

—Muscularis mucosae

—Submucosa

—Submucous gland

FIG. 8.   Section of mucous membrane of esophagus. (After Piersol.)

cornea and lining of the mouth and vagina, there are several strata of cells. The deepest ones are cuboidal or columnar: those covering the surface are squamous. Between these two types is a series of layers whose cells decrease in thickness in each successive stratum nearer the surface. This type of tissue is termed *stratified squamous* epithelium.

The linings of the respiratory, digestive and genito-urinary tracts are called *mucous membranes*. These consist of a layer or several layers of epithelial cells laid upon a foundation of connective tissue, called the *submucosa*. Beneath the submucosa throughout the greater part of the alimentary tract (esophagus, stomach and intestines) but not in the respiratory or genito-urinary passages, lies a thin layer of smooth muscle called the *muscularis mucosae*. This is separated from the muscle proper of the organ by a thin layer of loose connective tissue (Fig. 8). The mucous membranes secrete a slimy, tenacious material called *mucus*. This secretion, which contains a protein material (a glyco-protein, p. 290) known as *mucin*, is formed within the cytoplasm of the epithelial cells. As the material accumulates the cell becomes distended and finally bursts, discharging its contents. The mucus coats the epithelial surface, serving as a protection against injurious substances or to trap small foreign particles. From their flask-like appearance when filled with mucus, cells

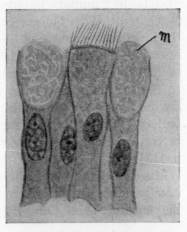

FIG. 9. Goblet cells from mucosa of the trachea. m, mucus.

of this type are referred to as *goblet cells*. Though a certain proportion of the epithelial cells constantly secrete mucus, the number is greatly increased by mechanical stimulation, or by infection or other harmful action. We are all familiar with the running nose of the common cold, and with the expectoration of mucus which accompanies inflammation of the trachea or bronchi (Fig. 9).

Endothelial tissue consists of extremely thin, wafer-like cells laid edge to edge to form delicate linings for the heart, blood vessels and lymphatics (Fig. 10).

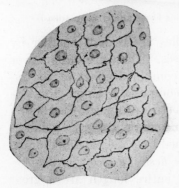

FIG. 10. Endothelium.

The smallest blood vessels (the capillaries) are delicate tubes formed of a single layer of endothelial cells. Though usually classed as a type of epithelial cell, endothelial cells differ from the latter in certain fundamental particulars.

Muscular tissue is of two main types, *striated* or *striped* and *unstriated* or *unstriped* (also called *plain* or *smooth*). Skeletal or voluntary muscle, e.g., the muscles of the limbs, is striated. With the exception of that forming the heart, the involuntary muscle of the internal organs (e.g., stomach, intestines, bronchi and bronchioles, uterus, Fallopian tubes, etc.) is non-striated. The muscle fibers in the skin attached to the hair follicles, in the walls of the blood vessels and around the alveoli of various glands are also of the unstriated variety. The muscle of the heart though striated differs in certain important respects from voluntary muscle (see p. 112).

Muscle cells are long and slender and for this reason are usually referred to as muscle fibers. In the large muscles of the skeleton great numbers of such fibers are massed to-

Fig. 11. A skeletal muscle fiber showing fibrils with cross striations.

gether into bundles. The bundles are bound together by connective tissue into larger masses. The contractile power of a muscle depends upon the combined effect of the innumerable fibers of which it is composed. Upon close examination under the microscope a striated muscle fiber shows a series of alternating light and dark transverse bands (Fig. 11). Each fiber is ensheathed by a delicate membrane called the *sarcolemma* (*Sarx* = *flesh* (*muscle*), *lemma* = *husk*), and running through its entire length are a great number of fine parallel filaments — the *myofibrils*. The latter are embedded in the cytoplasm, which is usually referred to as the *sarcoplasm*. Each myofibril is constituted of a number of alternating light and dark sections. The sections in the different myofibrils lie more or less in line across the fiber — light with light, dark with dark. It is to the combined effect of these sections that the cross-striated appearance of the whole fiber is due. The fine longitudinal lines seen in striated muscle are due to the myofibrils themselves. The striated muscle fiber usually shows several ovoid nuclei beneath the sarcolemma.

Unstriated or smooth muscle fibers are usually shorter than the striated variety, and somewhat spindle-shaped, i.e., thicker in the middle than at either end. They do not possess a sarcolemma and the myofibrils are few and in-

Fig. 12. Smooth muscle fibers.

conspicuous. They show no regular cross markings. The nucleus is usually single and situated near the center of the cell (Fig. 12).

The connective tissues. Connective tissue serves as a connecting and supporting material. It binds together masses of other types of cell, and forms a supporting framework for various organs. Thus, it holds bundles of muscle fibers together, forms fibrous investments (capsules) for the kidney, liver, etc., and enters largely into the composition of the deeper layers of the skin. It also serves to fill in spaces between neighboring organs and parts, and replaces tissue which has been destroyed by injury or disease (scar tissue). Connective tissue proper consists of a mass of long slender fibers embedded in a homogeneous jelly-like ground substance. In many types of connective tissue the fibers possess elastic properties, due to the presence of a protein known as *elastin.* In some regions, such as in the walls of the trachea and bronchioles, in the larynx, in the deeper layers of the skin, and in certain ligaments of the spinal column, the connective tissue is composed largely of *elastic fibers*. The tendons of muscles, the ligaments of the majority of the joints, and the membranous coverings of the internal organs are composed of bundles of strong, tough fibers which, though possessing little or no elastic property, are highly flexible. These fibers contain a protein known as *collagen*, and are therefore spoken of as the *collagenous* type of connective tissue fiber.

Areolar tissue is the most generalized and widely distributed form of connective tissue. It is loose in texture and composed of an interlacement of collagenous and elastic fibers running in all directions, a gelatinous ground

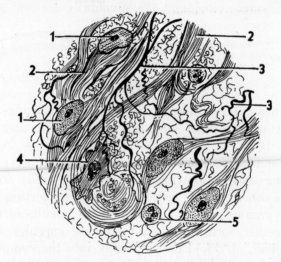

Fig. 13. Areolar tissue. 1, fibroblasts; 2, collagenous fibers; 3, elastic fibers; 4, fixed macrophage (histiocyte); 5, leucocyte.

substance and a variable number of cells of different types scattered throughout. The meshes (areolae) between the fibers have suggested the name for this type of tissue. Areolar tissue is found beneath the skin (subcutaneous tissue), filling the spaces between muscles and the internal organs, and ensheathing the blood vessels.

The typical cell of the connective tissues is the *fibroblast*. From these the numerous fibers are derived. The fibroblast is a long, flat, spindle-shaped cell with elongated processes or fibers. In tendons, membranes, ligaments, etc., cell bodies are relatively scarce, the substance of the tendon, membrane or ligament being composed almost entirely of fibers. Areolar tissue is much more cellular and contains leucocytes, fat cells and various reticulo-endothelial elements (p. 50), as well as the fibroblasts just mentioned (Figs. 13 and 14).

Adipose or *fatty tissue* is a modified connective tissue. Certain cells of areolar tissue have the special ability

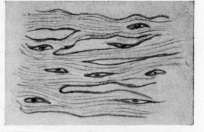

Fig. 14. Showing fibrous tissue in tendon.

to withdraw fat from the blood stream and deposit it within their bodies. The fat collects within the cytoplasm as a droplet which gradually increases in size until it occupies most of the cell, the original cytoplasm and the nucleus being displaced to the periphery and flattened against the cell membrane (Fig. 15). Adipose tissue consists of a mass of such fat-laden cells. Other cells of the areolar tissue have been crowded out while the fibers have largely disappeared. When the body loses weight, fatty tissue is one of the first to become reduced. The fat cells undergo a transformation. The fat droplets

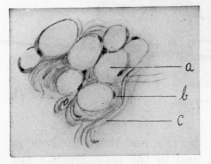

Fig. 15. Adipose tissue. a, fat globule; b, nucleus of fat cell; c, fibers of areolar tissue.

disappear; the cells shrink and, developing elongated processes, assume the appearance of fibroblasts. Adipose tissue is developed chiefly in subcutaneous situations and in the areolar tissue in relation to the abdominal organs.

Cartilage or *gristle* is also a modified connective tissue. There are three main types, *hyaline (glass-like) cartilage,* *elastic cartilage* and *fibrocartilage.*

Hyaline cartilage is translucent and of a bluish white color. It consists of large spherical or oval cells embedded in a nearly homogeneous ground substance. The cells are frequently found in pairs or groups and are then flattened where they are in contact with one another (Fig. 16). A narrow zone immediately surrounding the cartilage cells stains more deeply and is thus marked off, though not very sharply, from the rest of the ground substance. It is referred to as the *capsule.* Hyaline cartilage is found covering the ends of the bones inside joints (articular cartilage), be-

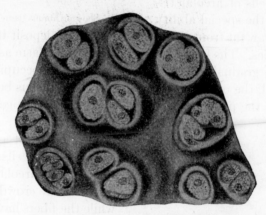

FIG. 16. Hyaline cartilage. (From Maximow after Krause.)

tween the anterior ends of the ribs and the breastbone or sternum (costal-cartilages), and in the nose, trachea and bronchi. The greater part of the skeleton of the embryo is first laid down in cartilage which undergoes gradual conversion into bone (ossification) during the development of the embryo and throughout the growth period of the young animal after birth. The process of ossification is not complete in the human subject until adult life.

Elastic cartilage is yellow in color. It contains the same type of cell as that seen in hyaline cartilage, but the ground substance is not homogeneous, being reinforced by numerous elastic fibers. This type of cartilage is found in the external ear, epiglottis and Eustachian tube.

Fibrocartilage is tough and dense. Its ground substance contains bundles of collagenous fibers. This type is considered to hold a transitional position between hyaline cartilage and the dense connective tissue constituting ligaments and tendons. It is found in the form of discs between the vertebrae (intervertebral discs) and in the shoulder, knee and hip joints. In each of the latter three situations it forms a

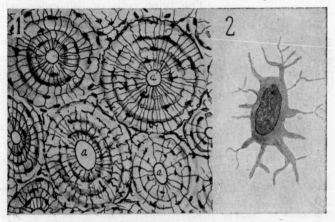

FIG. 17. Compact bone. 1, cross section showing Haversian canals (a) with concentric lamellae; 2, enlarged drawing of a bone cell.

rim to the articular cartilage, thus serving to deepen the joint socket.

Bone contains a large proportion of mineral matter, chiefly calcium and phosphorus (as tricalcium phosphate and calcium carbonate), but, also, smaller amounts of magnesium and traces of fluorine, chlorine and iron. Some bones, e.g., those of the limbs, are developed by the deposition of minerals in cartilage. Others, e.g., the bones of the cranium, are formed by the mineralization of membranous tissue.

Two types of bone enter into the construction of the long bones of the limbs. The *shaft* or *diaphysis* consists of a tube of hard *compact* bone, while the ends or *epiphyses* are composed of *cancellous* or *spongy* bone, covered by a shell of compact bone.

A section of compact bone from the shaft of the femur (thigh bone) is shown in Fig. 17. The heavily mineralized substance is laid down in a series of concentric plates or *lamellae* around narrow channels, called Haversian canals. The latter run for the most part parallel to the long axis of the bone; they contain blood vessels and connective tissue.

FIG. 18. Showing spongy bone in head of humerus. 1, shell of compact bone; 2, trabeculae.

The bone cells or *osteocytes*, which have oval bodies and numerous fiber-like processes, lie in small cavities — *Howship's lacunae* — between the lamellae. Fine canals leading from the lacunae lodge the processes of the osteocytes. The canals of neighboring lacunae communicate with one another. The bony lamellae are thus pierced in all directions by a system of fine interconnected channels. The hollow center of the shaft of the bone is filled with a soft, fatty material called the *yellow marrow.*

Cancellous bone is made up of slender bars of osseous tissue called *trabeculae* which interlace with one another (Fig. 18), and give a sponge-like pattern to the bony structure. The spaces between the trabeculae are filled with a soft, dark red material called the *red marrow* which is responsible for the manufacture of red blood cells, granular leucocytes, and probably also, of the blood platelets. The ribs and bodies of the vertebrae as well as the ends of the long bones are composed of cancellous bone covered by a thin layer of compact bone. In the cranial bones, the spongy bone is also found sandwiched between two layers of dense bone.

CHAPTER II

THE BLOOD, LYMPH AND TISSUE FLUIDS;
THE SPLEEN AND THE RETICULO-
ENDOTHELIAL SYSTEM

THE blood and tissue fluids of multicellular animals serve those purposes which in the case of unicellular organisms are served by the water in which the latter live. Thus, the ameba receives its oxygen through diffusion from the surrounding water. Carbon dioxide produced within the cell diffuses outwards through the cell membrane. Respiration, the absorption of oxygen and the elimination of carbon dioxide, is therefore a relatively simple process for the ameba. The processes of nutrition and excretion are accomplished in a manner equally primitive. Food materials pass through the cell membrane either in solution or as fine particles, and waste products pass into the surrounding medium. Other requirements of the unicellular organism, such as the maintenance of an optimum temperature and the proper degree of moisture, are dependent upon the immediate environment.

The elemental needs of each cell in a multicellular form, from the most primitive type to the highest vertebrate, are the same as those of the unicellular organism; yet in the evolution of the higher form, the cells constituting their bodies have become far removed from immediate contact with the outside world. No longer can the exchange of respiratory gases, the acquisition of nutriment and the excretion of waste products be carried out in the direct and simple manner practised by the unicellular forms. The more primitive of the multicellular types overcame the difficulty by the development of canal systems which opened upon their exteriors and through which the water flowed freely, in and out, bringing oxygen and nutriment to the more deeply lying cells and bearing carbon dioxide and other excretory products away. This, the first attempt at a circulation, was an open one. As higher forms evolved the circulation became closed — the waters of the environment no longer flowed through the body. Yet, the vessels of this closed circulatory system were filled with a liquid which took the place of, and fulfilled the duties of the watery environment of the more primitive types. The blood and other body fluids may be looked upon as that environment which has been enclosed within the bodies of the higher forms, but which has undergone certain modifications in composition to meet the requirements of the more specialized types of cell which it bathes.

Functions of blood and body fluids. The functions of the blood and body fluids are summarized as follows:

1. *Respiratory*. The transport of oxygen from the air in the lungs to the tissues, and of carbon dioxide from the tissues to the lungs.

2. *Nutritive*. The conveyance of food materials, glucose, amino-acids and fats, from the alimentary canal to the tissues.

3. *Excretory*. The removal of the waste products of metabolism, e.g., urea, uric acid, creatinine, etc.

4. *The maintenance of the water content of the tissues*. Though the blood itself is contained within definite channels — arteries, capillaries and veins (p. 80) — a constant interchange of fluid through the walls of the blood vessels takes place (p. 28). This fluid which comes in contact with the cells is known as the tissue fluid. It closely resembles the blood plasma (see p. 19) in chemical composition. Through the medium of this transuded fluid, the final stage in the passage of oxygen and food material to the cells, and the first stage of the journey of carbon dioxide from the tissues to the lungs, and of other waste products to the kidneys, is made.

5. *To regulate the body temperature* (see p. 295).

6. *Protective and regulative*. The blood, tissue fluids and

lymph contain certain chemical substances of a complex nature, antitoxins, lysins and other antibodies which are the basis of the body's defense against bacteria and injurious agents of various kinds. The blood is also the vehicle by which the hormones of the different ductless glands (Chapter VIII) are carried to and enabled to exert their effects upon the cells of the tissues.

COMPOSITION OF THE BLOOD

The blood is a highly complex fluid in which are suspended solid elements — the *blood cells* or *corpuscles*. Though blood is fluid, it must be classed as a tissue. As a matter of fact, the water content of blood is not greatly higher than that of most of the so-called solid tissues. If a tube is filled with blood and rotated rapidly in an instrument known as a centrifuge, the cells are thrown down to the bottom of the tube. The blood is thus separated into two portions — a packed mass of cells which constitute about 45 per cent of the volume of the specimen and an almost clear, faintly yellow fluid called the *plasma*, which makes up the remaining 55 per cent. To obtain a precise measurement of the proportion of red cells to plasma an instrument called a *hematocrit* is employed (see Pl. A and Fig. 21 B). The plasma contains *proteins* as well as many organic and inorganic substances in solution — nutritive and waste materials, antibodies, hormones and other compounds of an unknown or imperfectly known chemical constitution. The specific gravity of whole blood is about 1.055; that of plasma about 1.027. The cells of blood are of three types — the *red corpuscles* or *erythrocytes*, the *white corpuscles* or *leucocytes* and the *platelets* or *thrombocytes*.

The composition of blood is summarized as follows:

Whole blood
  A. *Cells:*
    (1) Red corpuscles or erythrocytes
    (2) White corpuscles or leucocytes
    (3) Platelets or thrombocytes

B. *Plasma:*

(1) Water, 91 to 92 per cent
(2) Solids, 8 to 9 per cent
  (a) Proteins, 7 per cent. Serum albumin, serum globulin and fibrinogen.
  (b) Inorganic constituents, 0.9 per cent. Sodium, calcium, potassium, magnesium, phosphorus, etc.
  (c) *Organic constituents* (other than protein). Nitrogenous substances (urea, uric acid, xanthine, hypoxanthine, creatine and creatinine, ammonia and amino-acids), neutral fats, phospholipids, cholesterol, glucose.
(3) *Respiratory gases*, oxygen and carbon dioxide.
(4) *Internal secretions, antibodies* and *various enzymes.*

The plasma proteins. The total protein concentration of the plasma is around 7 per cent. The plasma proteins are of three types — *serum albumin* (4 per cent), *serum globulin* (2.7 per cent) and *fibrinogen* (0.3 per cent).[1] The origins of the serum albumin and serum globulin are not known, but it is very probable that the fibrinogen is produced in the liver. It was thought at one time that plasma protein was food protein which was being transported from the digestive tract to the tissues. It is now known, however, that food protein is not absorbed as such, but must first be broken down into its constituent amino-acids (p. 288).

The proteins of the plasma serve several important *functions.* (a) They exert an osmotic pressure amounting to from 25 to 30 millimeters of mercury, which is a factor of first importance in the regulation of the blood volume (p. 26), and in the excretion of urine (p. 212). (b) They give viscosity to the blood, and thus aid in the maintenance of the blood pressure (p. 100). (c) The fibrinogen, but not the other types, plays an essential role in the coagulation of the blood (p. 58). (d) The manufacture of immune sub-

---

[1] Plasma from which the fibrinogen has been removed through clotting is called *serum.*

stances appears to be associated with the serum globulin. The concentration of this protein is increased during the process of immunization.

Most of the organic constituents of the plasma other than protein represent waste products of metabolism, e.g., urea, uric acid, etc., together with nutritive materials, e.g., amino-acids, glucose and fats, absorbed from the intestinal tract. Of the inorganic constituents of plasma, sodium chloride is in highest concentration. The plasma also contains potassium, calcium, magnesium, sodium bicarbonate and minute amounts of iodine and iron. Phosphorus is present in both inorganic and organic forms. The concentration of inorganic phosphorus is about 3 milligrams per 100 cc. of blood.

The proportions of the inorganic elements in plasma, blood cells, and whole blood are given in the following table.

TABLE 1

Inorganic constituents of plasma, red cells and whole blood, milligrams per 100 cc., average values

	Sodium	Potassium	Calcium	Magnesium	Chlorine	Iodine	Iron
Plasma........	340	20	10	2.7	370	0.001	0.1
Cells.........	0	420	0	6.0	190		100
Whole blood...	160	200	5	4.0	250		50

THE RED BLOOD CELLS OR ERYTHROCYTES

The human erythrocytes and those of most higher animals are circular disc-shaped cells possessing no nucleus. They have a mean diameter of 7.2 microns (0.0072 mm.), and a thickness of about 2.2 microns (Fig. 19). The central portion of the cell is much thinner than the circumference which, therefore, appears as a rim around a central depression. This construction gives the cell a biconcave contour or a roughly dumb-bell outline when viewed edgewise. In shed blood the red cells show a tendency to group themselves to-gether with their flat surfaces applied to one another. This arrangement, which resembles a stack of coins which has

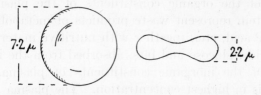

FIG. 19.   Showing the diameter and thickness of a red blood cell.

toppled over (Fig. 20), is spoken of as *rouleaux formation*. The cell is bounded by a membrane composed of protein in association with the lipid materials, *lecithin and cholesterol*. The main function of the red cell is to serve as a carrier of oxygen from the lungs to the tissues. It also serves, mainly in an indirect way, for the transport of carbon dioxide from the tissues to the lungs (pp. 68 and 191). The ability of the cell to carry oxygen is dependent upon its containing a remarkable pigment called *hemoglobin* (p. 29). It is to this pigment that the charac-teristic color of blood is due.

FIG. 20.   Red cells in rouleaux.

The number of red cells in a cubic millimeter of blood is usually stated to be 4,500,000 for women and 5,000,000 for men. As a matter of fact the values in health are somewhat higher than these, and in a robust young male 6,000,000 is not an unusual figure. The number shows some slight variation during the twenty-four hours, being lowest in the early morning, but increasing gradually throughout the day. The number of red cells is considerably higher (by a million or so) in new-born infants than in older children or adults.

The number of red cells in a cubic millimeter of a given specimen of blood is determined by counting the cells be-

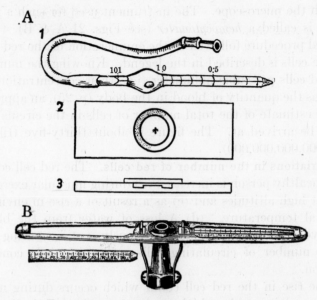

Fig. 21. A. Hemocytometer for counting the red blood cells. 1, pipette, 2, glass slide showing circular platform with scale; 3, slide in cross section with cover glass in position. The skin near the base of the thumb nail is pricked with a sterile needle or a fragment of glass, and blood drawn into the pipette as far as the mark 0.5. A suitable diluting fluid is then sucked up as far as the mark 1. The blood is thoroughly mixed with the diluting fluid (the glass bead in the dilated part of the pipette facilitates mixing); a drop of the blood diluted 1 in 200 is then expressed on to the surface of the platform of the glass slide and a cover glass laid on. The glass platform is ruled in $\frac{1}{400}$ mm. squares. The depth of the film of diluted blood between the platform and the cover glass is $\frac{1}{10}$ mm. The volume of fluid marked off by one square is therefore $\frac{1}{4000}$ cu. mm. The blood cells in a number of squares are counted and the average taken. The number of cells in a cubic millimeter of blood is then readily calculated. If the average number of cells in each square is 7, then the total number in a cubic millimeter is —

$$\underset{\substack{\text{volume of fluid over-}\\ \text{lying each square}}}{4000} \times \underset{\substack{\text{average red}\\ \text{cells per}\\ \text{square}}}{7} \times \underset{\text{(dilution)}}{200} = 5.600000$$

The white cells are counted in a similar manner, but the blood is diluted 1 in 20 by a fluid which destroys the red cells, a smaller pipette being employed.

B. Hematocrit. Blood to which sodium oxalate or other anticoagulant agent has been added, is drawn into the graduated tubes which are then placed in the holder and rotated in a centrifuge at a rate of 3000 revolutions per minute. The blood is thus separated into a red (cells) and a white (plasma) section, the proportions of each being easily determined by means of the graduations on the tubes.

neath the microscope. The instrument used for such a purpose is called a *hemocytometer* (see Figs. 21 A & B). The actual procedure followed in the enumeration of the red and white cells is described in the legend. Knowing the number of red cells per cubic millimeter (i.e., their concentration) as well as the quantity of blood in the body (p. 25), an approximate estimate of the total number of cells in the circulation may be arrived at. The figure is about thirty-five trillion (35,000,000,000,000).

Variations in the number of red cells. The red cell count of a healthy person is increased (a) during muscular exercise, (b) at high altitudes and (c) as a result of a rise in environmental temperature.   (d) A loss of water from the blood (anhydremia, p. 38) though, obviously, not increasing the total number of circulating cells, will raise their concentration.

The rise in the red cell count which occurs during muscular exercise, and at high environmental temperatures, is due mainly to contraction of the spleen which serves as a reservoir for red cells (p. 52). Contraction of the spleen also occurs when a person breathes rarefied air (i.e., air having a low percentage of oxygen) either in a closed chamber, in which the atmospheric pressure is reduced artificially, or in airplane or mountain ascents. An extra supply of red cells is thus discharged into the circulation. If the breathing of rarefied air is continued over a considerable period, as in the case of inhabitants of mountain villages, the red bone marrow — the tissue wherein the red cells are manufactured (p. 31) — is stimulated, its bulk is considerably increased and the red cell count is permanently raised. A count of 8,000,000 is not unusual in mountain dwellers. When the marrow is suddenly stimulated by a low pressure of oxygen large numbers of red cells are discharged into the circulation in a somewhat immature stage of their development. These are known as *reticulated cells* or *reticulocytes* (p. 31; see also Fig. 22 and Plate 1).

Blood whose concentration in red cells has been raised in this way, since it contains more hemoglobin, is capable of carrying a greater load of oxygen from the lungs to the tissues. This is a distinct advantage during muscular exercise, or when the pressure of oxygen in the atmosphere is low. In the latter instance the high red cell count helps to compensate for the low oxygen content of the atmosphere.

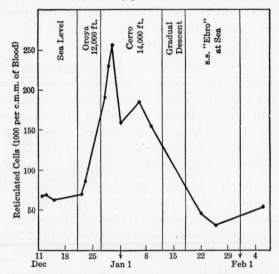

FIG. 22.   Showing reticulocyte response to a low oxygen tension in the atmosphere (high altitude).   (After Barcroft.)

When the temperature of the environment is raised, the discharge of blood from the spleen serves the useful purpose, through augmenting the volume of circulating blood, of increasing the capacity of the body's heat radiating system, and thus aiding in the regulation of the body temperature (p. 295 and Plate 1).

THE VOLUME OF THE BLOOD

The total quantity of blood in the body of an average sized man (70 kilograms) is around 6 liters (over 5 quarts), or about 1/11th of the total weight of the body. It can be measured in the living subject by injecting a solution of a harmless dye into a vein. *Vital red* is the dye most commonly used for this purpose. A couple of minutes after its injection the dye becomes thoroughly mixed with the circulating blood. A sample of blood is then withdrawn from a vein by means of a syringe, and the plasma separated from the cells by centrifuging. The plasma, which is now colored pink by the dye, is compared with a standard solution containing the dye in known dilution. The extent to which the sample of injected dye has been diluted in the blood stream is thus arrived at. From this the total volume of the plasma is calculated. But it is desired to know the volume of the *whole* blood, i.e., of cells and plasma. The next step is, therefore, to determine the proportion of cells to plasma in a sample of the subject's blood. This is done by centrifuging a sample of blood in an instrument known as an hematocrit (see Fig. 21 B). If the blood has the normal proportions of cells and plasma, namely, 45 per cent and 55 per cent, respectively, and the volume of the plasma as indicated by the dilution of the dye in the circulation is 3.4 liters (3400 cc.), then the total blood volume is $\frac{3400}{55} \times 100 = 6.1$ liters.

Regulation of the blood volume. The volume of the blood in health remains remarkably constant. There are two main factors in its regulation, (a) the *osmotic pressure* of the proteins of the plasma and tissue fluids, and (b) the *hydraulic or hydrostatic pressure* of the blood in the capillaries and of the fluids surrounding them.

Osmotic pressure may be best explained by citing an example. If an aqueous solution of sugar or salt is placed in a small membranous sac and immersed in water, and the membrane is permeable to water, but impermeable to the molecules of the dissolved substance, then water will pass into the sac, but the sugar or salt solution will not pass out. The pressure within the sac therefore rises; the walls of the sac become distended and may rupture. The force created in this way is spoken of as the osmotic pressure. The dissolved material appears to "attract" or "draw" the water through the membrane. A membrane which permits the passage of

water, but bars the passage of some water-soluble substance is said to be *semipermeable* with respect to that substance (Fig. 23). Now, the membrane forming the walls of the capillaries (which connect the small vessels on the ar-
terial side of the circulation with the small veins, see p. 76) is semi-
permeable only in so far as the plasma proteins are concerned. It permits the passage of water and the rela-
tively small molecules of sugar, urea, sodium chloride and other crystalloids, but hinders the passage of the large molecules of the plasma proteins. Only very small quantities of the latter pass through the capillary wall. The proteins of the plasma, therefore, exert a force which "draws" water from the surrounding tissue spaces, and tends to prevent the passage of water out of the vessels. The osmotic force thus exerted by the proteins of the plasma amounts to from 25 to 30 millimeters of mercury (mm. Hg). In order to overcome this osmotic pressure, and drive water and dissolved salts through the capillary wall, an opposing hydraulic pressure must be applied. This is provided by the pressure of blood in the capillaries. The capillary blood pressure must, of course, be greater than the protein

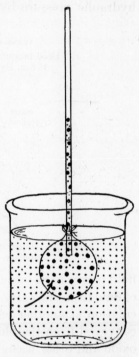

Fig. 23. Diagram illustrating osmotic pressure. A sac formed of a semipermeable membrane is fastened to one end of a glass tube. The large dots represent sugar molecules, the small ones, water molecules. Water passes through the pores of the membrane as indicated by the arrow. The pressure within the sac rises as shown by the height of the fluid column in the glass tube.

osmotic pressure. Such a relationship between osmotic and hydraulic pressures exists at the arterial end of the capillary. But a gradual fall in blood pressure occurs from the arterial end where it amounts to a little over 30 mm. Hg, to the ve-

nous end where it is around 12 mm. Hg. In the venous end
of the capillary the osmotic pressure, therefore, exceeds the
hydraulic pressure by several millimeters of mercury, and

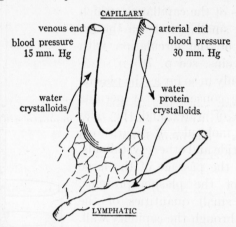

FIG. 24. Illustrating the exchange of fluid between blood
capillary, tissue spaces and lymph vessel.

fluid passes back into the vessels. Thus, through the passage
of fluid from one part of the capillary and its return to the circulation at another part, oxygen and nutritive materials are
conveyed from the blood to the tissue cells, and carbon dioxide and other waste products from the cells to the blood.

TABLE 2

	Blood	Tissue fluid
	Hydrostatic pressure 30 mm. Hg	*Hydrostatic pressure* 8 mm. Hg
	Effective hydrostatic pressure 22 mm. Hg	
Capillary wall		
	Osmotic pressure 25 mm. Hg	Osmotic pressure 10 mm. Hg
	Effective osmotic pressure 15 mm.	

Force driving fluid from vessels = 7 mm. Hg

The osmotic and hydraulic pressures of the tissue fluids surrounding the capillaries are also factors which must be considered in the transference of fluid across the capillary membrane. The osmotic pressure of these fluids will act to offset the osmotic pressure of the plasma. These fluids also exert a certain hydrostatic pressure which offsets somewhat the driving force of the capillary blood pressure.

HEMOGLOBIN

Hemoglobin, the coloring matter of the blood, is compounded of a substance called *heme* or *hematin* and a protein called *globin*. The heme is constituted of a pigment known as *porphyrin* combined with *iron*. Porphyrins are widely distributed throughout animal and vegetable life. The green coloring matter of plants, known as *chlorophyl*, and pigments in the plumage of certain birds are porphyrin compounds. The brown pigment in the shell of the hen's egg is a porphyrin very closely allied to the porphyrin in hemoglobin. Porphyrins possess the property of combining with various metals, copper, cobalt, magnesium (in chlorophyl), silver, nickel and iron. Such compounds are grouped as a class under the term *metalloporphyrins*. Heme is a member of this class, the metal in this instance being iron. Hemoglobin is therefore a *porphyrin-iron-globin compound*.

The constitution of the hemoglobin molecule may be shown concisely as follows:

porphyrin + iron = heme (or hematin)
heme (or hematin) + globin = hemoglobin

It has been mentioned that hemoglobin serves as a carrier of oxygen from the lungs to the tissues. This function is dependent upon the remarkable property which the pigment possesses of forming a very unstable compound with oxygen. Each hemoglobin molecule contains 4 atoms of iron, each of which combines with a molecule of oxygen. But a true oxide of iron is not formed; the hemoglobin is therefore said to be *oxygenated*, not *oxidized*. The oxygenation of hemoglobin may be represented thus: $Hb_4 + 4O_2 = Hb_4O_8$.

The affinity of hemoglobin for oxygen is remarkable. When exposed to air it combines rapidly with the gas — the compound being then called *oxyhemoglobin*. If the oxyhemoglobin is then exposed to an atmosphere in which the oxygen pressure is low, the compound readily decomposes, oxygen being liberated. That is, the oxyhemoglobin is reduced; the compound is then called *reduced hemoglobin*.

The quantity of oxygen which blood will absorb is some 60 times greater than that which can be absorbed by an equivalent volume of water. For example, if 100 cubic centimeters of water are exposed to an atmosphere containing the same percentage of oxygen as is present in the air of the lungs, about one-third of a cubic centimeter of the gas would be absorbed. Yet 100 cc. of blood exposed to the same atmosphere will absorb nearly 20 cc. of oxygen. The difference is due entirely to the hemoglobin. The total amount of blood in the human body will hold 1200 cc. of oxygen. This quantity of oxygen is used by the tissues in 5 minutes or so during rest, and in a fraction of a minute during strenuous muscular exercise. In the absence of hemoglobin, the entire duty for the carriage of oxygen would devolve upon the plasma (which is mostly water), and in order that this should be able to absorb the quantity of gas necessary to satisfy the requirements of the tissues, its volume would have to be some 60 times greater than it is. The circulating fluid instead of being 6 liters, or about 1/11th of the body weight, would need to be more than 350 liters — over 5 times the bulk of the solid tissues!

The quantity of oxygen which blood will absorb when fully saturated is called its *oxygen capacity*. As just mentioned, this depends almost entirely upon the hemoglobin. The oxygen capacity of a sample of blood is therefore directly proportional to the quantity of hemoglobin which it contains. Each gram of hemoglobin takes up a maximum of 1.34 cc. of oxygen. Now, each 100 cubic centimeters of normal human blood contains some 15 grams of hemoglobin.

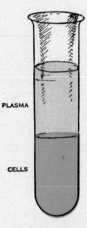

Plate A. Blood after centrifuging, showing separation of plasma (55%) from cells (45%).

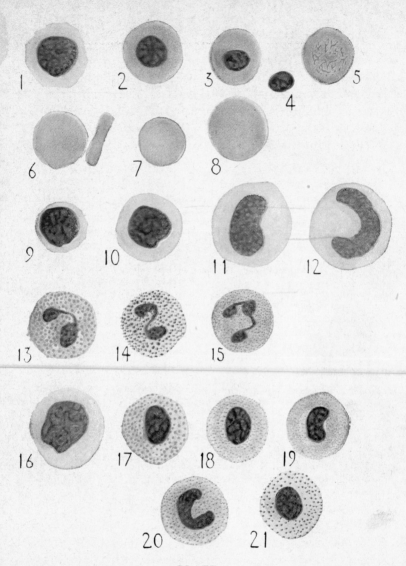

PLATE 1

The blood cells. 1–6, stages in the development of the red cells. 1, megaloblast; 2, erythroblast, note bluish tint of cytoplasm (polychromasia); 3, normoblast; 4, extruded nucleus; 5, reticulocyte; 6, fully mature erythrocyte, front and profile views; 7, microcyte, as seen in microcytic hypochromic types of anemia; 8, macrocyte, as seen in pernicious and certain other types of anemia. 9–15, varieties of leucocytes. 9, small lymphocyte; 10, large lymphocyte; 11 and 12, two types of monocyte; 13, eosinophil; 14, basophil; 15, neutrophil. 16–21, stages in the development of the leucocytes. 16, myeloblast; 17. eosinophil myelocyte; 18, 19 and 20, three ages of neutrophil myelocytes; 21, basophil myelocyte.

So then $(15 \times 1.34 =)20$ cc. is the oxygen capacity of 100 cc. of normal human blood. If, as in anemia, the hemoglobin content is below normal, the oxygen-carrying capacity of the blood is reduced. Further details of the role played by hemoglobin in supplying oxygen to the tissues, i.e., its respiratory function, will be given in Chapter IV.

THE FORMATION AND HISTORY OF THE RED CELLS

The red cells are manufactured in the red marrow of the bones — ribs, vertebrae and ends of the limb bones. The term *hemopoiesis* is applied to the process of blood formation, i.e., to the production of all types of blood cells. When it is wished only to refer to the manufacture of red cells the term *erythropoiesis* is employed. The red cells pass through several stages of development before they are discharged from the marrow into the general circulation. At one of the earliest stages leading to its maturation the cell is quite large, has no hemoglobin and possesses a nucleus. The cells of this stage are called *megaloblasts* (megas (megal-) × large; blastos = germ or sprout). A little later, the cell acquires hemoglobin, becomes reduced in size and is then called an *erythroblast*. The stage of the *normoblast* follows (Pl. 1). The cell is now about the size of the mature red cell; it contains its full complement of hemoglobin, but still possesses a nucleus. In the final stage of maturation the nucleus is expelled. The cell is now called a *reticulocyte* from the fact that when suitably stained its cytoplasm shows a fine reticulated or filigree pattern. Many cells of this stage of development, as well as normoblasts, may be seen in normal red marrow, but cells of the earliest stage, the megaloblasts, are very scarce, and erythroblasts are not plentiful. The reticulocytes are discharged into the general blood stream; normally, they constitute about 0.5 per cent of the total red cells in circulation. When the bone marrow is stimulated, as by the low oxygen tension of the atmosphere which exists at high altitudes, or by iron or liver administration in anemia

(p. 34), large numbers of reticulocytes appear in the general circulation.   A short time after their arrival in the general blood stream, the reticulocytes lose their reticulated pattern and are then mature red cells or erythrocytes.   In health, normoblasts, or any cells younger than these, do not leave the bone marrow.

The life of the red cell.   The average life of the erythrocyte is about 30 days.   There are no special means provided for its destruction.   It simply wears out as a result of the stresses and strains to which it is subjected, and breaks up in the blood stream.   Small fragments, *hemoconia* or *blood dust* as they are called, may often be detected during the microscopic examination of a specimen of normal blood.   The fragments are finally disposed of by the spleen, which contains large mobile cells which engulf them.

It has been estimated that in health something like a million cells per second undergo destruction in this way, and of course the same number must be formed afresh by the bone marrow.   The number of red cells in the body at any moment, therefore, represents the balance struck between the red cell wastage and the production of new red cells by the bone marrow.

Factors in the regeneration of blood.   The red cell, as we have seen, consists of a framework composed of protein and lipoid materials, and a complex pigment — hemoglobin. The well-nourished body possesses adequate supplies of building materials for the manufacture of the cell stroma. Not a great deal is known with regard to the mechanism of hemoglobin manufacture.   It might be thought that green foods, since they are rich in the pigment chlorophyl (which, as mentioned on p. 29, is related chemically to heme), would supply elements necessary for hemoglobin synthesis.   Yet it appears that chlorophyl is not utilized for this purpose.   Nor are the porphyrin and the iron in hemoglobin when taken in food utilized for the formation of hemoglobin.   The heme cannot apparently be split into its constituents by the digestive enzymes (see p. 222).   The globin, on the other hand, is utilized and the feeding of hemoglobin hastens the regeneration of blood pigment in certain forms of anemia. Not only is the iron in heme unavailable but the metal in other organic combinations is not utilized or is utilized very poorly. Iron in *inorganic* form (e.g., ferrous carbonate or ferrous sulphate) is absolutely necessary for normal erythropoiesis. A diet deficient in iron leads to anemia (p. 34), as does also the lack of first class protein.

The effects of various articles of diet upon the power of the dog to regenerate hemoglobin following hemorrhage were studied by Dr. Whipple and his associates (see table below).

TABLE 3

The influence of diet upon hemoglobin production

Diet, grams daily	Hemoglobin produced, grams in two-week period
Bread, 400	3
Milk, 450, Bread, 400	3
Cream, 100, Bread, 400	10
Spinach, 200, Bread, 300	15
Raisins, 200, Bread, 300	25
Eggs, 150, Bread, 300	45
Chicken gizzard, 250, Bread, 200	80
Chicken liver, 250, Bread, 300	80
Kidney, 250, Bread, 300	70
Beef liver, 450	95

Of all materials investigated, liver was found to cause the most rapid restoration of the hemoglobin.   Kidney and chicken gizzard were also highly effective. As we shall see presently, these experiments led to the discovery of a cure for a very grave type of anemia in the human subject.

It has been shown within recent years that *copper* in minute amounts is also necessary for the manufacture of hemoglobin. This element is not a constituent of the hemoglobin molecule, but it acts in some way not quite clear (but probably as a catalyst) to hasten the synthesis of hemoglobin.

ANEMIA

When the concentration of hemoglobin is below normal, the condition is called anemia. There are several varieties and grades of anemia. In very severe types the hemoglobin may be as low as ten per cent of the normal quantity, i.e., 1.5 grams per 100 cc. of blood instead of 15 grams, as in health. The reduction in the hemoglobin may be the result either of there being fewer red cells, as in the most severe types of anemia, or to there being less hemoglobin in each cell, the total number of cells being not very greatly reduced.

It has been mentioned that the number of red cells in the blood in health represents the balance struck between the loss of red cells through wear and tear in the circulation, and the production of new cells by the bone marrow. Anemia may result, therefore, from either increased destruction (or loss from the body) of red cells, or from diminished production. The anemias may be divided then into these two main categories.

A. **Anemias due to blood loss or increased destruction of red cells.** 1. *Post-hemorrhagic.* In this type a large amount of blood may be lost from the circulation either suddenly (*acute hemorrhage*) as a result of the opening of a large vessel, e.g., in accidental wounds, duodenal ulcer, etc., or by repeated small hemorrhages (*chronic hemorrhage*).

2. *Hemolytic.* In this type an abnormal number of red cells undergo destruction in the blood stream. Certain poisons, e.g., lead, arsenical preparations, etc., cause destruction of the cells. In another type of hemolytic anemia there appears to be some inherent defect in the erythrocytes themselves. They are more fragile and, in consequence, disintegrate more readily than usual.

B. **Anemias due to defective blood formation.** This group embraces anemias caused by:

1. *Iron deficiency.* Should the diet contain inadequate

amounts of iron, anemia develops. In this type the red cells, as a rule, are not greatly reduced in number, but they are smaller than the normal, and the concentrations of hemoglobin in each cell is low. The pale color of the erythrocytes is usually quite evident upon microscopic examination. The qualifying terms *microcytic* (micros = small; cytos = cell) and *hypochromic* (hypo = low; chromos = color) are frequently employed in referring to anemias of this class.

2. *Lack of the specific anti-anemic factor.* Anemia due to this cause is commonly referred to as *pernicious anemia* because, until a cure was discovered in 1926, it resisted all forms of treatment and invariably caused death. The hemoglobin may reach a very low percentage, the reduction being due to the great reduction in the number of red cells. Each cell actually contains more hemoglobin than a normal cell. The cells are also considerably larger than in health, and megaloblasts are present in the blood stream. The terms *macrocytic* and *hyperchromic* are frequently applied to this and certain other anemias in which the red cells show these characteristics. The observations of Whipple and his associates, already mentioned (p. 33), suggested to two physicians of Boston — Drs. Minot and Murphy — that liver might be of value in the treatment of pernicious anemia. The spectacular success which followed the feeding of liver to victims of this disease is now well known. As a result of this work of epochal importance, it is now evident that the liver normally discharges into the blood stream a principle which is essential for the maintenance of the erythropoietic function of the bone marrow, and that pernicious anemia is due to the absence of this so-called *anti-anemic* (or *hematinic*) principle. Fortunately, the anti-anemic principle obtained from the livers of farm animals is active when given to man, and can therefore replace that which the pernicious anemia patient lacks. It has since been shown that the anti-anemic principle is produced by the action of a specific substance, secreted by the stomach, upon certain articles of diet, e.g.,

beef muscle and other meats. The substance secreted by the stomach is called the *gastric* or *"intrinsic" factor;* the substance in the food upon which it acts to produce the antianemic principle is known as the *"extrinsic" factor.* The relationship of the three principles to erythropoiesis is shown diagrammatically in Fig. 25. A victim of pernicious anemia given the "intrinsic factor," as contained in the dried and

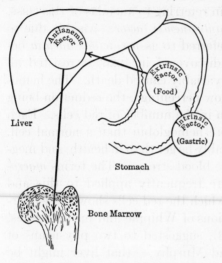

Liver

Stomach

Bone Marrow

ground-up stomach of the pig, is cured just as readily as by the liver principle itself. It appears, therefore, that the fundamental cause of this type of anemia is failure of the intrinsic factor to be secreted — the antianemic principle cannot then be formed.

3. *Toxic agents which depress the function of the bone marrow.* Certain chemical poisons, e.g., benzine compounds, radium salts or toxic substances produced in disease, e.g.,

Fig. 25.   Diagram illustrating the factors responsible for erythropoiesis. (From Best and Taylor, *The Physiological Basis of Medical Practice.*)

nephritis, and various infections, depress or destroy the function of the bone marrow. In some instances the bone marrow is almost functionless, is much reduced in amount and few red cells are produced to replace those which have been destroyed. Circulating red cells, as a consequence, fall to a very low level. The term *aplastic* is given to this type of anemia.

HEMORRHAGE

Hemorrhage may be defined as the loss of blood as a whole, i.e., of plasma and cells, from the blood vessels. The blood may escape from the body, as in accidents causing injury to an artery or vein — *external hemorrhage*. On the other hand, the blood may pass into the surrounding tissues, such as the brain or lungs, or into one of the hollow viscera, e.g., the stomach or intestine. This is called *internal hemorrhage*. However, the general effects are practically the same whether the hemorrhage is external or internal. If the quantity of blood lost is large, and especially if it occurs suddenly, the subject suffers severely from lack of oxygen as a consequence of the reduction in the number of erythrocytes. There is a fall in blood pressure, as a result of the reduction in volume of circulating fluid, and the heart beat increases in rate.

Of the physiological adjustments which ensue to safeguard the body against the dangers of blood loss, some are effected almost immediately after the hemorrhage; others not for some time. The first requisite, of course, is that the bleeding be staunched. This is accomplished through the clotting of the blood (p. 58) and the contraction of the walls of the divided vessels. In this way the leak in the circulating system is repaired. The *capacity of the circulating system* must also be reduced, in order to conform to the reduced volume of the blood. This is brought about through nervous reflexes. Messages are transmitted from the nervous centers to the small vessels in parts of the body such as the skin, muscles and intestines, whose functions are not immediately essential to life. The caliber of the vessels in these structures is reduced. The blood pressure is therefore raised (p. 99), and an adequate supply of blood to the heart and the vital centers in the brain thus maintained. The spleen responds to hemorrhage (p. 52) by contraction, and the discharge of a quantity of blood into the circulation, thus the blood volume is at once, in part at least, restored. The blood volume is also augmented by the passage of fluid — mainly water and salts — into the vessels from the tissue spaces. This process commences almost immediately after the blood has been shed, and may restore the blood volume to normal within a remarkably short time. The withdrawal of fluid from the tissues causes the subject to suffer from thirst, and the administration of fluids at this time is of value in hastening the return of the blood volume to its normal value. The time required for the replacement of the plasma proteins is longer, and longer still for the complete restoration of the blood cells by the bone marrow. The time following the hemorrhage, at which the blood cells are brought back to their normal concentration, varies with the nature of the diet (p. 33) and the recuperative powers of the individual subject.

TRANSFUSION

When more than 40 per cent of the blood is lost over a short period of time the body is usually unable to repair the loss unaided. Some artificial means of replacing the lost fluid must be resorted to. The intravenous injection of blood, plasma or serum, or of some artificial solution with the object of restoring the blood volume is called *transfusion*.[1]

Transfusion with whole blood. Blood obtained from another person (usually referred to as the donor) is the ideal transfusion fluid, for it is capable not only of restoring the blood volume but of furnishing erythrocytes as well. The transfused cells survive for a considerable length of time (probably for from 25 to 30 days). Not anyone's blood can be used for transfusion. Great care must be exercised in the choice of the person (the donor) from whom the blood is taken, for the blood of one person may result in the death of another into whose veins it is injected. The person receiving the blood is called the recipient. Death may occur even though donor and recipient are closely related. Such an untoward result is due to the patient's plasma containing a substance called an *agglutinin*, while the donor's erythrocytes contain a complementary substance called an *agglutinogen*. When unsuitable blood is transfused, the donor's

[1] Strictly speaking, the word *transfusion* refers to the use of blood serum or plasma and *infusion* to the use of other fluids.

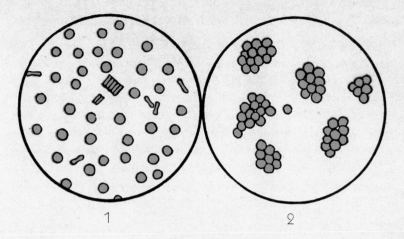

PLATE 2A

1, corpuscles mixed with compatible serum; 2, agglutination of corpuscles
caused by incompatible serum.

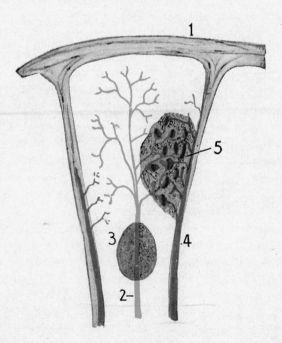

PLATE 2B

Section of a lobule of the spleen. 1, capsule; 2, branch of splenic artery;
3, Malpighian corpuscle; 4, vein; 5, splenic pulp showing blood sinuses (semidiagrammatic).

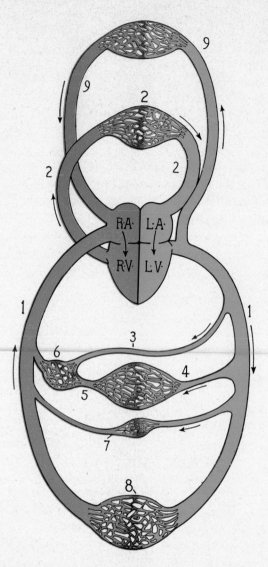

PLATE 3

Diagram of the circulation. 1, systemic circulation;
2, pulmonary circulation; 3, hepatic artery; 4, arteries to
gastro-intestinal tract and spleen; 5, portal vein; 6, hepatic
circulation; 7, renal circulation; 8, capillary bed of lower
limbs; 9, capillary bed of head and neck. R.A., right auricle;
R.V., right ventricle; L.A., left auricle; L.V., left ventricle.

erythrocytes become gathered together into clumps — *agglutination* (Pl. 2 A). Such clumps of cells block the small vessels; later the cells disintegrate and liberate their hemoglobin. The pigment in the process of excretion by the kidneys obstructs the urinary tubules, and the patient dies as a result of the suppression of urine. Types of blood which, when mixed, behave in this way are termed *incompatible*. It has been discovered that the entire human population of the earth — of no matter what race — can be divided into four groups according to the reactions of their bloods when mixed together. The groups are designated by the Roman numerals I, II, III, IV. Table 4 shows the reactions between plasma (or serum) and the corpuscles of the various groups according to the classification worked out by Jansky.

TABLE 4

Serum

		I	II	III	IV
Corpuscles	I	—	—	—	—
	II	+	—	+	—
	III	+	+	—	—
	IV	+	+	+	—

+ = agglutination; − = no agglutination

It will be noted that the *serum* of group IV (vertical row on extreme right) does not cause agglutination of the corpuscles of any group. That is, the red cells of any donor, it would be expected, could be injected with safety into a subject belonging to group IV. A person belonging to group IV has therefore been called the *"universal recipient."* It is also evident from the table that the *corpuscles* of group I are not agglutinated by any serum. A person of this group has therefore been called the *"universal donor."* Serious reactions and even death may result, however, when the donor belongs to group I or the recipient to group IV. The terms "universal donor" and "universal recipient" are therefore misleading. The donor should when possible be of the same group as that to which the recipient belongs; there is then no fear of incompatibility. Or better still, the compatibility of the two samples of blood should be tested before the transfusion is made. The clumping of the corpuscles which occurs when they are mixed with an incompatible serum is clearly seen under the microscope. Even to the naked eye the masses of agglutinated corpuscles may be seen as minute particles, like grains of cayenne pepper, floating upon the surface of the clear serum.

The blood characteristics are inherited according to Mendelian laws, and just as the offspring of a brown-eyed and a blue-eyed parent may have either brown or blue eyes, so it is impossible to predict the blood characters of a child from those of its parents.

Transfusion of blood is employed in other conditions besides hemorrhage, namely, in surgical shock, extensive burns, in certain severe infections, and in extreme malnutrition of infants.

Transfusion with plasma or serum. Within recent years it has been generally recognized that in many cases of hemorrhage it is unnecessary to transfuse with whole blood. The body possesses an immense reserve store of red cells, death from hemorrhage being as a rule due not to the reduction in the oxygen-carrying capacity of the blood but to the loss of the bulk of circulating fluid and the resulting fall in blood pressure which this entails. Plasma or serum has therefore come into very wide use as a transfusion fluid. There are certain very definite and great advantages to be gained by the use of these blood derivatives. In the first place, plasma or serum when collected from a number of donors and mixed together (pooled) does not cause agglutination of the transfused patient's corpuscles. That is, it is universally compatible. Another great advantage of plasma or serum over whole blood is that either can be dried and stored in bottles, and is thus ready at hand for almost immediate use. All that is then required is the addition of sterile distilled water in an amount equal to that which had been evaporated off in the drying process. In the preparation of the dried product the plasma or serum collected from a number of donors is separated from the cells by centrifuging and decanted off. The cells are discarded. The liquid part of the blood is frozen and then dried in the frozen state by subjecting it to a high vacuum (6 mm. Hg or less). This method, the *desivac process*, is now employed in the preparation of dried serum (or plasma) on a large scale for the armed forces in Britain, Canada, the United States, and other countries.

Artificial transfusion solutions. The search for a suitable substitute for blood or its derivatives, plasma or serum, as a transfusion material has engaged the attention of scientists for a number of years. Provided that the material resembles plasma or serum in its physical properties and is capable of restoring and maintaining the blood volume for a reasonable length of time and thus of raising the blood from a dangerously low level, the chemical composition of the transfusion fluid is of secondary importance. But the requirements of such an artificial transfusion material are many: (a) The molecule of the dissolved substance must be of such a size that the fluid will not leave the vessels too freely. (b) The solution must exert an osmotic pressure and possess a viscosity approaching as closely as possible that of whole blood; these qualifications depend upon molecular size and shape. (c) It should be as nearly as possible isotonic with the contents of the erythrocytes. (d) It must, of course, be non-antigenic and innocuous in every respect. In addition, it should be readily available, preferably cheap, and capable of being quickly and easily prepared for intravenous administration. Provided it is suitable in the respects just listed, there appears to be no valid objection to the use of some fluid other than blood or serum to fill the vessels after hemorrhage.

Among the solutions which have been used in the past or are under investigation and trial at the present time are (a) saline (0.9% solution of sodium chloride), (b) a 6% solution of gum acacia, and (c) a 6% solution of isinglass.

Saline is of little value in hemorrhage, for the simple reason that it is not held within the vessels. Its molecule is so small that it leaks through the capillary walls into the tissue spaces. When, however, the water of the blood alone is reduced (anhydremia), saline is of benefit.

Gum acacia was introduced during the first World War for the treatment of hemorrhage resulting from wounds, and was highly successful. The reason for its success lay in the fact that its molecule is large and does not readily escape from the circulation. In the dilution used (6% of gum in saline) this substance exerts an osmotic pressure about equal to that of the plasma proteins. The fluid is therefore retained within the vessels, the blood pressure is elevated and the circulation to vital structures maintained. Gum acacia has come into disfavor, however, since the discovery that it damages the liver.

Isinglass is a protein very closely allied in its chemical and physical properties to gelatin. It is prepared from the swim bladders of fish (hake, cod, sturgeon, etc.). In a 4% or a 6% solution it exerts an osmotic pressure comparable with that of the plasma proteins. It has proved successful in the treatment of acute hemorrhage in animals and in patients. It does not cause a foreign protein (antigenic) reaction or any other unfavorable effect.

HEMOLYSIS OR THE LAKING OF BLOOD

Ordinarily the plasma contains no hemoglobin. When normal blood is centrifuged, the red cells are thrown down and the supernatant plasma may then be seen to be almost colorless. Under the action of certain agents the hemoglobin is not retained by the erythrocytes, but escapes and colors the plasma. This process is termed *hemolysis* or the *laking* of the blood. The substance inducing the hemolysis is called a *hemolysin* or a *hemolytic agent*. Among the various agents which cause hemolysis are (a) *hypotonic solutions*, (b) *chloroform, ether* and *benzine*, and certain other *fat solvents*, (c) *bacterial poisons* (toxins), (d) the *venom of certain snakes* and (e) *specific hemolysins*. The depth of color given to the plasma varies from a faint pink to a deep red, according to the degree to which the erythrocytes have been attacked by the particular hemolysin.

Hypotonic solutions act by disturbing the osmotic equilibrium between the interior of the red cell and the surrounding plasma. When, for example, distilled water is added to blood, the salts of the plasma are diluted and the osmotic pressure of the plasma is reduced below that within the cells. Water is therefore "attracted" into the cell which, as a consequence, increases in volume and, finally rupturing, liberates its coloring matter. When the cell is completely hemolyzed in this way its colorless framework may still be seen. Such decolorized cells are referred to as "ghosts." Hemolysis commences in normal human blood when the inorganic salt concentration of the plasma is reduced to around 0.40 per cent. In certain conditions (e.g., hemolytic anemia) the red cells are more sensitive to hypotonic solution, hemolysis starting when the salts are reduced to a concentration of 0.5 or even 0.6 per cent. The cells are then said to be more fragile. The reverse change, i.e., reduced fragility, occurs in pernicious anemia.

Chloroform, ether, etc., cause hemolysis, apparently, by dissolving the lipoid materials composing the cell membrane and stroma. The manner in which bacterial and many other of the organic hemolytic agents act is not clear.

Specific hemolysins constitute a class of immune substances. For example, if an animal is given a series of daily injections of blood of another species, a substance is gradually developed in the serum of the recipient animal which has the power to hemolyze the erythrocytes of that species to which the donor animal belongs, but is not hemolytic for the erythrocytes of other species.

THE WHITE CELLS OR LEUCOCYTES

The leucocytes, unlike the red cells, possess a nucleus but no hemoglobin or other coloring matter. They number only about 8,000 (6,000–10,000) per cubic millimeter. That is, the red cells outnumber the white by about 600 to 1 (Fig. 26). The white cells are of two main types, (a) those

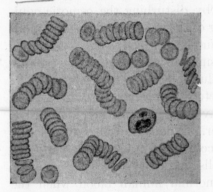

without granules in the cytoplasm and with an unlobed nucleus; these are called *agranular leucocytes*. (b) Those with granules in the cytoplasm and a nucleus possessing two or more lobes; these are termed *granular leucocytes*, *granulocytes* or *polymorphonuclear leucocytes* (see Pl. 1).

FIG. 26. A film of normal blood illustrating the relative numbers of red and white cells. A field as large again as that shown would probably contain no other white cell.

The agranular leucocytes are of three varieties — the *large* and *small lymphocytes* and the *monocytes*. The former two closely resemble one another except in size; the small lymphocyte is about 8 microns in diameter, the large from 10 to 12 microns. The small lymphocytes constitute about 25 per cent of the white cells, the large lymphocytes about 3 per cent. The monocytes are larger than the large lymphocytes, measuring about 15 microns in diameter; they are considered by most observers to belong to the reticulo-endothelial system of cells (p. **50**). They are relatively few in number — from 1 to 2 per cent of the total white cell count.

The granulocytes are also of three types, the eosinophils, the basophils and the neutrophils. The cytoplasm of the eosinophils contains coarse granules which stain with acid dyes (e.g., the red dye eosin); the nucleus has two lobes. Normally, these cells constitute about 3 per cent of the leucocyte population.

The granules of the basophils stain with basic dyes (e.g., methylene blue). Their nucleus is also bilobed. Basophils are scarce (not more than 0.5 per cent) in normal blood.

The neutrophils are about 10 microns in diameter, and contain numerous fine granules which stain with neutral dyes, or with a mixture of an acid and a basic dye (e.g., eosin and methylene blue). When so treated, the granules are colored violet. The majority of the neutrophil leucocytes possess

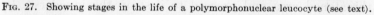

Fig. 27. Showing stages in the life of a polymorphonuclear leucocyte (see text).

nuclei which are divided into from 2 to 5 lobes (Fig. 27). The number of lobes depends upon the age of the cell, the oldest ones having 5 or more, while the youngest (which are very few in number) show only a suggestion of lobulation. The neutrophils are the most numerous type of white cell, constituting from 65 to 70 per cent of the total count.

The functions of the leucocytes. The neutrophilic polymorphonuclear leucocytes, together with the monocytes and other reticulo-endothelial elements, constitute probably the most important means which the body possesses for its defense against invading microorganisms. The ability of these cells to attack bacteria depends upon their motility, and a proclivity for the ingestion of solid particles (Fig. 28). The latter action, which was first demonstrated by Metchnikoff, is termed *phagocytosis* (phago = I eat). These two varieties of white blood cell are free lances among the body cells; they wander from place to place through the tissues, for practically no part of the body is barred to them. They insinuate a process (pseudopodium), improvised at the mo-

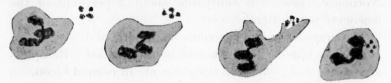

FIG. 28.   Drawing of a neutrophil at ½ minute intervals to show motility and phagocytosis. The dots represent a group of bacteria.

ment from their cell protoplasm, through one of the joints in the endothelium of the capillary wall (Fig. 29).   Then, by causing the semi-fluid substance of the cell body to stream into the protoplasmic protrusion, they pass out of the blood vessels.   By this process of *diapedesis*, as it is called, myriads of the white corpuscles may pass out of the vessels in a remarkably short time.   Reaching a point where the bacteria have entered the body, they surround the threatened area and proceed to destroy the invaders.   If,

FIG. 29.   Diapedesis. A leucocyte shown at short intervals during its progress through the wall of a capillary.

for example, an actively inflamed region should be examined under the microscope, masses of neutrophils would be seen, and many of these would be observed to hold bacteria imprisoned within their bodies.   As many as 15 or 20 organisms may be seen at times within a single cell.   It has been shown that the germs are ingested alive, and remain so for a time within the leucocyte.

When a tissue such as the mesentery or web of a frog, in which the capillaries are clearly visible, is examined in the living state a short time after a suspension of bacteria has been injected into it, the small vessels leading to the site of inoculation are found swarming with neutrophils. In the tissues round about, the ameboid cells are seen moving somewhat ponderously hither and thither to engulf the offending bacteria. The monocytes, though much less numerous, also join in the general attack and show their phagocytic propensities to a marked degree. After the first flooding of the tissues with neutrophils and monocytes, numbers of the latter come to rest and together with other reticulo-endothelial elements of the tissues surround and isolate the infected area from the neighboring healthy tissues. Until this is accomplished the danger of the infection becoming more widely spread always exists. In their struggle against bacteria, equipped as these are with powerful toxins, many of the white cells are killed. These collect within the infected area together with exuded plasma, liquefied tissue cells, and a few red cells that have escaped through the injured walls of the capillaries. This material constitutes pus, and the so-called pus cells are dead leucocytes. The circumscribing wall and its semi-fluid contents constitute an *abscess*. By the action of the phagocytes, aided by a protein-digesting ferment (protease) which they elaborate, the overlying structures whether connective tissue, mucosa or skin are, in part, removed piecemeal. In this way a communication with the exterior is effected and the contents of the abscess are discharged.

Not only bacteria but practically any foreign material, whether a rose thorn or a catgut suture, is attacked and removed if possible, or loosened by the phagocytes. The removal of dead tissue or of blood clot, or the separation of necrotic from living structures is accomplished in the same way. Devitalized bone, though not removed in its entirety, unless it is of very small size, is, nevertheless, eroded and separated from the living tissue by the leucocytes. The disappearance of effete organs, such as the tail and gills of the metamorphosing tadpole or the creeping muscles of insect larvae is effected in a similar manner.

The functions of the other varieties of granulocytes — the eosinophils and basophils — are unknown. They are not markedly motile and are not phagocytic. Nor is much known of the functions of the lymphocytes. A great migration of lymphocytes characterizes certain chronic types of inflammation. By being transformed into fixed connective tissue elements (fibroblasts) they are thought to aid in repair processes. They are not ameboid, that is, they do not progress by the protrusion of pseudopodia. They are capable of a certain slow progression, however, as a result of spasmodic movements of the cell nucleus. They have little phagocytic power and from all accounts possess no proteolytic ferment.

Variations in the number of leucocytes. A rise in the number of white cells of the blood is called *leucocytosis*. The increase may be due to any one of the various cell types. More specific terms are frequently employed, such as, *lymphocytosis*, *eosinophilia*, and *neutrophilia* for an increase in the number of lymphocytes, eosinophils and neutrophils, respectively. The neutrophil count is raised markedly by acute septic infections. Among physiological conditions which cause a moderate increase in this type of white cell are, muscular exercise, pregnancy and adrenaline injections. Lymphocytosis occurs in certain chronic infections; eosinophilia is seen in asthma, in some skin diseases and in diseases caused by parasites, e.g., intestinal worms. In order to determine which type of white cell is responsible for the leucocytosis it is necessary to perform a *differential count.* This consists in examining a stained smear of blood under the microscope and counting the numbers of the different types in a total of several hundred cells. The percentages of the various types are then calculated. In some instances the *proportions* of the different types are altered, though no change occurs in the *total* white cell count.

Leucopenia is the term applied to a reduction in the number of leucocytes below the normal; it occurs in certain infectious diseases, notably pneumonia and typhoid fever. Certain drugs (e.g., amidopyrine) used for the relief of headache, or pain in other parts of the body, are believed to be responsible for a fatal disease in which the granulocytes are reduced to a very low level. Resistance to infection is greatly lowered as a consequence.

The production and maturation of the leucocytes. The granulocytes are produced by the red bone marrow. Like the red cells they pass through several stages of development (see Pl. 1). The cells of the earliest stages are non-granular and show no division of the nucleus into lobes. These cells are called *myeloblasts*. Subsequent stages are marked by the appearance of granules which increase in number as maturation progresses and undergo differentiation into the three types, but the nucleus as yet shows no lobulation. These cells are called *myelocytes*. In the final stage, i.e., just before the cell is discharged from the marrow into the general circulation, constriction of the nucleus occurs at one point, but no definite division into lobes is evident. As already mentioned, the lobulation becomes pronounced and the number of lobes increases as the cell ages in the circulation. The life of a granulocyte is about 21 days.

The lymphocytes are produced in the lymphoid tissues, e.g., lymph glands, spleen, etc.

THE BLOOD PLATELETS OR THROMBOCYTES

These are small bodies about a quarter of the diameter of a red blood corpuscle. They do not possess a nucleus but their protoplasm contains distinct granules (Fig. 30). Their origin is not known with certainty. They are believed by some to be simply fragments of protoplasm broken off from large giant cells — the *megakaryocytes* — present in the bone marrow (Fig. 31). Others claim that they are derived from disintegrated erythrocytes. The platelets number about

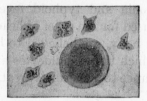

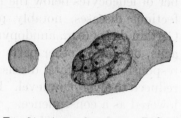

FIG. 30. Blood platelets. A red blood cell shown for comparison of size.

FIG. 31. A megakaryocyte. Red cell shown for size comparison.

250,000 per cubic millimeter. They play an important part in the coagulation of the blood (p. 58).

THE RETICULO-ENDOTHELIAL SYSTEM

This is a system of primitive cells normally present in the general connective tissue, lungs, spleen, liver, lymph glands, bone marrow and other situations. There are several varieties, but all possess phagocytic properties, and some of very large size are actively motile. One type of reticulo-endothelial cell, namely the monocyte, has already been mentioned as being present in blood. Reticulo-endothelial cells of the spleen are responsible for the final disposal of the fragments of red cells which they engulf, the hemoglobin being freed of iron and converted to bile pigment (p. 261). The reticulo-endothelial cells in the blood sinuses of the liver are known as Kupffer cells. These, as well as those in bone marrow and the general connective tissues, also possess the ability to convert into bile pigment the hemoglobin liberated from disintegrated red cells. The reticulo-endothelial cells of the general connective tissues are of exceptionally large size. They play a prominent role in the body's defense against invasion by microorganisms. These cells are actively motile, ingesting bacteria and any other foreign material which may be introduced into the tissues. After the injection of India ink (which consists of a suspension of carbon grains) into an animal, these macrophages,[1] as they are called, gorge themselves with the foreign particles. They are thus made conspicuous beneath the microscope (Fig. 32). In inflammatory conditions they gather in large numbers around and

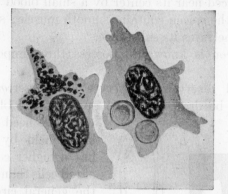

FIG. 32. Macrophages containing phagocytosed carbon grains (*left*) and red blood corpuscles (*right*).

within the inflamed part. In the lung, macrophages are active in the removal of foreign particles (e.g., dust, carbon particles) which have been carried into the alveoli by the inspired air.

THE SPLEEN

The spleen is an organ about the size of the fist situated in the abdomen behind the stomach and above, but to some extent overlapping, the left kidney. It contains under ordinary circumstances a relatively large amount of blood which is held in spaces (sinuses) lined by cells belonging to the reticulo-endothelial system. The blood is delivered into the substance of the spleen (splenic pulp) by small arteries. It then percolates into the sinuses through gaps between the cells forming the latter's walls (see Pl. 2 B). The sinuses are drained by veins through which the blood is con-

[1] The smaller phagocytic cells of the blood, namely the neutrophils, are sometimes referred to as *microphages*.

veyed to the portal vein and thence to the liver. Dotted throughout the spleen like islands, and surrounded by the pulp, are small lighter-colored areas composed of lymphoid tissue. These are the corpuscles of Malpighi (an anatomist of the seventeenth century who first described them). Each area is pierced near its center by a small blood vessel. The capsule of the spleen contains smooth muscle; smooth muscle also penetrates its substance.

The spleen is known to possess three important functions.

1. **Blood reservoir.** It serves as a *reservoir for blood* which can be drawn upon to augment the blood volume when the need arises. The blood held by the spleen has a higher concentration of red cells than the blood of the general circulation, so that, when the organ contracts, not only is the total volume of circulating blood increased, but the number of cells per cubic millimeter of blood is also raised. The several conditions which cause the spleen to contract are, a rise in environmental temperature, emotional excitement, carbon monoxide poisoning, hemorrhage and rarefied atmospheres. The immediate stimulus to splenic contraction in the last three conditions is a low oxygen tension in the blood, but its great sensitivity to nervous influence is illustrated by the observation that even a sudden sound, e.g., the slamming of a door, will cause it to contract (see Fig. 33). The spleen also shows spontaneous rhythmical contractions at the rate of about two per minute (Fig. 34). The small

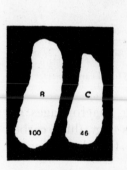

FIG. 33. Changes in volume of spleen as a result of emotional excitement (after Barcroft). Sketch on left, R, rest; C, dog sees cat. The numbers represent the relative sizes of the dog's spleen. Sketch on right, —·— rest; —— smells cat; .... hears cat; ———— sees cat; --------- chases cat.

changes in blood volume which such movements induce
cause corresponding variations in the blood pressure. The
value of the organ in certain emergencies associated with
a need for an additional supply of red cells is evident
from an experiment performed by Professor Barcroft upon
guinea-pigs. Two groups of animals were exposed to carbon
monoxide gas. The concentration of gas in the atmosphere,
and the length of exposure were the same for each group.
The animals of one group, however, had had their spleens
removed; these animals died, whereas those of the other
group which had not been operated upon survived.

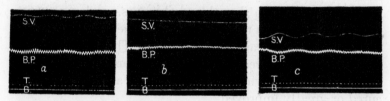

Fig. 34. S.V. = splenic volume. B.P. = general arterial blood pressure.
T = time, 5 sec. B = baseline at 40 mm. Hg. Spleen in plethysmograph; a,
before clamping splenic vessels, b, after clamping vessels, c, after removal of clamp.
(From Barcroft and Nisimaru.)

2. **Destruction of damaged red cells.** This function depends upon the presence of the large phagocytic cells (macrophages) already mentioned under the section on the
reticulo-endothelial system. Healthy red cells appear to be
immune to attack from these scavenger cells, but cells which
have outlived their usefulness, or those which are in some
way abnormal, are readily disposed of. Fragments of red
cells which have broken up in the blood stream are also ingested by the macrophages of the spleen.

3. **The formation of lymphocytes.** The lymphoid tissue
of the spleen, like similar tissue in other situations, lymph
glands, etc., manufactures lymphocytes. In embryonic life,
erythrocytes and granulocytes are also formed in the spleen,
but its ability to produce these types of blood cells ceases
before birth.

The spleen probably possesses other functions which have not yet been discovered. It exercises certain functions, e.g., bile pigment production and antibody formation, by virtue of the large numbers of reticulo-endothelial elements which it contains. It has not been demonstrated to possess an endocrine function (p. 328). That it is an important organ and guards the welfare of its possessor in several ways is undoubted. Nevertheless, it is not essential to life under ordinary circumstances, for when excised it is scarcely missed. Excision of the spleen (splenectomy) is practised for certain hemorrhagic diseases in which the platelets are reduced in number, presumably as a result of some abnormal action which it exerts upon these blood elements. Splenectomy is also performed for a type of hemolytic anemia in which the red cells are more fragile than normal. The spleen appears to be in some way responsible for the increased fragility of the cells, for, following its removal, the anemia is usually cured or greatly improved.

THE LYMPH AND THE LYMPHATIC SYSTEM

The formation and composition of lymph. The tissue fluid, as explained elsewhere, is derived from the blood plasma. A large part of the transuded fluid is returned to the capillary near its venous end. But the tissue spaces, as well as being in relation with the blood capillaries, are also drained by fine capillary vessels called *lymphatics*. Whereas the fluid reabsorbed by the blood capillaries is an aqueous solution of crystalloids (inorganic salts, sugar, urea, etc.), the fluid which passes into the lymph vessels contains some plasma protein as well. Small colloidal particles, such as those of India ink and other dyes which may have entered the tissue spaces from the blood, are also taken up by the lymphatics. Such particles do not return to the circulation through the walls of the blood capillaries. The fluid in the lymphatic vessels is called *lymph*, but it is almost identical in composition with tissue fluid. Lymph contains the same constituents as are found in blood plasma, though in different concentrations. It contains the three plasma proteins, but the total protein concentration is between 3 and 4 per cent as compared with around 7 per cent for plasma. The calcium and total phosphorus are both lower than in the plasma; the other constituents, e.g., sodium, potassium, magnesium, chlorine, sugar, urea, etc., are in about the same concentrations in the two fluids. Lymph contains numerous lymphocytes, an odd granulocyte, but no red cells, under normal circumstances. The lymphocyte count varies considerably in different specimens of lymph from 1,000 to 20,000 per cubic millimeter.

The lymph vessels (lymphatics). The lymphatic system commences at the periphery in a network of capillary vessels. Such vessels are found in the subcutaneous tissues (see Fig. 35), in the connective tissues of muscles and of the abdominal and thoracic viscera. Those in the villi of the small intestine are called *lacteals*. Through them a large proportion of the fat of the food is absorbed into the circulation, their name having been suggested by the milky appearance of their contents (usually referred to as the *chyle*) after a meal of fat. The lymph capillaries join to form larger vessels which ultimately form two main trunks — the *thoracic duct* and the *right lymphatic duct*. The former receives all the lymph of the body except that from the right side of the head, neck and thoracic wall, right arm, right lung, right side of the heart and upper surface of the liver. Lymphatics of these parts drain into the right lymphatic duct. Each of these large vessels opens into the subclavian vein of the corresponding side of the body (see Fig. 35).

The lymph nodes. At certain strategic points in the course of the medium-sized lymph vessels are situated small ovoid or round structures composed of lymphoid tissue. These are the *lymph nodes* (Fig. 36). The lymph in its course from the tissue spaces to the point where it is returned to the blood must pass through the lymph nodes,

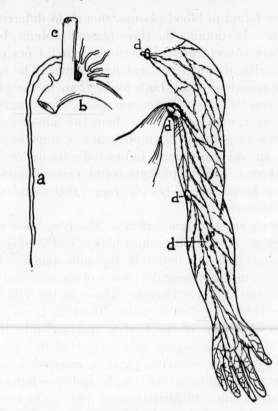

Fig. 35. *On left*, thoracic duct showing opening into left subclavian vein (*b*); *a*, thoracic duct; *c*, internal jugular vein. *On right*, lymphatics of hand and forearm; *d*, lymph nodes.

which act, in a sense, as sieves; any bacteria which enter the lymph current and would, otherwise, enter the blood stream are thus removed. In the upper part of the body lymph nodes are situated beneath the skin on the inside of the front of the elbow (Fig. 38), in the armpit, behind the ear and running down either side of the neck. Those in the armpit and at the elbow drain lymph from the hand, those of the neck receive lymph from the head and throat. A group of lymph nodes can be felt as hard shot-like objects in the groin; another group, situated behind the knee, drain lymph from the foot and leg. Lymph nodes are also situated more deeply in the tissues of the neck and limbs, as well as along the course of the lymph vessels draining the viscera. When the hand or foot is infected the lymph glands at the elbow and armpit in the one instance, and at the knee or in the groin in the other, may become inflamed and swollen as a result of bacteria or their products which have been carried upwards by the lymph current. In septic conditions of the scalp, throat or ear, the nodes receiving lymph from the infected area become similarly involved. Within the nodes, bacteria are attacked by leucocytes and other phagocytic cells. The lymph nodes must, therefore, be looked upon as important elements of defense against the invasion of the blood by microorganisms travelling along the lymphatic channels. They constitute a second defense line, the phagocytic cells at the primary site of infection bearing the first shock of the attack.

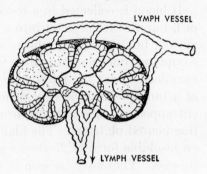

FIG. 36. A lymph node in cross section, diagrammatic.

The lymph nodes, and other collections of lymphoid tissue in the spleen, intestinal walls (Peyer's patches), tonsils, etc., are also hemopoietic organs, their functions in this regard being confined, however, in most animals and in man to the manufacture of lymphocytes.

Edema. An increase in the quantity of tissue fluid to the point where it causes definite swelling of a part is called *edema*. It is most frequently seen in the skin and subcutaneous tissues, as a symptom of heart or of kidney disease. The skin appears "puffy," and, when one presses it with a finger, a dent or pit is left which takes a little time to level up again.

Edema is due to an imbalance of those factors regulating the interchange of fluids between the vessels and the tissue spaces (see p. 28). It may result, therefore, from any of the following causes, (a) increased capillary pressure, as in heart disease, (b) reduced plasma osmotic pressure, as in chronic kidney disease, (c) increased permeability of the capillary wall, as in acute kidney disease, (d) obstruction of the lymph channels (lymphatic edema).

THE COAGULATION OF BLOOD AND LYMPH

If blood is collected in a test-tube it will be found after 5 or 6 minutes to have set into a jelly. The tube may be inverted, but the blood, which is now said to have *clotted* or *coagulated*, does not run out. When a section of this clot is examined under the microscope it is found to be composed of a tangled mesh of very delicate fibrils among which are entrapped, as in a net, erythrocytes, leucocytes and many fragmented platelets. The filaments are composed of *fibrin*, an insoluble form *of fibrinogen* produced during the clotting process. They may be seen in many places to radiate from centers formed of platelets. If the clot be allowed to stand for a while it undergoes shrinkage, and, as it shrinks, expresses from its meshes a clear faintly straw-colored fluid. This is the *serum*. The serum remains fluid indefinitely; it is quite incapable of clotting, for it contains no fibrinogen. Plasma separated from the blood cells by centrifuging, clots in a way similar to that of whole blood and expresses the clear serum. The clot is white, since it contains no cells, but except for this difference it is identical with that formed in whole blood. The clotting process is essentially, therefore, a phenomenon of the plasma. Lymph also clots though somewhat more slowly than does blood or plasma.

The clotting mechanism. Four substances are necessary for the coagulation of blood; *prothrombin*, *thromboplastin*, *calcium* and *fibrinogen*. Prothrombin and thromboplastin are ferments. Fibrinogen, prothrombin and calcium are present in circulating blood. Thromboplastin is present in all tissues but is absent or present in small quantities only in the free state in the circulation. When blood is shed, thromboplastin is liberated from injured cells and from the platelets and leucocytes of the blood itself. The thrombo-plastin, acting upon the pro-thrombin in the presence of calcium, converts it to the active ferment thrombin. Thrombin acts in turn upon the soluble protein fibrin-ogen, converting it to in-soluble fibrin which, as mentioned above, is depos-ited as fine threads to form the framework of the clot.

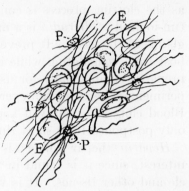

FIG. 36a. Showing section of blood clot. E, erythrocytes; P, platelets.

The foregoing is a descrip-tion of the clotting mecha-nism in the simplest possible terms. The chief factors are summarized in the following scheme.

Prothrombin + calcium + thromboplastin = thrombin
Thrombin + fibrinogen = fibrin

Blood does not clot in the living body because there is not sufficient free thromboplastin to convert the inactive pro-thrombin into the active thrombin. Clotting within the vessels is further safeguarded by the presence in the blood plasma of a substance which neutralizes the action of any thrombin which might be found. This antagonist to throm-bin is called the *normal antithrombin* of plasma. When, however, blood escapes from a cut vessel and flows from a wound, thromboplastin is liberated from the damaged tissue cells and also from disintegrated platelets. Thus the clotting process is immediately initiated.

Anticoagulants. Substances which prevent the coagula-tion of blood are called *anticoagulants*. Among such are *sodium* or *potassium oxalate, fluorides, citrates,* certain *neu-tral salts,* e.g., *sodium* and *magnesium sulphates, hirudin* and *heparin*. The oxalates act by precipitating the calcium of the blood which, as mentioned above, is required for the formation of thrombin. Fluorides and citrates form soluble compounds with the calcium, but the latter, in so far as the clotting process is concerned, is in an inactive form (un-ionized). *Hirudin* is a material secreted by the mouth glands of the leech. It prevents the blood of the parasite's host from coagulating while it is being sucked. Hirudin is prepared commercially for use, chiefly, in physiological experiments; heparin, however, has largely taken its place. Blood clots less readily if kept cold, but its coagulation is only postponed for a short time by this measure.

Heparin (hepar = liver) is an anticoagulant of special interest, since it is found in mammalian liver, lung, muscle and other tissues. It is very powerfully anticoagulant, 1 milligram of a highly purified preparation being capable of preventing for 24 hours the coagulation of 500 cc. of blood, if kept at a temperature of about 50° F.

A substance known as *dicoumarin* has recently been isolated from spoiled sweet clover. This material has been responsible in the past for a fatal hemorrhagic disease occurring in farm animals which have been fed upon spoiled clover. Dicoumarin produces its effect by reducing the prothrombin concentration of the blood to such a low level that clotting cannot occur. Prothrombin is produced in the liver, and it is probable that the poison damages this organ and interferes in some way with prothrombin production.

A low prothrombin concentration of the blood and a tendency to bleed is associated in some animal species with a dietary lack of a vitamin found in certain green foods, e.g., alfalfa, spinach, cabbage, etc. This is known as vitamin K (see p. 320).

We have seen that after calcium has been precipitated from blood by the addition of oxalate, clotting will not occur. Likewise the essential importance of prothrombin in the clotting mechanism is demonstrated by the failure to clot of blood with a low prothrombin concentration.

The importance of the two other primary factors in the clotting process, namely, thromboplastin and fibrinogen, may be illustrated by the following observations. Thromboplastin, as mentioned above, is derived from tissue cells and from damaged platelets in the blood itself. If the blood is drawn by means of a syringe directly from a blood vessel into a clean glass container made smooth by a coating of liquid paraffin, the platelets remain largely intact. For this reason, and because the blood does not come into contact with the tissues, it receives a minimum quantity of thromboplastin and as a consequence clots much more slowly than usual. The experiment of the "living test tube" also demonstrates the indispensability of thromboplastin for the clotting of blood. When a short section of the jugular vein in the living animal is isolated by ligatures from the rest of the vessel and removed, the blood within it, since it remains undisturbed and in contact with the smooth and uninjured lining of the vein's wall, does not clot for many hours.

Defibrinated blood is blood from which the fibrin has been removed; it is incapable of forming a clot. Defibrination is carried out by whipping the blood with a bundle of thin twigs or wires. As clotting occurs the fibrin collects upon the twigs and can in this way be removed, leaving only the serum and cells.

Means used to hasten coagulation. The coagulation of blood as it issues from a wound can be accelerated by several measures. Heat, powder dusted on the wound, tissue extracts (containing thromboplastin) and various chemicals (known from their action in this regard as *styptics* or *hemostatics*) accelerate the clotting process. Among the latter are alum, ferric chloride, zinc chloride and silver nitrate. Such substances arrest bleeding in two ways; they hasten clotting of the blood through the precipitation of the plasma proteins which, by forming a sticky mass, mechanically impede the flow of blood and thus favor platelet disintegration; they also cause constriction of the walls of the small bleeding vessels. Certain physiological conditions hasten coagulation. Blood shed after muscular exercise or emotional excitement clots more quickly than usual owing to the discharge of *adrenaline* into the circulation (p. 347). Adrenaline injected into the body also causes a sample of blood, drawn shortly after the injection, to clot more quickly, but no such effect results from adding adrenaline to blood outside the body, or by applying it to a bleeding vessel. In the latter instance, however, adrenaline tends to stop the bleeding by constricting the small vessels with which it comes into contact. Thus, superficial bleeding or slow oozing of blood is very quickly arrested. The arrest of bleeding either by hastening coagulation of the blood or by constriction of the bleeding vessels is called *hemostasis*.

HEMORRHAGIC STATES DUE TO FAILURE OF THE CLOTTING MECHANISM

In rare instances a deficiency of *fibrinogen* is the cause of the blood failing to form a firm clot, with the result that severe hemorrhage may follow a wound which in a normal person would be of little concern. It is a very common practice to give *calcium* in the belief that it will promote coagulation of the blood in hemorrhagic states. It appears, however, that the blood is never so low in calcium that clotting fails. Contrary to what might be expected, a hemorrhagic tendency is never due to a low concentration of calcium in the blood. Certain serious effects (e.g., tetany) ensue before the blood calcium is reduced to the point where the clotting mechanism is interfered with. The common use of calcium to promote the coagulation of the blood in hemorrhagic states is therefore without any scientific foundation.

A depression of the prothrombin of the blood (hypoprothrombinemia) is one of the commonest defects of the clotting mechanism. The tendency to bleed in *obstructive jaundice* and in the *hemorrhagic disease of the newborn* is due to this cause which is the result in turn of a lack of vitamin K.

In obstructive jaundice bile, which is an essential for the absorption of vitamin K, does not reach the intestine. The body fails, therefore, to secure the vitamin required for the manufacture of prothrombin.

In the newborn child the prothrombin concentration of the blood is in some instances far below the normal value. The hemorrhagic tendency is corrected by the administration of vitamin K.

The fatal hemorrhagic disease of farm animals which have been poisoned with *dicoumarin*, a material formed in spoiled sweet clover, has been mentioned.

Hemophilia is a disease in which the blood takes an abnormally long time to clot. The blood of a normal person clots within 5 or 6 minutes after its withdrawal from the body. In hemophilia the blood may remain fluid for an hour or more. There is grave danger, therefore, of a person afflicted with this disease bleeding to death, even from a trivial wound. Hemophilia is hereditary but it occurs solely in males and is transmitted only by females. This sex-linked type of heredity is also seen in the case of color blindness.

The manner in which the disease is carried from generation to generation may be illustrated by an example. If a man suffering from hemophilia — commonly known as a *bleeder* — marries a normal woman, none of the offspring of the union will show the disease. The daughters, nevertheless, but not the sons, will, when they marry, transmit the disease to *their* sons, but not to their daughters. The latter, however, can transmit it. The disease, therefore, skips a generation, a bleeder inheriting it from his mother's male forebears. Thus:

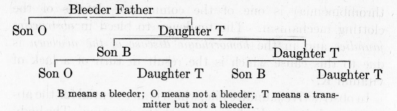

B means a bleeder; O means not a bleeder; T means a trans-
mitter but not a bleeder.

What part of the clotting mechanism is at fault in this disease is uncertain.   There is not a deficiency of calcium, of thrombin or of thromboplastin, and heparin is not present in excess.   According to Howell it is due to an abnormality of the platelets which are said to be less fragile than normally and, therefore, do not break up as they should and supply thromboplastin.   Bleeding due to this disease is treated most successfully by blood transfusions.

Purpura is another hemorrhagic disease, in which blood leaks from the small vessels of the skin and mucous membranes.   When the hemorrhages are from the cutaneous vessels, the skin is discolored by small purplish patches. Some defect in the capillary walls and a reduction in the number of thrombocytes appear to be the chief factors concerned in the production of the disease.   A sample of blood is usually found to clot within the normal time.   One severe type of purpura is apparently due to some destructive action of the spleen upon the platelets.   Removal of the spleen is followed in most instances by an increase in the platelet count and a cessation of the hemorrhages.

THE REACTION OF THE BLOOD

The acidity or alkalinity of a solution is dependent upon its concentration in hydrogen ions (H^+) or hydroxyl ions (OH^-), respectively; that is, upon the degree to which the molecules are dissociated into their constituent ions.   A tenth normal solution of hydrochloric acid (H^+Cl^-), for example, contains a high concentration of hydrogen ions, whereas the hydrogen ion concentration of a tenth normal solution of acetic acid is very much lower. The acid properties of hydrochloric acid are, therefore, much greater than those of acetic acid. Similarly, a tenth normal solution of sodium hydroxide (Na^+OH^-) has a much higher concentration in hydroxyl ions than has a tenth normal solution of sodium bicarbonate. The former solution is therefore more alkaline. It must be emphasized that it is the concentration of the *hydrogen ion*, i.e., the extent to which the molecule is dissociated, and not the total number of *hydrogen atoms* which determines the acid reaction. Thus, HCl though it contains only one hydrogen atom in its molecule undergoes almost complete dissociation into H^+ and Cl^- and is, in consequence, a much stronger acid than acetic, whose molecules dissociate to a relatively small extent. Water undergoes dissociation to a very slight degree into H^+ and OH^-. The ionized hydrogen in a liter of water is 0.0000001 gram, or more conveniently expressed, 1×10^{-7} gram. We therefore say that the H ion concentration of water is 1×10^{-7}. The symbol $^{-7}$ to the right of the figure 10 is termed the *negative exponent* or *index*, and means that to express the value in the form of a decimal fraction the figure 1 must be placed 7 places to the right of the decimal point (0.0000001). Expressed as a vulgar fraction the 10^{-7} would be $\frac{1}{10000000}$.

Other examples of this system of notation are:

10^{-1} means 0.1 or $\frac{1}{10}$

10^{-2} " 0.01 or $\frac{1}{100}$

10^{-3} " 0.001 or $\frac{1}{1000}$, and so on

The concentration of OH ions in water is also 1×10^{-7} gram. That is, the H^+ ions and OH^- ions are in equal concentration; water is therefore neutral in reaction. Now the *product* of the concentrations of H ions and OH ions in water is 1×10^{14} [$(1 \times 10^{-7}) \times (1 \times 10^{-7}) = 1 \times 10^{-14}$]. Furthermore, in any aqueous solution, whether acid, neutral or alkaline, the product of the concentrations of H^+ and OH^- ions is constant at 1×10^{-14}. This means that in an acid solution the H^+ ion concentration increases, whereas the OH^- ion concentration is reduced reciprocally. It is evident, then, that in order to express the reaction of an aqueous solution it is not necessary to give the concentrations of both H^+ and OH^- ions, but only of the H^+ ion. The reaction of water or any other neutral solution is indicated, therefore, by stating that it has an H^+ ion concentration (usually designated cH) of 1×10^{-7}. The hydrogen ion concentrations of alkaline solutions are less than 1×10^{-7}, i.e., 1×10^{-8}, 1×10^{-9}, 1×10^{-10}, and so on, according to the degree of alkalinity. The hydrogen ion concentration of acid solutions is more than 1×10^{-7}, i.e., 1×10^{-6}, 1×10^{-5}, 1×10^{-4}, etc.

To summarize: neutral solutions have 0.0000001 gram of ionized hydrogen per liter, i.e., a cH of 1×10^{-7}.

Alkaline solutions have a lower H^+ ion concentration, i.e., from 1×10^{-7} to 1×10^{-14}.

Acid solutions have a higher H^+ ion concentration, i.e., from 1×10^{-7} to 1×10^{-1}.

Within recent years a more convenient method of expressing the hydrogen ion concentration has been introduced, in which the symbol pH, instead of cH, is used. Thus the expression $cH \times 10^{-7}$, indicating a neutral solution, becomes pH 7. Alkaline solutions have pH's ranging from pH 7 to pH 14, acid solutions from pH 7 to pH 1. It will be noted that the lower the pH the higher is the hydrogen ion concentration, i.e., the less alkaline or the more acid is the solution. More advanced texts should be consulted if the reader wishes to understand the mathematical basis for this method of expressing the hydrogen ion concentration in terms of pH.

Arterial blood has a pH of between 7.35 and 7.45. Venous blood is very slightly *less* alkaline; the change is due to carbon dioxide and small quantities of lactic acid which the blood absorbs in passing through the tissues. Though large quantities of acid (carbonic, lactic, sulphuric, hydrochloric, etc.) are constantly being produced in the body as a result of various metabolic processes, the reaction of the blood and

other body fluids remains remarkably constant around the
figures just given.   The three important mechanisms responsible for the maintenance of this constancy of reaction
are:

1. The elimination of CO_2 by the lungs (p. 186).

2. The excretion of acid by the kidney [the urine is de-
cidedly acid in reaction (p. 210)].

3. The buffer systems of the blood.

Buffers may be defined as chemical substances which permit only a very slight change in the reaction of a solution to
occur upon the addition of acid.   It is from this action in
buffering the shock, one might say, of the added acid that
these substances derive their name.   For example, when
hydrochloric acid is poured into a solution of sodium bicarbonate the very weak carbonic acid, together with sodium
chloride, a neutral salt, is produced.   Furthermore, the carbonic acid is volatile; it escapes into the atmosphere.   The
result is that little change in the reaction of the solution occurs, even though it has received relatively large amounts of
acid.   The sodium bicarbonate acts as a buffer.   Thus:

$$HCl + NaHCO_3 = NaCl + H_2CO_3 \nearrow CO_2$$

| Hydrochloric acid | Sodium bicarbonate | Sodium Chloride | Carbonic acid |

The chief buffer of the plasma and tissue fluids is sodium
bicarbonate.   A fixed acid such as lactic, formed during
muscular activity, reacts with the bicarbonate as shown in
the following equation.

$$LA + NaHCO_3 = NaL + H_2CO_3 \nearrow CO_2$$

| Lactic acid | Sodium bicarbonate | Sodium lactate | Carbonic acid |

The sodium bicarbonate of the plasma thus serves as a store
of alkali available for the protection of the body against
poisoning with the acid products of metabolism.   It is therefore called the *alkali reserve*.

Hemoglobin is a weak acid; it is combined in the red blood cells with alkali (potassium) to form potassium hemoglobinate (KHb). This alkali acts to buffer carbonic acid entering the blood from the tissues. The contents of the erythrocytes, however, are separated from the plasma by a semipermeable membrane which will not permit the passage of K^+, Na^+ or Ca^+ ions but allows the free passage of Cl^-, HCO_3^- and other negative ions, as well as the H^+ ion. When, therefore, the carbon dioxide produced in the tissues enters the plasma the following interchange of ions occurs across the erythrocyte boundary. The carbon dioxide (CO_2) diffuses freely into the cell and, through the action of a ferment called *carbonic anhydrase*, combines with H_2O to form carbonic acid (H_2CO_3). The carbonic acid being a stronger acid than reduced hemoglobin seizes the base combined with the pigment to form potassium bicarbonate — $K^+HCO_3^-$ which dissociates into K^+ and HCO_3^- ions. The membrane of the cell as just mentioned is permeable to HCO_3^- ions but not to K^+ ions. HCO_3^- ions diffuse across the cell boundary into the plasma; the K^+ ions are retained. In order to maintain the balance between negative and positive ions on the two sides of the cell membrane Cl^- ions derived from the Na^+Cl^- of the plasma pass into the cell in exchange for the HCO_3^- ions which pass out. In the plasma the HCO_3^- ions unite with the Na^+ ions, which had been coupled with Cl^- ions, thus forming sodium bicarbonate (Na^+HCO^-). The mechanism just described is termed the *chloride shift* (see Fig. 37). This mechanism is responsible for the phenomenon, now well recognized, that an increase in the carbon dioxide of the plasma causes a rise in the alkali reserve (sodium bicarbonate). In the lungs, ionic interchanges in the reverse order occur. The hemoglobin when it becomes oxygenated is a very much stronger acid than is reduced hemoglobin or carbonic acid. It therefore recaptures the alkali (K^+) bound to carbonic acid. The carbonic anhydrase, whose action is now reversed, decomposes the carbonic acid into

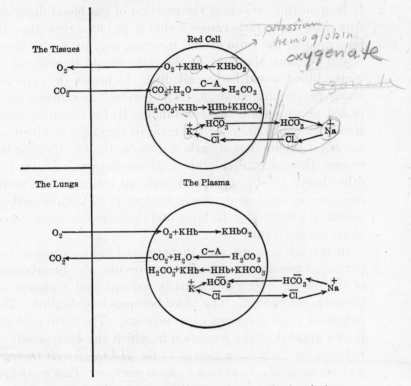

Fig. 37. Diagram illustrating chloride shift. C–A = carbonic anhydrase.

carbon dioxide (CO_2) and water (H_2O). The carbon dioxide diffuses out of the cells, as they traverse the capillaries of the lungs, and is exhaled. The concentration of HCO_3^- ions within the cells is reduced as a result of these reactions. HCO_3^- ions pass from the plasma into the cells and Cl^- ions are transferred from the cells to the plasma. The sodium bicarbonate of the plasma is reduced, the sodium chloride increased by the interchange.

Acidosis and alkalosis. The proportion of carbonic acid to sodium bicarbonate in the plasma is about 1 to 20, thus:

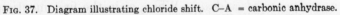

$$\frac{H_2CO_3}{NaHCO_3} = \frac{1}{20}$$

It is upon this ratio that the reaction of the blood depends. Any shift in the ratio causes a change in blood reaction. If, for example, the ratio should increase, say, to $\frac{1}{25}$ the blood would be more alkaline. If the ratio should be reduced to $\frac{1}{15}$ the blood would be less alkaline. In health the ratio remains practically constant. The several mechanisms mentioned above ensure this constancy. If, for example, there should be a tendency for the ratio to rise, as a result of an increased production of carbon dioxide, the bicarbonate increases through the chloride shift mechanism. If, on the other hand, the bicarbonate is reduced owing to the accumulation of fixed acids (see equation, p. 67), more carbon dioxide is excreted by the lungs and the ratio thus maintained at its normal value.

In certain diseases, e.g., diabetes and kidney disease (nephritis), excessive acid production occurs, the bicarbonate of the plasma becomes markedly reduced and a change in the ratio may result. The blood becomes less alkaline. The condition is then spoken of as *acidosis*. The term acidosis is also applied to the condition in which the bicarbonate is reduced *but there is no change in the* $H_2CO_3/NaHCO_3$ *ratio and, consequently, no change in blood reaction*. This is spoken of as *compensated acidosis*. When, as in the first mentioned instance, the acidosis is accompanied by a change in blood reaction it is said to be *uncompensated*.

It should be emphasized that the $H_2CO_3/NaHCO_3$ ratio does not vary from its normal value of $\frac{1}{20}$ unless serious disease exists. There are two possible exceptions to this statement. First, in very strenuous muscular exercise the large quantities of carbon dioxide and lactic acid produced might result in a slight and *temporary* reduction in the alkalinity of the blood. Secondly, forced breathing (p. 193) if prolonged may, through the excessive loss of carbon dioxide, cause the blood to become temporarily slightly more alkaline.

It should be remembered, moreover, that the blood practically never, except in the last stages of some fatal disease, becomes *actually acid* in reaction, i.e., with a pH less than 7, and rarely does it even approach the neutral point. The range of blood reaction compatible with life is from about pH 7.8 to 6.8. It is quite evident then, that the term acidosis is frequently used — especially by the advertisers of quack remedies — without any clear understanding of its meaning.

Alkalosis is the corresponding term used to denote an increase in sodium bicarbonate with or without a change in the H_2CO_3/$NaHCO_3$ ratio. As in the case of acidosis it is called compensated or uncompensated, respectively, according to whether or not a change in the ratio and so, of course, in the blood reaction has occurred. Alkalosis may result from the ingestion of large quantities of sodium bicarbonate, from persistent vomiting, when hydrochloric acid is removed in the gastric juice, or from forced breathing when, as already mentioned, unusually large quantities of carbon dioxide are eliminated.

CHAPTER III

THE CIRCULATION

GENERAL DESCRIPTION OF THE CIRCULATORY SYSTEM

THE blood circulates through the body in a completely closed system consisting of a pump — the *heart* — and a network of tubes — the *blood vessels*.

The heart is a hollow muscular organ, roughly cone-shaped, situated near the center of the thoracic cavity, and in close relation to the lungs. About a third of its bulk lies to the right and two thirds to the left of the mid-line of the body. The heart is divided by partitions or septa into four chambers — the *right* and *left auricles* (or *atria*), and the *right* and *left ventricles*. The auricles are situated above, posteriorly and to the right; the ventricles below, anteriorly and to the left. The broad upper part of the heart formed by the auricles is called the *base*. Its somewhat pointed lower part formed by the left ventricle is called the *apex;* this is directed downwards, forwards and to the left (Fig. 38).

The right and left halves of the heart — the right auricle and ventricle, on the one hand, and the left auricle and ventricle, on the other — are not in communication. The partition interposed between the two auricles is called the *interauricular septum;* that separating the two ventricles from one another is named the *interventricular septum.* The auricle of each side communicates with the corresponding ventricle through an opening, the *auriculo-ventricular orifice,* guarded by the *auriculo-ventricular valve.* These valves open toward the ventricles and close when the ventricle contracts, thus preventing the passage of blood backwards into the auricles. The auriculo-ventricular valve on the left side is also known as the *mitral* valve, that on the right side as the *tricuspid* valve (see also p. 127). The muscular walls of the auricles are thin as compared with the muscle of the ventricles. The left ventricle has a wall about double the thickness of that of the right ventricle, since the work which it must perform is much greater than that performed by

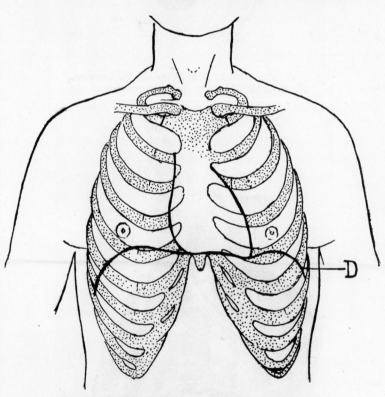

FIG. 38. Showing position of heart in relation to the front of the chest wall. D, diaphragm.

the right ventricle (Fig. 39). The heart chambers are lined by a delicate endothelial membrane called the *endocardium*. Springing from the wall of each ventricular cavity are two small muscular pillars, somewhat conical in shape and known as the *papillary muscles* (*musculi papillares*). From the apices of the latter, slender bands, the *chordae tendineae*, arise

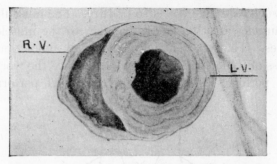

FIG. 39. Cross section of heart through the ventricles.
R.V., right ventricle; L.V., left ventricle.

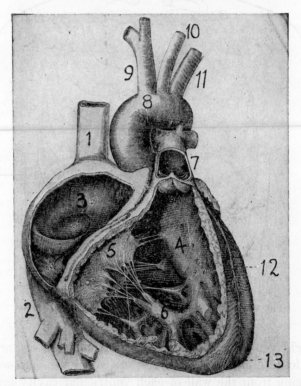

FIG. 40. Showing interior of the right auricle and ventricle. 1, superior vena
cava; 2, inferior vena cava; 3, right auricular cavity; 4, right ventricular cavity
(figure is on interventricular septum); 5, right auriculoventricular (tricuspid)
valve; 6, musculus papillaris; 7, pulmonary artery with part of wall removed;
8, arch of the aorta; 9, innominate artery; 10, left common carotid artery;
11, left subclavian artery; 12, outside of left ventricle; 13, left ventricle at apex.
(After Allen Thomson.)

and are attached to the ventricular aspects of the auriculo-ventricular valves (Fig. 40).

The arrangement of the fibers of the ventricles is very complex. They are disposed in a superficial and a deep series of layers. Of the superficial layers some course from the upper and anterior part of the right ventricle, downwards and to the left, looping around the apex, in the form

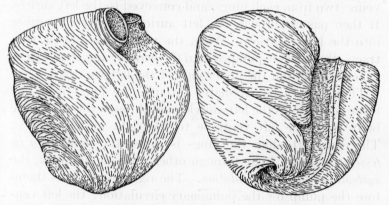

Fig. 41. Dissection to show the muscle fibers of the ventricles. (After Mall.)

of a vortex (Fig. 41). Passing upwards and inwards they end in the papillary muscles of the left ventricle. Other superficial groups of fibers pass diagonally across the posterior surface of the heart from right to left. Of the deep layers, some pass from the papillary muscles of one ventricle to those of the other, encircling both ventricles in a scroll-like or S-shaped manner. Other groups encircle the left ventricle alone.

The right side of the heart contains venous blood, that is, blood which has passed through the tissues and given up a proportion of its load of oxygen (p. 187). The left side contains bright red (arterial) blood — blood which has been oxygenated in the lungs. The venous blood is delivered to the right auricle by two large veins — the *superior vena cava* which drains blood from the upper part of the body (head, neck and arms), and the *inferior vena cava* which conveys blood from the lower part of the body (lower limbs and abdominal organs). The blood flows from the right auricle through the auriculo-ventricular orifice, into the right ventricle, from which it is discharged during ventricular contraction into the *pulmonary artery* and thence through the vessels of the lungs. After passing through the vessels of the lungs, the oxygenated blood is collected by the four pulmonary veins (two from each lung), and conveyed to the left auricle. It then passes through the left auriculo-ventricular orifice into the left ventricle. When the ventricular muscle contracts, the blood is pumped into the *aorta* — the great artery which arises from the upper part of the left ventricle.

Thus, the blood circulates through the lungs from the right ventricle to the left auricle, and through the rest of the body from the left ventricle to the right auricle (Pl. 3). The course through the lungs is called the *pulmonary* or *lesser circulation*, that through other parts of the body, the *systemic* or *greater circulation*. The right ventricle is therefore the pump for the pulmonary circulation; the left ventricle serves a corresponding function for the systemic or greater circulation. Both ventricles contract at the same instant.

Though it is now a matter of general knowledge that the blood circulates in this way, the truth lay hidden until William Harvey, an English physician of the seventeenth century, made the discovery. By his clear reasoning from a number of observations and simple experiments he convinced those who were not blinded by preconceived notions that the blood must take the course outlined above. In 1628 he published his great work *Exercitatio anatomica de motu cordis et sanguinis in animalibus* (*Anatomical Exercise on the Motion of the Heart and Blood in Animals*). Before Harvey's day the dogmas of Galen, a Greek physician who practised medicine in Rome in the second century of the Christian era, dominated all medical thought. His views on physiology were accepted without question as the infallible pronouncements of a god. According to Galen the food material absorbed from the intestines was conveyed by the portal vein to the liver where it was converted into blood. This newly formed and somewhat crude type of blood then passed to the right side of the heart where it was purified, the impurities, finding vent through the pulmonary artery and lungs, were exhaled in the breath. The blood formed in the liver did not circulate, but was conceived as simply ebbing and flowing in the veins; from it the tissues derived their nutriment. A small part of the blood in the right heart was believed, however, to find its way through invisible pores in the septum to the left side where, mixing with air received from the lungs through the pulmonary veins, it was transformed into a more refined type of blood. This arterial blood, as the result of the action upon it of a vital essence — the *pneuma* — contained in the air, possessed a life-giving principle which Galen called the *vital spirit*.

This brief description of ancient and medieval physiology will give the reader an idea of the fundamental nature and immense importance of Harvey's discovery. Galen was a great and wise physician and experimentalist of his day, and we can see that in his theory of the pneuma, by which he sought to explain the difference between venous and arterial blood, he was groping for an essential life-sustaining principle in air which we now identify as oxygen. Oxygen was not discovered and its importance to living processes recognized until Lavoisier's work in the eighteenth century.

The blood vessels. There are four main types of blood vessel: — *arteries, arterioles, capillaries and veins*.

The arteries are of various sizes; the largest in the body are the *aorta* — which is the sole outlet for the blood from the left ventricle — and the *pulmonary artery*, which receives the contents of the right ventricle. In the human subject each of these vessels is a little over an inch in diameter. Traced peripherally the channels of the arterial system divide and subdivide extensively like the branches and twigs of a tree. The aorta ascends from its origin for a short distance and then, arching, descends in front of the vertebral column through the thorax. At the level of the 4th lumbar vertebra it divides into two vessels — the *right* and *left common iliac arteries*. Each common iliac divides into two branches — the *external iliac* and *hypogastric* arteries. The former carries blood to the lower limbs; after entering the thigh it is called the *femoral artery*. The hypogastric artery is distributed to the pelvis.

The thoracic and abdominal viscera are supplied by branches which spring from the aorta in its course through these cavities. Three large arteries spring from the arch of the aorta; the *left common carotid*, the *left subclavian* and the *innominate arteries*. The last one is a short trunk which divides into the *right common carotid* and the *right subclavian* arteries. The common carotid arteries are the main arterial trunks to the head. They ascend on either side of the neck and at the upper border of the thyroid cartilage divide into the *external* and *internal carotid* arteries. The subclavian arteries convey blood to the upper limbs; at the root of the limb it is called the *axillary artery*, and in the arm the *brachial artery* (see Fig. 42). It will be noted that the common carotid and subclavian arteries on the right side spring from the innominate, whereas the left common carotid and subclavian arise directly from the aorta.

The walls of the arteries are thick and strong; they contain a large proportion of elastic tissue and a smaller amount of smooth muscle. Their interiors are lined by endothelium which is called the *internal coat* or *tunica intima*. The *middle coat* or *tunica media* is made up of elastic and muscular tissues. The *outer coat*, composed of connective tissue, is called the *tunica adventitia* (see Fig. 43). The proportions of smooth muscle and elastic tissue in the arterial wall vary with the size of the artery. Though elastic tissue enters largely into the construction of the largest vessels, e.g., the pulmonary artery and aorta, muscular tissue is relatively small in amount. In the medium and smallest arterial

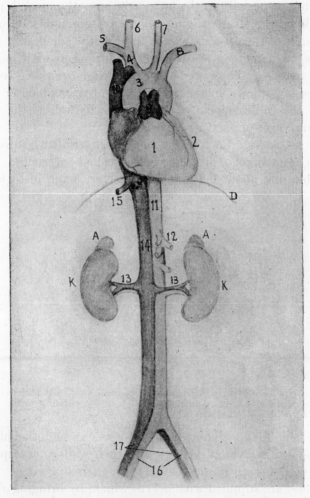

FIG. 42. Diagram of main vessels of the body. Veins and pulmonary artery in darker shading. 1, right ventricle; 2, left ventricle; 3, arch of aorta; 4, innominate artery; 5, right subclavian artery; 6, right common carotid artery; 7, left common carotid artery; 8, left subclavian artery; 9, pulmonary artery; 10, superior vena cava; 11, abdominal aorta; 12, abdominal branches of aorta; 13, renal vein and artery; 14, inferior vena cava; 15, hepatic veins; 16, common iliac arteries; 17, common iliac veins; A, adrenal gland; D, diaphragm; K, kidney.

branches, especially in the latter, the smooth muscle is more abundant, the elastic tissue being correspondingly reduced. The walls of the arteries, except those of the smallest (1 mm. or less in diameter), are themselves furnished with minute blood vessels. These vessels, called *vasa vasorum* (vessels of vessels), ramify in the tunica adventitia and outer layers of the tunica media. The arteries, as well as the vasa vasorum, are supplied with nerves.

The arterioles. Each of the smallest arterial twigs divides into a number of still finer vessels, called arterioles. The arterioles are about 0.2 mm. in diameter, being just visible

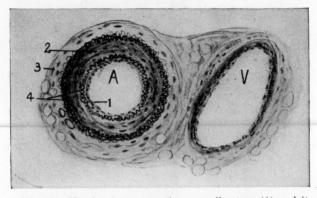

Fig. 43. Showing in cross section a small artery (A) and its companion vein (V). 1, tunica intima; 2, tunica media; 3, tunica adventitia; 4, elastic fibers.

to the naked eye. Though they possess an endothelial lining and a thin layer of elastic tissue, their walls are composed mainly of smooth muscle which form encircling rings. The arterioles are supplied with nerves which, by bringing about contraction or relaxation of the rings of smooth muscle, control the caliber of the arteriole. Thus, the quantity of blood passing through this part of the circulatory system may be altered from time to time as occasion requires (see pp. 99, 149).

The capillaries. An arteriole when traced peripherally is found to break up into a number of extremely narrow tubes, the capillaries. These vessels have a length of from

½ to 1 mm. and a bore which in many instances is no greater, and may be less, than the diameter of a red blood corpuscle (7 to 8 microns). The wall of a capillary consists of a single layer of endothelial cells — a membrane of exquisite thinness which, as mentioned elsewhere (p. 27), permits the free passage of water and crystalloids, but is almost impermeable to the plasma proteins. Lying close to, or in contact with, the capillary wall are peculiar cells whose slender processes form a lattice-work which embraces the vessel (Fig. 44). They are called *Rouget cells*. The capil-

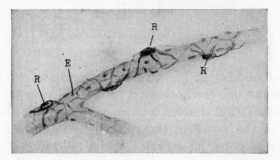

FIG. 44. A capillary. E, endothelial wall; R, Rouget cells.

laries though constituting such an inconspicuous part of the circulation are, nevertheless, the *raison d'etre* for the rest of the circulatory system. The heart is the pump and the relatively thick-walled arteries and veins simply conduits which convey blood to and from the capillaries; at this point the object of the circulation, namely, to convey oxygen and nutritive materials to the tissues and to carry carbon dioxide and waste products away, is fulfilled.

The veins, like the arteries, have walls composed of three coats, but the tunica media is poorly developed as compared with an artery of about the same size. The wall of a vein is, consequently, much thinner than that of its companion artery, but its caliber is considerably larger (see Fig. 43).

HEMODYNAMIC PRINCIPLES

In order that certain features of the circulation may be understood, some of the physical laws governing the flow of liquids through tubes must be briefly reviewed. Some of the more important of these laws may be illustrated by

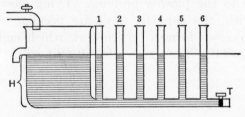

Fig. 45. See text.

means of models. In Fig. 45 is shown a glass reservoir whose outlet is through the horizontal tube H. The latter is fitted with a tap T, and gives off a series of vertical branches. The height of the water in the reservoir represents a certain quantity of potential energy. When the tap is closed, all this energy appears as pressure in the system. The pressure on the wall of the horizontal tube at any point is equivalent

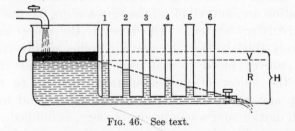

Fig. 46. See text.

to the height (in millimeters of water) of the water column in the vertical tube at that point. It will be noted that the fluid columns (in the vertical tubes and reservoir) are all of the same height.

When the tap is opened water flows along the horizontal tube. A part of the potential energy is converted to energy

of flow — *kinetic energy* (Fig. 46). The level of the first
water column is lower than that of the reservoir, the second
column is lower than the first, the third lower than the
second, and so on. The difference between the water level
in the reservoir and that in the *first tube represents* the proportion of the total potential energy which has been expended in giving velocity to the liquid. This is therefore
called the *velocity head.* The height of any given tube represents, as in the first model, the lateral pressure exerted at
that point upon the wall of the horizontal tube. The height
of the reservoir represents the quantity of potential energy
remaining in the system, and is called the *reservoir head.*
The slope in the levels (pressures) of successive tubes, that

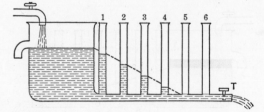

FIG. 47. See text.

is, the difference between the levels of columns 1 and 2, or
between any other two columns, represents the energy which
has been dissipated in overcoming the frictional resistance
offered by the walls of the horizontal tube between the two
points from which the tubes arise. The farther the liquid
has to travel along the horizontal tube, the greater will be
the proportion of the original supply of energy which will
be dissipated in overcoming frictional resistance. The difference between the levels between any two columns is
therefore called the *resistance head.*

When the tap is opened further, as in the model in Fig.
47, the velocity of flow along the horizontal tube increases,
the difference between the water levels of the reservoir and
the first tube (i.e., the velocity head) is greater; also, the
slope in the levels of the liquid columns in successive tubes

is steeper. That is, the pressure at any point in the horizontal tube is less and the velocity greater, while the energy expended in overcoming frictional resistance is increased.

The main facts in the foregoing account can be summarized in the following laws:

1. The lateral pressure is inversely proportional to the velocity, i.e., an increase in velocity reduces the lateral pressure and vice versa.

2. Resistance varies with the length of the horizontal tube, i.e., is proportional to the frictional surface.

3. Resistance is proportional approximately to the square of the velocity. If, for example, velocity is doubled, the resistance is increased fourfold.

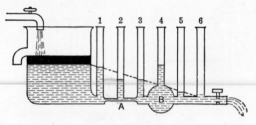

Fig. 48. See text.

Now let us consider a model in which the bore of the horizontal tube, instead of being uniform throughout, as in the models shown in Figs. 45, 46 and 47, is dilated at one part and constricted at another (Fig. 48). The velocity of flow in the dilated portion will be slower and that in the constricted part more rapid than in other parts of the tube. This must be so, since the quantities of water which enter and leave the horizontal tube in a given time, or pass between any two points in the tube, are exactly equal. But a smaller volume of water can be accommodated at any instant in the constricted section (B) than in the dilated section (A). Consequently, in order for the same volume of water to be transmitted per minute, the flow through the constricted part must be more rapid than through the di-

lated part. It is well known that the current of a river becomes more rapid where the river bed is narrowed, but slows
again when the river broadens out, or flows into a lake.
Since, as stated in the first law above, pressure is inversely
proportional to velocity, the pressure rises in the wide part of
the horizontal tube (as indicated by the vertical tube 2)
and falls in the narrowed portion (tube 4).

A fourth law may now be enunciated:

4. In a tube of varying diameter the velocity is inversely
proportional to the sectional area of the stream.

If, as in the model shown in Fig. 49, the tap is placed
about half-way along the horizontal tube, then opening or
closing it will produce opposite effects upon the liquid in the

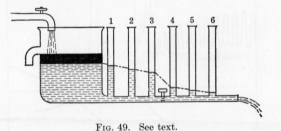

Fig. 49. See text.

sections on either side of it. When the tap is opened the
velocity increases, and the pressure falls in the left hand
section. But, since more liquid enters the right hand section, and thus raises the pressure head, which is equivalent
to raising the height of the reservoir column, both velocity
and pressure in the right hand section are increased.

The tubing through which the blood flows differs, of
course, from that of the models. The vascular walls are not
rigid, but composed of resilient elastic material. For this
reason, and also because certain other factors of a physiological nature exert a modifying influence, the physical
principles outlined above cannot be applied absolutely and
unreservedly to the circulation. Broadly speaking, however, these principles do apply.

THE CIRCULATION

The contraction of the heart furnishes the energy which drives the blood through the vascular system; it is represented in the glass models by the reservoir (reservoir head). The aorta and other arteries are represented by the horizontal tube and its series of upright tubes. The arterioles which, as mentioned on p. 80, can, through nervous influences, be varied in caliber from time to time, correspond

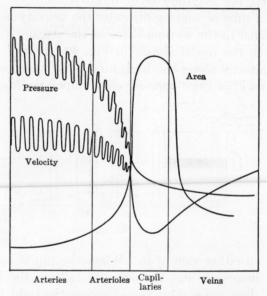

Pressure

Velocity

Area

Arteries   Arterioles   Capillaries   Veins

FIG. 50. Diagram showing the pressure and velocity of the blood in different parts of the vascular system. (Modified from Fredericq.) Note the relation between blood velocity and vascular area, and the absence of rhythmical variations in pressure and velocity in the capillaries and veins.

to the taps in the models. When the arterioles are constricted, the flow from the arterial system to the venous system increases, the pressure in the arteries rises, whereas the venous pressure tends to fall. Dilatation of the arterioles tends to cause the reverse effects. A large part of the energy derived from the contraction of the heart is expended in overcoming the resistance to the flow of blood through the arterioles; a pronounced fall in pressure therefore occurs in the region of these vessels (see Fig. 50). The arterioles, therefore, divide the vascular system into two sections — a high pressure or arterial system, and a low pressure or venous system.

The work of the heart — the cardiac output. The work performed by a machine is expressed in foot-pounds or in kilogram-meters, that is, the vertical distance, in feet or meters, through which a given weight, in pounds or kilograms, is lifted. Thus, if a weight of 2 kilograms is raised to a height of 4 meters the work done is 8 kilogram-meters. The efficiency of the machine is the proportion of the total energy expended which appears as work. Thus:

$$\frac{\text{Work}}{\text{Total energy expended}} = \text{Efficiency}$$

The work performed by the heart when it contracts may be expressed in the same way, for it ejects a certain weight of blood at a mean pressure of about 1.3 meters of water (or blood) which is equivalent to saying that the heart raises the blood to a height of 1.3 meters. As we shall see (p. 93), if a long glass tube be inserted into a large artery, and held vertically, the blood actually rises to a height of several feet.

Under ordinary conditions of bodily rest the greater proportion of the work performed by the heart may be calculated from the following formula.

$$W = \tfrac{7}{6} Q R$$

W = work in kilogram-meters
Q = quantity of blood ejected, in kilograms
R = mean blood pressure in the aorta, in meters of blood

The pressure in the pulmonary artery is only $\tfrac{1}{6}$ of that in the aorta. That is, the pressure developed by the right ventricle is only $\tfrac{1}{6}$ that developed by the left. The quantity of blood ejected by each ventricle is, however, the same. The fraction $\tfrac{7}{6}$, therefore, is used to obtain the work of the whole heart, i.e., of both ventricles.

The cardiac output. The amount of blood ejected by one ventricle per minute is called the *minute volume* of the heart or the cardiac output. The minute volume of the human heart under ordinary resting conditions amounts to from 3 to 4.6 liters, depending upon the size of the individual. It must be remembered, however, that, per minute, an equal volume of blood is ejected by the right ventricle, and that an equal volume passes through the lungs and through the systemic circulation. The minute volume of the heart is therefore also referred to as the *circulation rate*. In other words, it is the quantity of blood which passes per minute through the circulatory system. The quantity of blood ejected by one ventricle at each *beat* of the heart is called the *stroke volume;* it amounts to about 60 cubic centimeters under resting conditions. The cardiac output or minute volume is the product, therefore, of the stroke volume and the heart rate.

The cardiac output is greatly increased during muscular exercise. In a robust healthy young man doing strenuous work, it may amount to over 35 liters. The minute volume of the heart is raised by increasing the output per beat (stroke volume) and usually by increasing the number of beats per minute (pulse rate) as well. In persons of poor muscular development the heart rate accelerates in response to exercise to a greater extent than in those of athletic build. That is, the former individual in order to increase his cardiac output, depends upon increase in heart rate to a greater extent than does the latter. In some athletes, for example, the minute volume may be increased several fold with little or no change in heart rate.

The minute volume of the heart is also increased during *digestion*, at *high environmental temperatures*, during *emotional excitement* and in the *later months of pregnancy*. Among pathological conditions which increase the cardiac output are *hyperthyroidism* (p. 336), *fever* and *severe anemia*. It is reduced in *hypothyroidism* and in certain forms of *cardiac disease*.

The cardiac output in man can be measured only indirectly. The method of measurement is based upon what is generally known as the Fick principle. Fick pointed out that, if the quantity of carbon dioxide which was given off in the lungs by each 100 cc. of blood were known, and the *total* quantity of CO_2 given off over a given period of time were also known, then the volume of blood which had passed through the lungs in that time could be calculated. For example, if the venous blood coming to the lungs contained 58 cc. of carbon dioxide per 100 cc. and the arterial blood leaving the lungs contained 52 volumes per 100 cc., then 6 cc. of carbon dioxide per 100 cc. must have been given off by the blood in its passage through the lungs. The quantities of the gas in the venous and arterial bloods are determined by analyzing samples of the subject's alveolar air; the details of this procedure cannot be given here. The total quantity of carbon dioxide eliminated over a period of a few minutes is next determined (p. 185). Let us say that this amounts to 240 cc. per minute. We have now all the data necessary for the calculation of the cardiac output. Thus:

$$\frac{\text{(Total } CO_2 \text{ eliminated per min.)} \quad 240 \text{ cc.}}{\text{(Difference between volumes of } CO_2 \text{ in venous and arterial bloods)} \quad 6 \text{ cc.}} \times 100 = 4000 \text{ cc. cardiac output or minute volume}$$

THE VELOCITY OF THE BLOOD

The velocity of the blood varies in different parts of the vascular system. It does not, like the blood pressure, show a continuously progressive diminution from the left to the right side of the heart. The blood moves swiftly through the large arteries. In the human aorta, for example, its speed is around 0.4 meters per second when the body is at rest. The velocity decreases moderately throughout the arterial tree, but is greatly reduced in the capillaries, where it averages only 0.5 millimeters per second. The blood upon reaching the venous system speeds up again, and, in the great veins feeding the heart (superior and inferior venae cavae), flows at a velocity not greatly less than that of the blood in the aorta. It must be remembered that (except for very brief periods) the quantity of blood returned to the right side of the heart in a given time must equal that ejected by the left ventricle. Variations in the velocity of the blood in different regions of the circulatory system are dependent simply upon corresponding variations in the cross area of the bed of the blood stream for, as was stated on p. 85, in a tube of varying diameter the velocity is inversely proportional to the cross area of the blood stream. Now, in a closed system such as the circulation it is immaterial whether a broadening of the bed of the stream is caused by the dilatation of a single tube or by the division of the tube into a number of channels. So long as the sum of the cross areas of the channels is increased, even though the diameter of each channel is much less than that of the rest of the tube, the velocity of flow is reduced. The human aorta is a little over an inch in diameter. All the blood ejected by the left ventricle must pass through this channel; the blood velocity must therefore be much greater here than in more peripheral parts of the vascular tree where, as a result of the numerous branchings and rebranchings, the total cross area of the vascular bed is increased. In the region of the capillaries where, as just mentioned, the flow is greatly slowed, the most pronounced widening of the bed is found. For this reason the capillary area is frequently referred to as the "*capillary lake*." Though the cross area of each capillary is only a very small fraction of that of the aorta, the sum of all the cross areas of the capillaries is from 600 to 800 times greater (see Figs. 50 and 51).

In the venous system, the successive junctions of smaller veins to form larger trunks results in a progressive narrowing of the cross area of the vascular channels until, at the

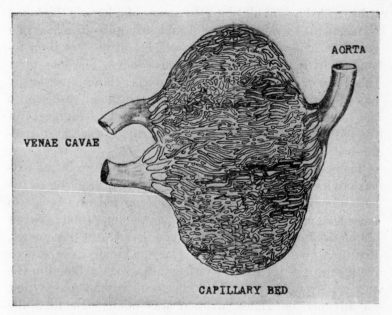

AORTA

VENAE CAVAE

CAPILLARY BED

FIG. 51. Diagram illustrating the relative sectional area of the aorta, capillary bed and great veins. The area of the "capillary lake" is actually much greater relatively than is shown. (After Best and Taylor, *The Physiological Basis of Medical Practice.*)

entrance to the right auricle, the two blood columns (in superior and inferior venae cavae) have together a cross area only about double that of the aorta.

The velocity of the blood in the arteries, but not in the veins, varies with the heart beat above and below a mean value. During the ejection of blood from the ventricle the velocity of the blood rises to a maximum, but falls again when the heart pauses. The minimum value is reached just before the next heart beat.

THE ARTERIAL BLOOD PRESSURE

That the blood in the arteries is under a relatively high pressure was not demonstrated until about a century after Harvey's discovery of the circulation. In 1733 an English clergyman, the Rev. Stephen Hales, inserted a small glass tube (called a cannula) into the artery of a horse's thigh and connected it by means of the flexible windpipe (trachea) of a goose (in lieu of rubber tubing which had not yet been invented) with a glass tube some 8 feet long. The long glass tube was placed vertically. When the clamp, previously placed upon the artery, was released the blood rushed into the tubing and rose nearly to its upper end. The height of the blood column was observed to fluctuate several centimeters with each beat of the heart.

This method of measuring the blood pressure in animals has obvious disadvantages. In the first place, owing to the length of the tubing required, it is inconvenient. It is also inaccurate, since the blood which fills the long tube is out of circulation and the pressure as recorded is, in consequence, less than that which actually exists. Finally, the experiment is soon interrupted by coagulation of the blood in the tubing. It was not until another century had passed that an advance on Hales' method was made. In 1828 the French physicist Poiseuille used a U tube filled with mercury to register the pressure, and an anticoagulant fluid to fill the tubing connecting the U tube (now usually referred to as a *manometer*) with the cannula in the artery. Since mercury is some 13.5 times heavier than blood, the mercury rises only a few inches instead of several feet, as when the pressure is measured by the height of a column of blood itself. Before the clamp is released from the artery the anticoagulant fluid is introduced under a pressure equivalent to what the blood pressure is expected to be. If the pressure of the fluid is adjusted so that it exactly equals the blood pressure, blood does not leave the artery, nor does an appreciable amount of anticoagulant enter the circulation. It has been customary ever since Poiseuille introduced the mercurial manometer, to express the blood pressure in millimeters of mercury (mm. Hg). Some years later Ludwig improved the method by placing a float, fastened to a wire bearing a writing point, upon the mercury column. Movements of the mercury could in this way be recorded upon a writing surface — a revolving drum covered with smoked paper — and permanent tracings of the blood pressure secured. The instrument bearing the writing surface is run by clock-work, and is known as a *kymograph* (see Fig. 52).

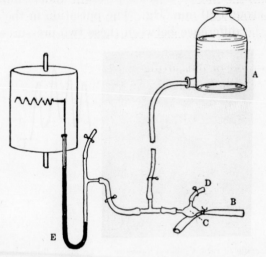

Fig. 52. Showing method of recording blood pressure in animals. A, reservoir filled with anticoagulant solution; B, artery; C, cannula; D, tube for cleaning cannula; E, mercurial manometer.

The phases of the arterial blood pressure. The arterial blood pressure of warm-blooded animals has a value of from 110 to 150 mm. of mercury. Unlike certain other physiological functions, e.g., heart rate, output of the heart, basal metabolism, etc., no relationship exists between the height of the blood pressure and an animal's size. The blood pressure of the rat, for example, is about the same as that of man. The arterial blood pressure, like the velocity of the arterial blood, varies rhythmically with the beating of the heart, rising to a maximum during the cardiac contraction (systole), when blood is pumped into the arteries, but falling again when the heart relaxes (diastole). The pressure reaches its lowest level just before the next beat. These variations are shown in Fig. 53, which is a blood pressure tracing obtained from the artery of an animal by the method described above.

The maximum or *systolic pressure* in a young man has an average value under ordinary resting conditions of 120 mm. Hg. The minimum or *diastolic pressure* under similar conditions is around 80 mm. Hg. The pulsation in the arteries is due to the difference between these two pressures, and is

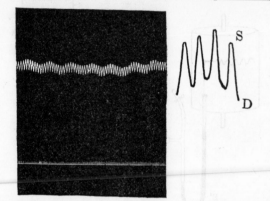

Fig. 53. Tracing of rabbit's blood pressure. The larger fluctuations in blood pressure are due to the respirations, the smaller ones to the heart beats. The tracing near the bottom of the figure is made by a time marker. On the right a section of the tracing is enlarged; s = systolic pressure; d = diastolic.

therefore called the *pulse pressure;* it amounts to $(120 - 80 =)$ 40 mm. Hg. The value obtained by dividing the sum of the values for the systolic and diastolic pressures by two, is called the *mean pressure*. Under resting conditions, therefore, the mean pressure amounts to $\left(\dfrac{120 + 80}{2} = \right)$ 100 mm. Hg.

The clinical measurement of the arterial blood pressure. The blood pressure is measured indirectly in the human subject, by means of an instrument called a *sphygmomanometer* (see Fig. 54). The latter comprises a flat rubber bag about 5″ wide and 8″ long, enclosed in an envelope of cotton cloth to prevent stretching. Two tubes, one connected to a manometer (mercurial or aneroid) and the other to a small

hand pump provided with valves, lead from the interior of
the bag. The cloth-covered bag, which is usually referred
to as the *cuff or armlet*, is
wrapped around the arm
above the elbow, the tails
of the cloth being wound
bandage fashion to hold it
snugly in position. The
pressure within the bag
is raised by a few com-
pressions of the hand bulb
until the pulse at the wrist
disappears; that is, until
the air pressure overcomes
the blood pressure and
occludes the artery. The
observer listens with a
stethoscope placed over
the artery (brachial) in
front of the elbow just
below the armlet, while
he gradually reduces the
pressure by opening the
valve close to the bulb.
As the blood escapes from
beneath the cuff and en-
ters the artery below,
faint tapping sounds syn-
chronous with the heart
beats are heard. The
reading of the manometer
at which the sounds are
first heard is taken as the

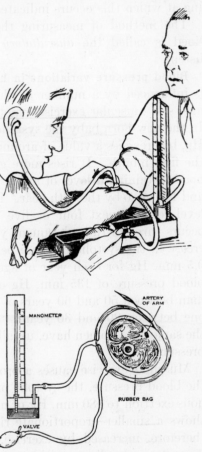

FIG. 54. Photograph illustrating the auscultatory method of determining the blood
pressure in man. *Below*, drawing to illustrate
the principle; cross section of the arm with
the armlet wrapped around it and connected
with the manometer.

systolic pressure. The sounds become progressively louder
as the air pressure is reduced further, then undergo a series
of changes in quality and finally disappear. At a pressure

level about 5 mm. above that at which they disappear the sounds acquire a muffled character; the manometer reading at which this occurs indicates the diastolic pressure.

The method of measuring the blood pressure just outlined is called the *auscultatory method* (L. *auscultare*, to listen).

Blood pressure variations in health. The blood pressure is influenced by a number of physiological conditions, e.g., age, sex, muscular exercise, emotion, digestion and posture. In the new-born baby the systolic pressure averages 40 mm. Hg, but reaches a value of around 80 mm. Hg by the end of the first month. It rises more gradually throughout childhood, attaining a level of about 100 mm. by the 12th year and 120 or so by the 17th year. It remains around the latter level for the next four or five years. A progressive rise occurs through the subsequent years of life, the rate of increase in the systolic pressure being in the neighborhood of 0.5 mm. Hg for each year of age. For example, a systolic blood pressure of 135 mm. Hg or so, though normal for a man between 50 and 60 years of age, would be too high for one between 20 and 30 years. As compared with men of the same age, women have, usually, a somewhat lower blood pressure.

Muscular exercise causes a pronounced temporary rise in the blood pressure, the systolic pressure rising during strenuous exertion to 180 mm. Hg or more; the diastolic pressure shows a smaller proportionate rise. The pulse pressure is, therefore, increased by exercise. A change from a lying down to a standing position causes a rise in the diastolic, but little change as a rule in the systolic pressure; the pulse pressure is therefore reduced.

Emotion, e.g., fear, worry, excitement, etc., may cause a rise of several millimeters of mercury in the systolic pressure; the diastolic pressure is raised to a smaller extent. During digestion a moderate rise in the systolic pressure with little change in the diastolic occurs. A reduction of from 20 to 30 mm. Hg in the systolic pressure occurs during restful sleep, but if the sleep is disturbed by exciting or terrifying dreams, the systolic pressure may be elevated to 180 or 200 mm. Hg.

Arterial hypertension. A persistent elevation of the arterial blood pressure above the normal level is called hypertension. The abnormally high pressure is due to spasm of the arterioles (i.e., to an increase in the peripheral resistance, see p. 99): this, at any rate, is the general belief. The cause of the vascular spasm is, however, quite unknown. The condition leads to serious consequences; it throws extra work upon the heart and subjects the arterial system to undue strain. Enlargement of the heart, followed eventually by cardiac failure, and deterioration of the arterial tissue (arteriosclerosis) result. Rupture of a diseased cerebral vessel may cause death; or death may result from the kidneys failing to perform their functions as a result of pathological changes in the renal vessels. There are two types of arterial hypertension. In one type, called *primary* or *essential hypertension*, the condition occurs unpreceded by kidney or any other disease. Essential hypertension, therefore, may cause, but is not itself the result of, kidney disease. In the other form, the hypertension is a consequence of kidney disease.

Dr. Goldblatt and his associates in Cleveland have carried out some experiments of great interest and importance which have shed light upon the origin of arterial hypertension and its relation to kidney disease. By means of a specially devised clamp, the renal artery to one kidney or to both was constricted and the renal blood flow thus reduced. When the renal artery of one side alone was narrowed in this manner, the blood pressure rose moderately but returned to normal again within a few weeks. When, however, the blood flow to the both kidneys was reduced or to one kidney only and the other kidney then removed, the blood pressure rose to a higher level and remained permanently elevated. There now seems to be little doubt that the high blood pressure so commonly associated with kidney disease is the result of some interference with the renal blood supply. It is also not improbable that primary or essential hypertension is dependent upon some fault in the renal circulation.

It has been shown that a reduction in the renal blood flow results in the production by the kidney of a chemical substance which, being discharged into the circulation, acts upon the muscular walls of the arterioles throughout the body to cause narrowing of the caliber of these vessels. Such vascular constriction is the direct and immediate cause of high blood pressure.

The factors responsible for the maintenance of the normal blood pressure. These are five in number:

1. *The amount of blood discharged per minute by the heart into the systemic arteries,* i.e., the cardiac output.
2. *The blood volume.*
3. *The peripheral resistance.*
4. *The viscosity of the blood.*
5. *The elasticity of the arterial walls.*

The cardiac output. It has been mentioned that the cardiac output is increased, as a rule, by increasing both heart rate and the stroke volume, but that the extent to which each of these factors participates varies. The larger amount of blood discharged into the arterial system can be accommodated within the arterial system only by further stretching of the arterial walls. Both systolic and diastolic pressures rise, but both pressures are not necessarily raised to the same degree. When the increase in cardiac output is the result mainly of an increase in the stroke volume, the systolic pressure rises to a greater extent than the diastolic, with a consequent increase in pulse pressure. If, on the other hand, the pulse rate is markedly increased, the diastolic pressure tends to rise to a greater extent than the systolic because, since the time between beats is

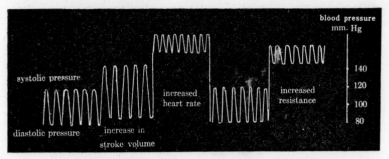

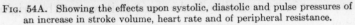

FIG. 54A. Showing the effects upon systolic, diastolic and pulse pressures of an increase in stroke volume, heart rate and of peripheral resistance.

shortened, the decline in pressure during the diastole of the heart is arrested at a higher level by the arrival of the next beat. The pulse pressure is therefore reduced.

The blood volume. The arterial system is, under ordinary circumstances, overfilled. That is to say, the arterial walls even at the lowest pressure (diastolic) are stretched. A reduction in blood volume, as by hemorrhage, causes the blood pressure to fall. Restoration of the blood volume by transfusion of blood or of a suitable blood substitute (p. 38) is followed by a rise in pressure.

The peripheral resistance. This refers to the small vessels at the periphery — the arterioles and capillaries — but particularly the former, which, as already mentioned, offer resistance to the passage of blood from the arterial system into the veins. The arterioles and capillaries are furnished with nerves through which their caliber may be altered from time to time.

Constriction of the peripheral vessels reduces, temporarily, the outflow from the arterial system, and in accordance with the first law stated on p. 84, a rise in arterial pressure occurs, provided the minute volume of the heart is not at the same time reduced. The arterial system must, therefore, contain more blood than formerly, and the arterial walls are more forcibly stretched. The pressure rises to the point at which the quantity of blood leaving the system again equals that which is pumped into it (the cardiac output); no further rise in pressure then occurs. Opposite effects are produced when the peripheral vessels dilate. The pressure falls until the outflow from the arterial system again just balances the inflow. The peripheral resistance may be compared to a dam in a river. If the dam is raised or lowered, the water continues to rise or fall, respectively (i.e., its pressure increases or decreases) until it reaches the new level. From then on, the quantity of water which overflows in a given time is the same as it was at the original level.

Variations in the caliber of the vessels of the abdominal (splanchnic) region are more effective than those of other vascular areas in causing changes in the blood pressure. The splanchnic vessels when fully dilated have a relatively immense capacity — sufficient to accommodate almost the entire blood volume. Some sudden and strong emotion may cause their dilatation, when a fall in arterial pressure and loss of consciousness (fainting, or syncope) may result. On the other hand, stimulating the great splanchnic nerve (the large nerve of the abdomen through which nervous impulses reach the vessels, p. 149) in an anesthetized animal, as by the application of an electric shock, causes constriction of the abdominal vessels and, in consequence, a pronounced rise in blood pressure.

Viscosity of the blood. Viscosity may be defined simply as the "thickness" of a liquid or the resistance offered by a liquid to its movement along a tube. The viscosity of a particular liquid is determined by measuring the time which it takes, when acted upon by a constant force, to pass through a given length of a capillary tube. The viscosity of water is taken as unity, and that of various other liquids is expressed relatively to that of water. Thus, alcohol and ether are less viscous than water, while glycerine, oil and syrup are much more viscous. Blood itself is some 5 times more viscous than water. We know that should two piston syringes be filled, one with a highly viscous liquid, such as syrup, the other with water, a greater effort would be required to drive out the syrup than to drive out the water, and a higher pressure would be created in the first syringe than in the second. The relatively high viscosity of blood increases the resistance in the vascular system; it tends to impede the flow through the arterioles, and so to enhance the effect which these narrow vessels themselves have in maintaining the arterial pressure. Variations in viscosity, therefore, have an effect upon the blood pressure similar to that caused by alterations in the caliber of the peripheral vessels. The relatively high viscosity of blood is due to the plasma proteins, and, to an even greater extent, to the corpuscles. The viscosity is lowered in conditions associated with low plasma protein concentration and in some anemias. It is increased in conditions associated with a high corpuscular concentration or when, as a result of the loss of blood water (anhydremia), the protein concentration of the blood is raised.

The elasticity of the arterial walls. Did the arteries possess rigid and not elastic walls, the systolic pressure would be higher, other things being equal, but there would be no diastolic pressure. That is to say, the arterial blood pressure would fall to zero between the beats of the heart. The disappearance of a pulse in the capillaries and veins is due, in turn, to the existence of a pressure in the arteries during diastole. These facts are best illustrated by means of a model.

In Fig. 55 is represented a bulb syringe, S, valved at A, and having a short tube, B, which dips into a basin of water. Leading from the opposite pole of the bulb is a longer tube, C. If the bulb is alternately compressed and released, fluid will be drawn from the basin, and discharged from the mouth of the tube (Fig. 55, 1). If the walls of the latter are composed of some rigid material, e.g., glass, it will be found that when the pump is worked the fluid issues from the tube in

spurts or jets synchronous with each stroke, but no flow occurs between the strokes. An increase in the frequency or
force of the strokes does not alter the intermittent character
of the flow, nor does lengthening the tubing. If the peripheral resistance of the vascular system is imitated by attach-
ing a nipple of small bore to the mouth of the delivery tube,
thus increasing the resistance to the outflow of fluid, the
issuing stream is finer and its velocity is increased, but it
still remains intermittent (Fig. 55, 2). Now let the elasticity
of the arterial wall be imitated by replacing the rigid tube

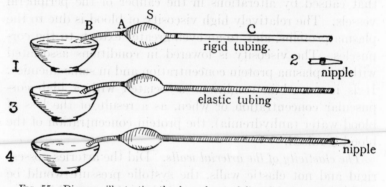

FIG. 55. Diagram illustrating the dependence of diastolic pressure upon the
arterial elasticity and peripheral resistance. Description in text.

(C) by one of rubber, but let the mouth of the tube be left
free and not constricted in any way (Fig. 55, 3). The intermittent character of the flow from the tubing is unaffected.
However, if the *small-bored nipple* representing the peripheral resistance be fixed into the mouth of the *elastic tubing*
the stream will be found to have lost its pulsatile character
and to have become continuous (Fig. 55, 4). Two factors
are therefore necessary to produce a continuous outflow,
(a) *elastic tubing* and (b) *resistance to the outflow*. The reasons
for this are clear. If the tubing is made of elastic material,
its wall is distended by the force of the pump and energy is
thus stored up which is expended between beats as the elastic
wall recoils. Thus the fluid is driven along the tube during
the pauses of the pump. Nevertheless, if the fluid has free

egress from the tube, the pressure does not rise to a sufficient height to distend the rubber wall, i.e., elasticity is
not called into play, over-filling of the tube does not occur,
and in consequence the latter acts simply as though it were
composed of rigid material.

The foregoing facts apply directly to the arterial system.
The elasticity of the vascular walls and the peripheral resistance are both essential for the development of the diastolic pressure. As the contents of the ventricle are forced
into the already over-filled arterial system during systole,
the added pressure which is then exerted upon the vascular
walls causes their further distension. After the completion
of systole, the elastic walls rebound and, pressing upon the
blood within their embrace, force it onwards through the
peripheral vessels. In other words, the arterial lumen returns to its previous diameter and the energy that had been
stored up during the stretching of the elastic tissue is in this
way gradually expended during diastole.

It may then be said that the elastic recoil of the arterial
wall acts, in a sense, as a subsidiary pump to drive the blood
onwards in a continuous stream between the heart beats.
Otherwise the pressure would fall to zero after each systole.

In health, the several factors mentioned in the foregoing
paragraphs interact with one another to maintain the blood
pressure at a fairly constant level. When a change occurs in
one factor which, acting alone, would raise or lower the pressure, a compensating reaction occurs which tends to offset
its effects. For example, a moderate fall in the cardiac output or in blood volume (as through hemorrhage) is not
necessarily followed by a fall in blood pressure, since narrowing of the calibers of the small vessels occurs, that is, the
peripheral resistance is increased. Again, dilatation of the
arterioles in one region, which of itself would lower the blood
pressure, is balanced by constriction of the minute vessels in
another (Lovén reflex). Also, increased blood volume or a
rise in blood viscosity which alone would cause an elevation
of the blood pressure, is counteracted by vasodilatation.

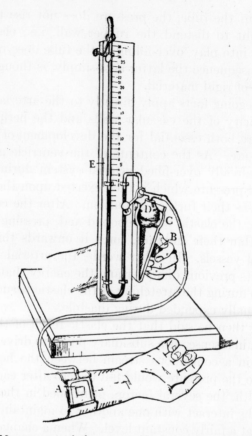

Fig. 56. Measurement of the venous blood pressure. The small chamber with transparent top (A) is cemented to the skin over a superficial vein. The pressure within the chamber is raised by means of the pressure bulb arrangement B, C, D until the vein collapses. E, manometer. (After Hooker and Eyster.)

CAPILLARY AND VENOUS PRESSURES

It has been mentioned that, except for the sharp drop which occurs in the region of the arterioles, the blood pressure falls in a gradual slope from the left to the right side of the heart. The pressure is about 30 mm. Hg at the arterial end of the capillary and about 12 mm. at the venous end. The pressure of blood in the great veins is low, and at the entrance of these vessels into the right auricle is only some 5 mm. H$_2$O. In other words the energy of the cardiac contraction has been almost entirely expended in overcoming the resistance offered to the flow of blood through the vascular system.

The venous pressure may be measured in man by a method based upon the same principle as that employed for the measurement of the arterial blood pressure. A vein is selected upon the back of the hand and a small chamber with a transparent top is hermetically sealed by means of a special cement to the overlying skin (Fig. 56). The chamber is provided with two tubes, one of which is connected to a water manometer, the other to a hand bulb. The pressure within the chamber is raised by a few compressions of the bulb until the vein is seen to collapse. The pressure, which at this point just balances the pressure in the vein, is read from the manometer. While the measurement is being made, the vein under observation must be brought to the level of the right auricle; otherwise, the hydrostatic pressure of the venous blood, i.e., the weight of the blood column extending from the vein level to the auricle, would be added to the pressure due to contraction of the left ventricle.

The pressure of blood in the peripheral veins, such as those of the limbs, amounts to from 60 to 100 mm. H$_2$O.

THE EFFECT OF GRAVITY UPON THE CIRCULATION

When the human subject assumes the erect posture the blood pressure in the arteries of the head and arms is not reduced; as mentioned on p. 96, the diastolic pressure actually rises. This is so, even though the subject makes no effort, but is tilted on a moveable table from the horizontal to the upright position. If a fall in blood pressure of sufficient magnitude to deprive the brain of an adequate supply of blood did occur when one changed from the recumbent to the standing position, fainting would result. Now, in order to maintain the blood pressure, the heart pump must receive an adequate supply of blood. The question then arises, "How, when the body is standing, is the blood conveyed against gravity up the great veins to the heart?" The factors concerned are four in number:

1. The contraction of the left ventricle, the *vis a tergo* (force from behind), as it is termed, drives the blood through the arterioles and capillaries and along the veins to the right side of the heart.

2. The respiratory movements. The pressure within the thorax (see intrathoracic pressure, p. 169) is always a little below that of the atmosphere. This "negative" pressure fluctuates with the respiratory movements, being increased (i.e., becoming more negative) during inspiration, when it amounts to about − 6 mm. Hg, and decreased during expiration to about − 2.5 mm. Hg. The intrathoracic pressure thus exerts a suction effect or pull (*vis a fronte*) upon the column of blood in the large veins of the abdomen. The blood is also *forced* upward during inspiration, for when the diaphragm descends it increases the intra-abdominal pressure. The increased pressure is transmitted to the blood in the veins; since the blood is prevented by the presence of valves in the large veins of the lower limbs from passing downwards, it is propelled upwards. The respiratory movements thus act both as a force pump and as a suction pump to move the venous blood toward the heart.

3. The abdominal and limb muscles. When one is standing, the abdominal muscles contract and offer a firm support for the large veins of the abdomen. The venous walls are prevented from becoming over-distended under the weight of their contained blood. If the walls of the veins stretched and so increased their capacity, a larger mass of blood would be accommodated in the large veins of the abdomen, and the flow to the heart correspondingly reduced. The muscles of the limbs perform a similar duty for the limb veins. Furthermore, they exert, during muscular movements, a varying pressure or massaging action upon the

veins. By virtue of the venous valves, any pressure upon
the column of venous blood is converted into an upward
propulsive movement.

4. Constriction of the vessels of the splanchnic area.
Through the action of the vascular nerves (p. 149) the small
vessels — arterioles, capillaries and small veins — in the
abdomen undergo a reduction in caliber, and so in capacity.
Thus, blood, which otherwise would collect in these areas
when the erect posture is assumed, is directed upwards into
the large venous trunks.

In quadrupeds, the mechanisms for raising the blood
against gravity are much less efficient than they are in man
or in the apes. The dog, however, is able to compensate
fairly well for the gravity effect, but the domestic rabbit
may become unconscious or even die, if held up by the ears
for any considerable length of time. This result is due to
the heart being inadequately supplied with blood which,
owing to the flabbiness of the abdominal muscles of the tame
rabbit, collects in the large veins. Sheep also not infrequently become unconscious if held in a vertical position
during shearing. Fainting (syncope) in the human subject
is in most instances due, not to any affection of the heart
itself, but to reduction of the venous flow to the heart.
Fatigue or some strong emotion such as fear or shock may,
by inducing splanchnic vasodilatation and imperfect cardiac
filling, cause loss of consciousness. Also, a person who
stands quietly for some time, a soldier standing at attention
on parade, for example, may fall in a faint because the venous flow is unaided by muscular movement. Such a result
is the more likely to occur if he is fatigued, or if the day is hot
and the vessels of the skin are, therefore, dilated. The treatment of a subject in a faint is simple; he is laid in the horizontal position, the effect of gravity upon the circulation
being thus abolished. He should not be supported in the
sitting position. As a matter of fact, the subject of a faint
usually does the right thing himself — he falls to the ground.

Pressure may be applied to the abdomen in order to force blood along the veins to the heart, but such a procedure is usually unnecessary.

THE EFFECTS OF ACCELERATION UPON THE CIRCULATION

A constant speed, however great, has in itself no effect upon the circulation, but acceleration, that is, a change in velocity either in the line of motion (*linear acceleration*) or a change in direction, as when a body traveling along a straight course turns into a curvilinear one (*centrifugal acceleration*), may cause profound circulatory effects. Such effects not uncommonly result from the sudden and strong changes in direction entailed in military flying. For example, a pilot pulling out of a power dive, that is, changing direction at high velocity from a downward to a horizontal and upward movement, has his head directed inward toward the center of a circular course and the lower part of his body directed outward. His blood, as a result of centrifugal acceleration, is therefore "forced" away from the head into the lower part of the body. The high pressure of blood in the capillaries in the skin of the lower limbs may result in small cutaneous hemorrhages. The return of venous blood to the heart is reduced, with a consequent fall in the blood pressure in the cerebral and retinal vessels. Vision is temporarily lost and the pilot may become unconscious. Such effects are commonly referred to in the flier's parlance as "blackout." The abdominal organs may also be forced downward and drawing upon the diaphragm embarrass respiration. Any manoeuver in which the head is directed outward causes the reverse effect upon the circulation. The blood is now "forced" toward the head. The vessels of the head and neck become engorged and severe throbbing pain in the head is experienced. The eyes feel as if they were being forced from their sockets. There may be mental confusion. Rupture of a cerebral or retinal vessel may result.

THE ARTERIAL PULSE

The pulse in the arteries is due, of course, to the beat of the heart. It is felt most conveniently by placing the finger upon the radial artery, which lies near the outer border of the palmar aspect of the wrist. In health the rate of the pulse, when the body is at rest or engaged in some light occupation, is around 70 per minute. The pulse is a *pressure change* transmitted as a wave through the arterial wall and blood column to the periphery. Though caused by the discharge of blood into the arterial system, it is in the nature of a transmitted impact, and *is not due to the passage of the ejected blood itself*. For example, when one places a finger upon the artery at the wrist the pulse beat which is felt is not due to the arrival of blood which has been discharged an instant before from the left ventricle into the arterial system, but is due rather to the shock or impact given to the resilient arterial walls by the sudden entrance of that blood into the aorta. The wave thus set up in the wall of the aorta and in the column of blood therein travels from 10 to 15 times more rapidly than does the blood itself, and quite independently of it. The blood, as we have seen, has a velocity of around half a meter per second in the aorta, and less than that in the smaller arteries. The speed of the pulse wave is from 5 to 8 meters per second, and is practically the same throughout the arterial tree. That the pulse travels quite independently of the blood flow is evident from the observation that in an artery which has been tied across so that no blood flows through it, the pulse persists in the vessel up to the point of occlusion. The velocity of transmission of the pulse wave is dependent upon the character of the arterial wall. Were arteries made of unyielding material (e.g., glass), they and the incompressible blood within them would constitute a rigid system and, therefore, transmit an impact almost instantaneously from end to end. The arteries are, however, elastic and, in consequence, transmit a shock applied to their walls much more slowly.

The arteries become less resilient with age and the speed of the pulse wave therefore increases. At five years of age, for example, the velocity of the pulse wave is around 5 meters per second, whereas at the age of 80 it is in the neighborhood of 8 meters per second. In arteriosclerosis, in which condition the arteries are abnormally rigid, the pulse wave has a still higher velocity. The speed of the pulse wave may be measured by placing two levers, one upon an artery near the heart, the other near the periphery, and timing the arrival of the pulse at the two points. The distance between the two points is then measured. This distance (in millimeters) divided by the time (in seconds) which the pulse wave has taken to pass between the two points will give the velocity (in millimeters per second). Thus, $\frac{D}{T} = V$, where D = distance in millimeters, T = time, in seconds and V = velocity in millimeters per second.

The instrument employed for obtaining a record of the pulse wave is called a *sphygmograph* (see Figs. 57 and 58). The upstroke of the curve drawn by this instrument during the passage of the pulse wave is abrupt and is called the *anacrotic* limb (G. *ana* = up, *crotos* = pulse). The downstroke has a more gradual inclination and is called the *catacrotic* limb (G. *cata* = down). The catacrotic limb shows, a short distance from the peak of the primary wave, a secondary elevation known as the *dicrotic wave,* which is immediately preceded by a slight negative fluctuation called the *dicrotic notch.* The latter is due to the backward movement (i.e., toward the heart) of the blood column in the artery, when the ventricle commences to relax. The dicrotic wave is caused by the checking of this backward movement of the blood column and its rebound from the aortic valves which, coming into accurate apposition at the end of ventricular systole (see p. 127), prevent the leakage of blood into the relaxing ventricle. When the aortic valves are prevented from closing, the dicrotic wave is not seen. In normal circumstances dicrotic fluctuations can be revealed only by

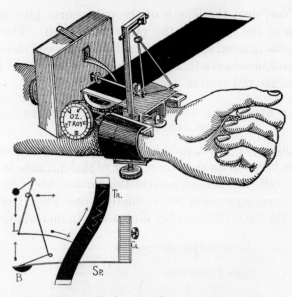

FIG. 57. *Upper drawing*, Dudgeon's sphygmograph in position. *Lower*, diagram of mechanism. Cl, clock-work driving the smoked paper, Tr., under the writing point of the lever, L. Sp. is a steel spring with a button, B, which is applied over the radial artery. With each expansion of the artery the button is moved upwards and causes a movement of the system of levers as indicated by the arrows.

means of some graphic method of recording; they cannot be felt by the finger placed upon the pulse. In certain conditions, however, in which the blood pressure is abnormally low and the arterial wall, in consequence, less tense, the

FIG. 58. Tracing of radial pulse. 1, anacrotic limb; 2, dicrotic wave; 3, dicrotic notch.

dicrotic wave may be felt as a distinct tap following the main wave. A pulse of this character — the so-called *dicrotic pulse* — is not uncommonly present in typhoid fever.

It should be mentioned that the height of the pulse tracing gives no indication of the height of the systolic blood pres-

sure. Nor, does the length of the pulse curve give any indication of the length of the pulse wave itself. The pulse
wave in the arterial system is actually a long swell measuring
from 5 to 6 meters (16 to 20 feet), that is, several times longer
than the arterial system itself.

THE STRUCTURE AND PHYSIOLOGICAL PROPERTIES OF CARDIAC MUSCLE

The fibers of heart muscle possess cross striations, but
these are less well marked than those of skeletal muscle. Unlike the cells of skeletal muscle the cardiac fibers have no
sarcolemma separating or insulating one fiber from another. On the contrary, they give rise to branched processes

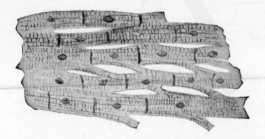

FIG. 59. Heart muscle fibers.

which join with one another and thus establish continuity
from fiber to fiber. The heart muscle is therefore in reality a
syncytium, i.e., a large multinucleated mass of protoplasm
rather than, like skeletal muscle, a number of separate units
bound together (see Fig. 59).

The physiology of cardiac muscle will be taken up under
the following heads: (1) *excitability and contractility*, (2) *rhythmicity* and (3) *conductivity*.

1. **Excitability and contractility.** Heart muscle responds
by a contraction of its fibers to the various types of stimulus,
thermal, chemical, mechanical or electrical, which excite
skeletal muscle. Its response follows the *"all or none" law*.
This law, which also applies to the conduction of the nerve

impulse (p. 390) and to the contraction of an isolated fiber of skeletal muscle (p. 399), states that a stimulus, if it produces a response at all, will produce the maximum response of which the tissue is capable under the conditions existing at the moment. That is to say, increasing the strength of stimulus above that which is just necessary to excite the heart muscle (threshold strength) does not increase the force of the contraction.

Treppe. When the heart muscle is stimulated at regular intervals the first few contractions increase progressively in

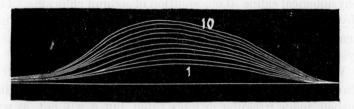

FIG. 60. Treppe. Record of a series of contractions of frog's heart caused by electrical stimulation of the ventricle of a Stannius preparation. Tracings taken on a rapidly moving surface. First contraction (1) the lowest, last contraction (10) the highest. (After Halliburton)

amplitude. From the appearance given to the tracing by the initial contractions (Fig. 60) this behavior is referred to as *treppe* or the *staircase phenomenon*. It is probably due to the beneficial effect exerted upon one contraction by the rise in temperature and the acid metabolites (carbon dioxide and lactic acid) produced during the contraction or contractions which have preceded.

Refractory periods. Heart muscle will not respond to a stimulus while it is contracting; in this it differs from skeletal muscle (p. 399). This time, during which the cardiac muscle is unresponsive to stimulation, is called the *absolute refractory period*. The absolute refractory period of heart muscle is, therefore, coterminous with the period of contraction. The absolute refractory period is followed by one in which the muscle gradually recovers its excitability. At the beginning of this period, i.e., at the commencement of cardiac relaxation, a stronger stimulus is required for excitation, and the force of the contraction which results is less than the normal. Excitability increases progressively and reaches its full value only when relaxation is complete. This phase of depressed but gradually increasing excitability is called the *relative refractory period*.

2. Rhythmicity. This is an outstanding characteristic of cardiac muscle. The heart of the frog will contract spontaneously and rhythmically for a considerable length of time after its removal from the body, if simply kept moist with physiological saline (0.6% solution of sodium chloride). The rhythmicity is also an inherent property of the mammalian heart; it occurs quite independently of the central nervous system (see perfusion of the heart, p. 115).

When the heart of an animal is stimulated by an electric shock or a series of such shocks, the rhythm may be disturbed, made irregular or more rapid, but it will not, as will skeletal muscle, give a sustained (tetanic) contraction. The cardiac contractions are always intermittent; fusion or summation of contractions (p. 400) does not occur. This fact is dependent upon the refractory period. The heart muscle must first cease to contract and recover at least part of its excitability before another contraction can be evoked.

If, when the heart is beating naturally, the ventricle is stimulated during its relaxation phase, a contraction occurs which varies directly in strength with the excitability of the muscle; this, as just mentioned, rises progressively throughout the relative refractory period. The maximal response is therefore obtained at the end of the latter. The response caused by the artificial stimulus is called a *premature beat* or *extrasystole*. Such premature beats occur in the human heart as a result of some abnormal stimulation (p. 136). An unusually long resting interval known as the *compensatory pause* follows the extrasystole (see Fig. 61). The pause is caused in the following way. The impulses causing the normal heart beat originate at regular invervals in the upper part of the right auricle and, spreading downwards, excite the rest of the heart. When an extrasystole of the ventricle occurs, the next regular impulse from the auricle usually reaches the ventricle while it is absolutely refractory, i.e., while it is still in the contracted state as a result of the abnormal stimulus. The muscle therefore fails to respond. Not until the next normal impulse arrives is the heart capable of contracting.

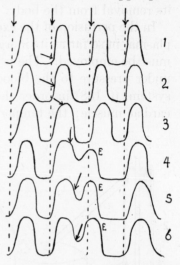

3. **Conductivity.** It has already been mentioned that, as a result of the fusion of branches or slips of one fiber with those of its neighbors, the heart muscle is a continuous protoplasmic mass. When, therefore, one part of the muscle is stimulated, the excitatory process spreads without interruption to all its parts. The mammalian heart has developed a conducting system of specialized tissue which transmits the impulse from the right auricle to the ventricles. This system will be dealt with presently (p. 118).

Fig. 61. Extrasystoles. Record of contractions of frog's ventricles. Upper row of arrows and dotted lines indicate the arrival of the auricular impulse in the ventricular muscle. Slanting arrows in this and succeeding tracings indicate the application of the artificial stimulus. In tracings 1, 2 and 3 the artificial stimulus is applied during the contraction of the muscle, and is therefore ineffective (absolute refractory period). In 4, 5 and 6 the stimulus falls in the relative refractory period and gives rise to an extrasystole, its amplitude being greater the later in the relaxation phase that the stimulus is applied. A long pause follows the extrasystole because the auricular impulse reaches the ventricular muscle during the refractory phase, and is therefore ineffective. E = extrasystole.

PERFUSION OF THE EXCISED HEART

Under appropriate conditions the excised mammalian heart will continue to beat for several hours. Even the human heart has been revived after death, and made to beat after its removal from the body.

In the perfusion of the excised heart a fluid resembling the plasma, in so far as its inorganic constituents are concerned, must be employed. The perfusion fluid should be delivered under pressure to the blood vessels of the heart (coronary system, p. 158) in order that it shall reach all parts of the cardiac muscle; the temperature of the fluid should be that of a warm-blooded animal, namely, about 98.6° Fahrenheit. The perfusion is performed in the following way. A cannula is tied into the aorta and connected by rubber tubing to a reservoir filled with the perfusion fluid and placed at a height of about 5 feet above the level of the heart; the fluid is thus driven into the coronary arteries which arise from the root of the aorta just beyond the semilunar valves. The valves are closed by the pressure of the fluid so that no fluid enters the ventricle directly.

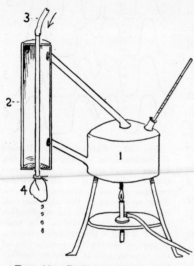

FIG. 62. Perfusion of the isolated mammalian heart. 1, warm water container; 2, water jacket with front wall removed; 3, tube conveying solution from reservoir; 4, heart.

After passing through the coronary system (arteries, arterioles, capillaries and veins), the fluid enters the chambers of the heart from which it is allowed to escape through knife cuts made in the walls of the ventricles (see Fig. 62).

The heart muscle must be supplied with *oxygen*. This is accomplished by bubbling oxygen or simply air through the fluid in the reservoir.

It is of the utmost importance that the perfusion fluid contains the three inorganic cations Na^+, Ca^+ and K^+, in properly balanced proportions. This fundamental fact was demonstrated many years ago by Sidney Ringer, an English physiologist (see Fig. 63). Experimenting with the excised frog's heart he found that the heart beat could be maintained for a short time only, when physiological saline (0.6% sodium chloride solution) was used. The addition of a very small amount of calcium restored the beat, but the pauses between beats (diastolic periods) became shorter and shorter, and the heart came to a standstill in a firmly contracted state; this condition is called *calcium rigor*. When potassium instead of calcium was added to the physiological saline the diastolic

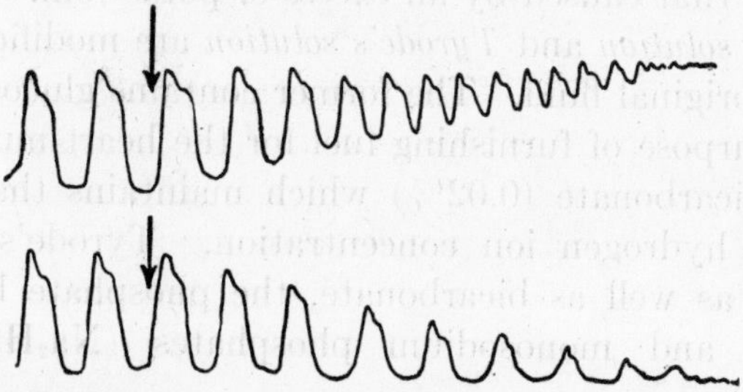

FIG. 63. Effects of calcium and potassium upon the action of the perfused heart. *Upper curve* shows effect of excess of calcium; the heart enters into *calcium rigor*. *Lower curve*, the effect of potassium (*potassium inhibition*). Arrows indicate the points where the cations were added.

periods became longer and longer and the heart ceased to beat in a fully relaxed state (diastole). This effect is referred to as *potassium inhibition*. A fluid made up to contain sodium, calcium and potassium chloride in suitable proportions (sodium chloride 0.6% for the frog heart or 0.9% for the mammalian heart, calcium chloride 0.024% and potassium chloride 0.035%) was found to sustain the beat for long periods. This is known as *Ringer's solution*. If the perfusion fluid contains calcium in excess, the effect upon the heart is the same as if it contained calcium in normal concentration but lacked potassium; calcium rigor ensues. On the other hand, when potassium is in excess the effect is the same as when calcium is lacking but potassium is present in the correct amount; potassium inhibition is induced. The effects of these two cations upon the action of the heart muscle are therefore antagonistic, one favoring contraction, the other relaxation. Only when they are present in balanced proportions, as in blood plasma, can the normal rhythm of the heart be sustained.

The reaction of the perfusion fluid is also of prime importance. The optimum reaction is around a pH of 7.4. If the fluid is too alkaline, an effect is produced upon the heart resembling that of an excess of calcium; if the hydrogen ion concentration is too high (pH 7.0) it induces an effect similar to that caused by an excess of potassium.

Locke's solution and *Tyrode's solution* are modifications of Ringer's original fluid. The former contains glucose, added for the purpose of furnishing fuel for the heart muscle, and sodium bicarbonate (0.02%) which maintains the fluid at optimum hydrogen ion concentration. Tyrode's solution contains, as well as bicarbonate, the phosphate buffers — disodium and monosodium phosphates (Na_2HPO_4 and NaH_2PO_4).

Until quite recently it had been thought that glucose constituted the chief fuel of cardiac muscle. It now appears that the heart uses glucose to a minor extent; its main fuel is lactic acid. Lactic acid is formed during muscular contraction from the breakdown of glycogen (p. 407). It is also formed from glucose in the blood, and in the lungs at all times. The lactic acid so produced is utilized by the heart muscle to furnish energy for its contraction.

THE ORIGIN AND CONDUCTION OF THE HEART BEAT

In the slowly beating heart of the frog each beat may be seen to arise at the junction of the great veins with the sinus venosus — a chamber situated between the great veins and the right auricle (see Fig. 64). This chamber is present in the mammalian embryo, but disappears during development. The beat spreads from the sinus venosus through the muscle of the auricles and ventricles. When a ligature is drawn tightly around the frog's heart at the junction of the sinus with the auricle (1st Stannius ligature), or at any lower level, the impulse is blocked and the heart below the block ceases to beat for a time. In the adult mammalian heart a ring of fibrous tissue is interposed between the auricles and the ventricles; the beat therefore cannot be transmitted from the upper to the lower cardiac chambers by muscular tissue. But a system of specialized tissue — the *junctional tissues* —

has been developed in the mammalian heart, which possesses the property of rhythmical impulse formation and conductivity to a higher degree than the cardiac muscle itself. The beat is generated in a small mass of tissue belonging to this system, situated in the wall of the right auricle near its junction with the superior vena cava. This rather circumscribed knot of tissue differs in structure from the surrounding auricular muscle, being composed of muscle cells of a primitive type, together with nerve fibers and a few nerve cells. It

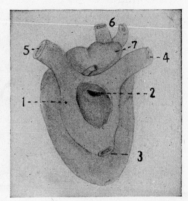

Fig. 64. Diagram of the frog's heart from the back. 1, sinus venosus; 2, opening from sinus into the auricle; 3, inferior vena cava; 4, right superior vena cava; 5, left superior vena cava; 6, aortae; 7, auricle.

is called the *sino-auricular* (S-A) *node* (Fig. 65), and is believed to be derived from the wall of the sinus venosus of the embryonic heart where this chamber joined the auricle. Heating or cooling the S-A node accelerates or slows, respectively, the rate of the heart. From such and other facts, it seems quite certain that the impulse which causes the beat of the heart is generated within this node of special tissue. It is therefore commonly referred to as the *pacemaker* of the heart. The impulse spreads as a wave

— the *excitation wave* — in all directions through the muscle of the auricles. The nature of the excitation wave cannot be defined precisely, but at any rate it is known to be accompanied by an electrical change, and is followed immediately (within 0.02 second) by contraction of the muscle.

The remainder of the specialized system of the mammalian heart consists of the *auriculo-ventricular (A-V) node*, the *auriculo-ventricular bundle* and the *Purkinje network*.

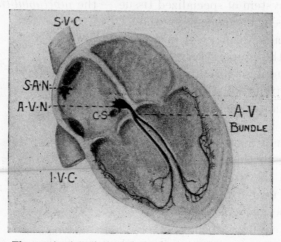

Fig. 65. The conducting tissues of the heart. S.V.C., superior vena cava; S-A.N., sino-auricular node; A-V.N., auriculo-ventricular node; I.V.C., inferior vena cava; C.S., coronary sinus.

The auriculo-ventricular node is situated in the lower part of the interauricular system. It is composed of tissue similar to that of the sino-auricular node. The auriculo-ventricular bundle arises from the auriculo-ventricular node and, after descending for a short distance, divides into two branches — one to each ventricle. Each branch descends beneath the endocardium covering the interventricular septum and, after giving off twigs to the papillary muscles, breaks up into a rich network of fine filaments — the *Purkinje network* — which is continued beneath the endocardium of the ventricular wall to the base of the heart.

The impulses are discharged rhythmically from the S-A node, and conducted at a uniform rate through the fibers of the auricular muscle. The impulse is then picked up by the A-V node, and conducted to the ventricular muscle by the bundle and its ramifications. Each part of the muscle of the ventricle is excited when the impulse arrives at the part of the Purkinje system immediately underlying it. The impulse, normally, is not conducted from point to point in the ventricle through muscular tissue, but follows this specialized pathway. The rate of conduction through ventricular muscle is around 500 mm. per second, whereas the rate through the specialized tissue is about 5000 mm. per second.

The specialized tissues of the heart may be compared to a radio system, the S-A node to the broadcasting station, and the A-V node to a receiving center which after picking up the message transmits it by a telephonic system. In the heart, the bundle and its branches and the terminal network of Purkinje correspond to the telephone wires.

It should be noted that the S-A and A-V nodes are not connected by a tract of specialized tissue; the impulse in this part of its course is conducted solely through the muscular tissue. Also, *the A-V bundle is the only pathway along which the impulse can reach the ventricles*. This slender strand of tissue is therefore a very important and vulnerable point in the conducting system of the heart. It is a "bottle neck" which the impulses must traverse. If interrupted, either experimentally in animals, or by disease in man, the path of the impulse from auricle to ventricle is completely and permanently blocked. The ventricle does not, however, cease to beat; for the specialized tissue below the block also possesses, though to a less degree than does the S-A node, the power of generating rhythmical impulses. The ventricular muscle excited by impulses arising below the block then beats at the relatively slow rate of about 35 per minute. The auricle being still under the control of the S-A node beats at the usual rate of 70 per minute. This dissociation of the rhythms of the auricles and ventricles, which follows interruption of the A-V bundle above its point of division into the two main branches, is called *complete heart block* or *auriculo-ventricular block* (see p. 135).

In other instances one or other *branch* of the A-V bundle may be interrupted by disease. This is called *bundle branch block* or *intraventricular block* (see p. 133).

THE ACTION OF THE HEART, THE CARDIAC CYCLE

The action of the heart consists of a succession of events which follow one another with great rapidity. It is therefore impossible, except by the use of special apparatus and improved methods, to analyze the beat into its different components. Starting with any given event in cardiac action (e.g., contraction of the auricle or of the ventricle), the succession of changes which takes place in the heart until the first-noted event is repeated, is called a *cardiac cycle*. The cardiac cycle in the human subject, when the heart is beating at the usual rate of about 70 per minute, is $\frac{6}{7}$ second. It is shorter than this, of course, when the heart rate is more rapid. Contraction of the auricular or of the ventricular muscle is called *systole;* so we speak of *auricular systole* or *ventricular systole*, respectively. *Auricular diastole* and *ventricular diastole* are corresponding terms which refer to the relaxation of the respective chambers. When the word systole or diastole is used alone, it is the systole or diastole of the ventricle that is meant.

We shall now describe in their proper sequence the several events in the cardiac cycle. The part of the cycle at which the description starts does not matter. The period immediately following the contraction (systole) of the ventricle may be chosen. At this time the ventricles are closed cavities. The valves guarding the orifices of the aorta and the pulmonary artery are closed, as are also those guarding the auriculo-ventricular orifices. The ventricular muscle is now relaxing but, since no blood can enter the ventricles from the auricles to stretch the muscle fibers, these are of the same length as during the preceding systole. This phase of the cardiac cycle at the commencement of ventricular diastole is, therefore, called the period of *isometric* (G. *isos* = same; *metros* = measurement) *relaxation* (Figs. 66 and 67); it has a duration (at a heart rate of 70 per minute) of about .06 second. At its termination, the auriculo-ventricular valves open and the blood flows rapidly into the ventricles from the auricles. This phase which lasts for about 0.1 second is called the period of *rapid filling* of the ventricles.

As the ventricles fill, the flow of venous blood slows, and then almost ceases. This interval following the period of

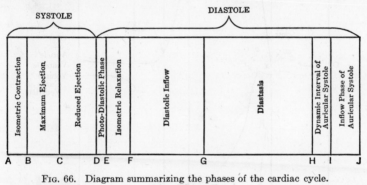

Fig. 66.   Diagram summarizing the phases of the cardiac cycle.
(After Wiggers.)

rapid filling is termed the *period of diastasis*. It varies considerably in length, being longer when the heart is beating slowly. During rapid heart action it may disappear entirely. *Auricular systole* follows the period of diastasis, the upper chambers discharging their contents into the ventricles. Auricular systole has a duration of about 0.1 second; at its termination the ventricle contracts.

It should be emphasized that throughout all the phases of the cardiac cycle just described, viz., isometric relaxation, rapid filling, diastasis and auricular systole, the ventricle is relaxing or is completely relaxed, that is, these events occur during the resting phase or diastole of the ventricle.

Ventricular systole which, as just mentioned, follows upon auricular systole is divided into two phases, the period of *isometric contraction* and the period of *ejection*. The rise in pressure within the ventricles when they contract brings the auriculo-ventricular valves firmly closed. The aortic and pulmonary valves which were brought into apposition at the end

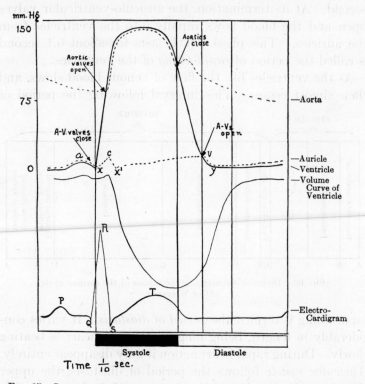

FIG. 67. Intraventricular, aortic and intra-auricular pressure curves, together with a ventricular volume curve and an electrocardiogram. The vertical lines pass through synchronous points in the five curves.

of the preceding systole have not yet opened; they are held closed by the pressure of blood in the aorta and pulmonary arteries. The ventricle being thus again a closed cavity but filled with blood, which of course is incompressible, the muscle fibers obviously cannot shorten during this phase of systole. They contract isometrically. This phase, therefore, is appropriately called the period of *isometric contraction*. The pressure within the ventricles continues to rise rapidly, however, during this time. When it reaches a height sufficient to overcome the diastolic pressure in the aorta (80 mm. Hg) and pulmonary arteries (15 mm. Hg), the valves guarding these vessels are thrown wide open and the ventricular contents ejected. The ejection period lasts for about 0.30 second (with heart rate of 70). It terminates with relaxation of the ventricular muscle. The pressure within the ventricles now falls below that in the large arteries, and the aortic and pulmonary valves close again as a result. The next phase of the heart's action is the period of isometric relaxation — the phase with which this description started. A cardiac cycle has been completed.

The phases of the cardiac cycle are shown diagrammatically in Fig. 66. In animals the cardiac cycle is most readily analyzed into its several phases by means of records, taken simultaneously, of the pressure changes occurring respectively in an auricle, a ventricle and the aorta. Instruments specially designed to record rapid variations in pressure are placed in these situations and compared with one another, as shown in Fig. 67. The *intra-auricular pressure curve*, it will be seen, consists of three positive waves, a, c and v and three depressions x, x_1 and y. The wave a is due to auricular systole, the depression x to auricular relaxation (auricular diastole). The wave c is caused when the ventricle contracts and bulges the thin auriculo-ventricular valves into the auricle. The depression x_1 is dependent also upon ventricular systole. When blood is ejected by the ventricle the volume of the ventricle of course is reduced; its fibers shorten, and in doing so they draw upon and depress the floor of the auricle. This causes a negative fluctuation in auricular pressure. Furthermore, the ejection of blood from the thorax — a closed cavity — causes a temporary fall in intrathoracic pressure which is transmitted through the thin wall of the auricle. There are, then, two factors —

both dependent upon ventricular systole — concerned in the production of the depression x_1.

V is called a stasis wave. Since the A-V valves are closed at this time the blood cannot enter the ventricle but, accumulating in the auricle, causes a gradual rise in pressure. The depression y is due to the opening of the valves and the fall in auricular pressure as the blood flows rapidly into the ventricle (i.e., during the period of rapid filling).

The *volume of the ventricles* may be recorded by means of an instrument known as a *cardiometer*. This consists of a hermetically sealed chamber which is fitted to enclose the ventricles. It communicates by means of rubber tubing, through which changes in ventricular volume during the cardiac cycle are transmitted, with a recording apparatus. A marked reduction in volume occurs during the ejection period of systole but not during the period of isometric contraction. No increase in volume occurs during the period of isometric relaxation but a marked increase occurs during the period of rapid filling when the ventricles are filling with blood (see Fig. 67).

THE MOVEMENTS OF THE HEART VALVES

The heart is a pump and its valves give direction to the movement of the blood. Those guarding the auriculo-ventricular orifices open toward the ventricles, thus allowing blood to pass from auricles to ventricles. They close at the commencement of ventricular systole and remain closed until the end of the period of isometric relaxation; their closure during systole prevents the blood from being driven backwards into the auricle when the intraventricular pressure rises. At the commencement of the ejection period the valves surrounding the orifices of the aorta and pulmonary artery open outwards, that is, toward the arterial lumen; but are closed during diastole. They thus prevent the leakage of blood into the ventricles when the intraventricular pressure falls below the arterial pressure.

The valves are composed of delicate membranes formed by the doubling of the endothelial lining of the heart. They form two or more somewhat triangular leaves or *cusps* which are attached by their bases to the fibrous rings surrounding the auriculo-ventricular and arterial orifices. Near the bases of the valves the two layers of endothelium are separated by a small amount of connective tissue and smooth muscle. The *auriculo-ventricular valve* of the right side (also known as the *tricuspid valve*) has three cusps which fit neatly together by their free margins when the valve closes. The corresponding valve of the left side (also known as the *mitral* or *bicuspid valve*) has only two leaves. Both auriculo-ventricular valves are strengthened by a number of tendinous cords — the *chordae tendineae* (p. 73) — which pass from the papillary muscles to be attached to the ventricular surfaces of the cusps near their free margins. The chordae tendineae act as guy ropes which prevent the valves from being inverted into the auricles by the pressure developed within the ventricles. The *pulmonary and aortic valves* (also called the *semilunar valves*) have each three leaves.

The opening and closing of the heart valves are not due to any active movement of the valves themselves. Though, as just mentioned, the valves contain a few strands of smooth muscle, these are not responsible for their movements. The blood current and the difference between the pressures on their two surfaces are the only operating factors. During auricular systole the A-V valves, and during the ventricular systole the pulmonary and aortic valves, are held open by the blood flowing through the respective openings. When auricular systole comes to an end, eddy currents arising in the ventricle bring the leaflets of the A-V valves gently into position. The pressure created immediately thereafter by ventricular systole closes them firmly. The closure of the aortic or of the pulmonary valves is effected in a similar manner, namely, by the higher pressure in the artery than in the ventricle when the ventricular muscle commences to relax.

The heart sounds. If one places his ear, or the receiver of an instrument called a *stethoscope*, upon a person's chest a little below the left nipple, the beat of the heart can be clearly heard. Two sounds, separated by a short silent interval and followed by a longer pause, can be distinguished. They are called, respectively, the first and second heart sounds, and have been compared to the syllables "*lub*" "*dup*." The first sound ("lub") is louder, of lower pitch and longer than the second ("dup"). The first sound is caused by two factors, (a) the contraction of the ventricular muscle and (b) the vibrations set up by the auriculoventricular (tricuspid and mitral) valves, and of the chordae tendineae as they are put upon the stretch by the rising pressure in the ventricles.

The second sound is caused by the closure of the aortic and pulmonary valves.

Valvular disease. The function of one or other valve of the heart may be interfered with as a result of some infectious disease, e.g., acute rheumatic fever or septicemia. The affected valve becomes deformed or partially destroyed so that its cusps do not come accurately into apposition to prevent leakage. The valve is then called *incompetent* and the leakage of blood is referred to as *regurgitation*. For example, when the aortic valves fail to close properly at the end of ventricular systole, blood flows from the aorta into the ventricle during diastole; when the mitral valve is incompetent, blood is driven into the auricle during ventricular systole. Now, these abnormal movements of the blood cause sounds or *murmurs* to be heard. In aortic incompetence the clear second sound of the normal heart is replaced by a murmur, and this is often continued through a part of, and sometimes throughout, the diastolic period, that is, a blowing or rushing sound is heard during the silent period which normally follows the second sound, and separates it from the first sound of the next heart cycle. In mitral or tricuspid incompetence the abnormal sound is heard during ventricular systole.

In other instances the diseased valve loses its resilient character, becoming stiff and its surface roughened. The cusps are not brushed aside by the current of blood but, projecting into the stream, offer an impediment. The orifice is therefore narrowed. This valvular condition is called *stenosis.* Thus, according to which valve is affected, *mitral, aortic, pulmonary* or *tricuspid stenosis* is spoken of. Owing to the narrowing of the orifice the blood passes through it at a higher velocity than usual. The blood flowing at high velocity over the roughened and irregular cusps causes a murmur. When an auriculo-ventricular valve is affected, the murmur is heard during those times when the blood normally enters the ventricle at highest velocity, namely, during the period of rapid filling, i.e., early in diastole, or during auricular systole, i.e., just before ventricular systole (presystolic murmur). In aortic stenosis the murmur is heard during the ejection of blood from the ventricle.

It must be evident that the rigidity and deformation of a stenosed valve is likely to render it incompetent as well. Two sounds will then be present, one being due to the stenosis, the other to regurgitation.

A diseased valve increases the work of the heart. The heart is at a mechanical disadvantage. Moreover, the disease which attacked the valve may have also injured the heart muscle. In order to carry on its work efficiently, the heart chambers must enlarge and the muscular walls become thicker. Dilatation of the heart and increased bulk of the heart muscle (hypertrophy) is therefore a consequence of valvular disease.

Electrical changes in the heart. Contracting muscle is relatively negative (electrically) to resting muscle. The electrical changes in skeletal muscle are described on p. 388. The same principles apply, in general, to heart muscle. When the excitation wave spreads through the heart, changes in electrical potential are created which may be recorded in animals by placing electrodes directly on the surface of

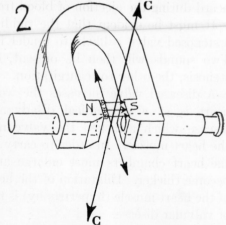

Fig. 68. 1 ($\times \frac{1}{4}$), Model of the string galvanometer. A A are the poles of the magnet; B B are the coils of the magnet, M N the terminals conveying constant current to it. D receives and condenses the beam of light which falls upon the string (or strings) through a mica window in the carrier. C carries the projecting lens, and the same tube has, at its exposed end, an eye-piece which focuses the light on the camera; R is a focusing screw; S moves the microscope from side to side. The carrier has a number of adjusting screws; an adjusting screw swings the whole carrier on pivots, moving the mica window to and fro across the beam of light; J and J' alter the tensions of the strings; T moves one string and thus adjusts the relative positions of the two strings; O O and P P are terminals connecting to the ends of the wires and through them the currents to be tested are conveyed. Carriers may be used which are fitted with one or two strings. (After Lewis.) 2, Diagrammatic representation. C C, galvanometer string; N⇄S, electric field set up between the poles of the electromagnet. The horizontal double-headed arrow represents the movements of the string, their direction depending upon the direction (ascending or descending) of the cardiac action currents through C C.

the heart and connecting them through wires to a galvanometer. It is, of course, impossible to take records (*electrograms*, as they are called) in this way of the potential changes in the human heart. Nevertheless, the blood and tissues of the body have a relatively high electrical conductivity; the beating heart may, therefore, be looked upon as an electrical generator immersed in a conducting medium, and the electric currents (action currents) produced during the cardiac cycle may be "tapped" by connecting two parts of the body with a sensitive galvanometer. Einthoven, a Dutch physiologist, was the first to devise a galvanometer for this purpose. The indicator of the galvanometer consists of a very fine fiber of quartz glass through which the cardiac action currents are transmitted. In order to render it conductive the fiber is coated with a silver deposit (as in the backing of a mirror), and suspended between the poles of an electromagnet. The fiber moves outward (away from the arch of the magnet) or inward according to whether the cardiac current at the moment is being transmitted in an upward or a downward direction. By means of a projection system and a camera of special design, the movements are photographed. The record thus obtained is called an *electrocardiogram* and the recording instrument, i.e., the galvanometer, projecting and photographic apparatus, an *electrocardiograph* (see Fig. 68). The parts of the body which are usually connected to the electrocardiograph are the two hands, or one hand and the left foot. There are three possible ways in which these members may be connected through the instrument. Each combination is referred to as a *lead* (see Fig. 69). Thus,

Right hand and left hand is called lead I,

Right hand and left foot, lead II, and

Left hand and left foot, lead III.

The normal electrocardiogram shows five *waves* or *deflections*, known simply by the letters P, Q, R, S and T (Fig. 70, p. 133). The P, R and T waves are positive, i.e., above the base line of the record; the Q and S waves are negative. P and T are blunt waves of low amplitude. The R wave is a tall spike. The P wave is caused by the spread of the excitation wave over the auricle, i.e., it precedes auricular systole by a fraction of a second. The Q, R and S deflections are produced during the transmission of the impulse through the junc-

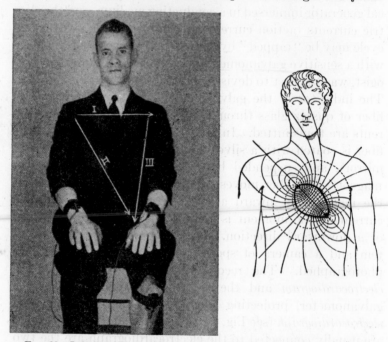

FIG. 69. *Left*, the electrocardiographic leads, represented by the arrows. (After Lewis.) *Right*, diagram showing the electrical currents caused by the beating heart. (After Waller.)

tional tissues — auriculo-ventricular bundle and its branches, and the Purkinje network. The actual contraction of the ventricular muscle commences a fraction of a second after the beginning of the R wave. The T wave is recorded while the ventricle is relaxing (see also Fig. 67, p. 124).

The electrocardiograph is one of the most valuable instruments which we possess for the investigation of the various abnormal heart conditions. It is now possible with its help to study diseases of the heart with a precision which was impossible hitherto. An electrocardiogram is now taken as a matter of routine, being almost as commonplace a procedure as the determination of the blood pressure. Important information is given by the electrocardiogram of the state of the conducting tissue of the heart. Since the P wave is caused by the excitation wave passing over the

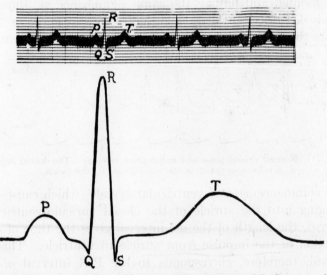

FIG. 70. *Upper curve*, normal electrocardiogram taken in lead I (Courtesy of Dr. John Hepburn). *Below*, diagrammatic representation.

auricle and the R wave by the excitation of the ventricle, the time interval between the commencement of P and the commencement of R (P-R interval) gives the conduction time from auricle to ventricle, i.e., over the A-V bundle. The normal time does not exceed 1/5 second. It is usually around 0.12 second. Lengthening of the interval indicates depression of conductivity through the auriculo-ventricular connections, i.e., incipient or partial heart block. Disease of one or other branch of the bundle (*intraventricular block*) is also readily detected by means of the electrocardiograph. Marked distortion of the record occurs in this condition.

The venous pulse. The arterial pulse is not transmitted through the capillaries to the venous system (p. 101). The peripheral veins, therefore, do not pulsate, but the *jugular vein* is in direct communication with the right auricle, and any change in intra-auricular pressure causes volume changes in this vein which can be recorded clinically by means of suitable apparatus. The jugular tracing shows a series of waves resembling, and having the same significance as, those already described for the intra-auricular pressure curve (p. 125). Since the *a* wave is due to auricular systole and the *c* wave to

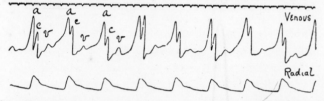

FIG. 71.　Normal venous pulse and radial pulse tracings.　The dotted line joins synchronous points in the two curves.　(After Lewis.)

the commencement of ventricular systole (which causes the bulging into the auricle of the closed auriculo-ventricular valve), the length of the *a-c* interval gives the time of conduction of the impulse from auricle to ventricle. This interval, therefore, corresponds to the P-R interval of the electrocardiogram (p. 133) and, like the latter, does not normally exceed 1/5 second.

The waves of the jugular record are not always easy to identify unless an arterial tracing (carotid or radial) is taken simultaneously with it. The instrument employed for taking synchronous records of jugular and arterial pulses is called a *polygraph*. The upstroke of the carotid tracing occurs simultaneously with the jugular *c* wave, which can thus readily be identified. The positive wave immediately preceding the *c* wave must therefore be the *a* wave and the positive wave immediately following *c* is the *v* wave (see Fig. 71).

The apex beat. The contraction of the heart causes a

slight impact upon the chest wall which can be felt by placing the fingers on the skin between the fifth and sixth ribs,
and in a line with the center of the left collar bone, i.e., about
an inch below the left nipple. This impact is called the *apex
beat*. The slight outward movement of the chest wall can
also be seen if the bare chest is looked at from one side, in
a good light.   The movement is caused by the pressure
exerted by the left ventricle during its contraction.   All
dimensions of the ventricles are reduced when they contract, but no change in the level of the apex of the heart
occurs. The base of the heart, therefore, must move
toward the apex. The auricles and great vessels are thus
elongated; they cannot move downwards as a whole, for
they are fixed above. At the same time the heart rotates to
the right, bringing the wall of the left ventricle and particularly that part forming the apex, against the chest wall.
During ventricular diastole the base of the heart moves upwards again. The up and down movement of the auriculo-
ventricular groove (the junction between the auricles and
ventricles) during the cardiac cycle can be seen quite plainly
in the exposed heart of an animal.

Disorders of the heart beat. Certain abnormalities of
cardiac rhythm in the human subject, e.g., heart block and
extrasystoles, have already been mentioned. These, and
some of the other cardiac irregularities, will now be briefly
described.

Heart block or *auriculo-ventricular block* results from disease, usually of a degenerative nature, affecting the auriculo-
ventricular bundle. Interference with the blood supply to the
heart through "hardening" (sclerosis) of the coronary vessels is a common cause of defective conduction through the
bundle. The disease may completely interrupt the passage of
impulses from auricles to ventricles; the auricles and ventricles then beat quite independently. In such an event the
radial pulse is around 35 per minute while the *a* (auricular)
waves in the venous pulse occur at the rate of 70 per minute.

In less severe grades of the disease the conduction time is lengthened, but no actual block exists. The P-R intervals of the electrocardiogram and the *a-c* intervals of the jugular tracing are prolonged. In other instances block occurs intermittently. That is, after every 2, 3 or 4 auricular beats the impulse fails to get through to the ventricle which, in

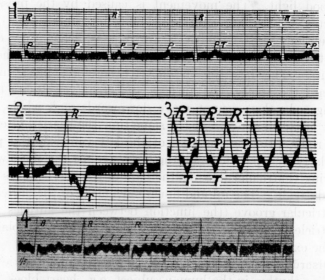

FIG. 72. 1, heart block. Note absence of the normal relationship between the auricular (*P*) and the ventricular waves (*Q*, *R*, and *S*). 2, an extrasystole. Note the long pause following it. 3, ventricular paroxysmal tachycardia, actually a series of extrasystoles. 4, auricular fibrillation. Waves marked *f* replace the normal *P* wave. (1, 2 and 3 by the courtesy of Dr. John Hepburn, 4 from Lewis.)

consequence, misses a beat. Three stages in disease of the A-V bundle are therefore recognized, namely, (a) delayed conduction, (b) missed beats or incomplete heart block and (c) complete heart block (Fig. 72, 1).

Extrasystoles or *premature beats* (see also p. 114). The abnormal impulse which excites the heart may arise in the auricle, the A-V node or in the special conducting tissue of the ventricle. Thus, three types of extra systole, *auricular*, *nodal* and *ventricular*, occur. In the auricular type, the impulses arise in some part of the auricle other than the

S-A node; each of these impulses spreads to the ventricle, excites it in the usual way and causes a premature beat of the the whole heart. There is, as a rule, no compensatory pause (p. 114). In the nodal type, the impulse arising in the A-V node passes upwards through the auricular muscle and downwards to the ventricle. Both chambers, therefore, beat almost or quite simultaneously. In the ventricular type, which has already been described on p. 114, the premature beat is followed by a compensatory pause. In this variety, the abnormal impulse, since it excites one ventricle before the other, disturbs the electrical balance of the heart. The Q R S group of waves of the electrocardiogram is therefore distorted (Fig. 72, 2).

Paroxysmal tachycardia. This name is given to a condition in which the heart suddenly commences to beat at an extraordinarily rapid rate and continues to do so for a period which varies in length in different instances from a few seconds to several hours or even days. The heart rate is from 150 to 250 per minute. The rapid beating is caused by impulses arising in some part of the heart other than the S-A node. They may be generated in the auricle, the A-V node, or the ventricular part of the special conducting system. The condition therefore consists, actually, of a series of rapidly recurring extrasystoles (Fig. 72, 3).

Auricular flutter. In this heart condition the auricle beats more rapidly than in paroxysmal tachycardia, namely, from 250 to 300 per minute. Attacks of flutter are also usually of longer duration than those of paroxysmal tachycardia. Furthermore, the A-V bundle, even though healthy itself, is unable to transmit impulses at as high a frequency as they are produced by the fluttering auricle. Only a proportion of the impulses get through; the ventricle, therefore, beats at a slower rate than the auricle. In other words, there is a *relative* heart block. The ratio of auricular to ventricular beats is usually 3 : 1 or 2 : 1.

Auricular fibrillation. The auricle in this disorder does

not contract as a whole, or in an effective manner. Its walls twitch rapidly and incessantly at a rate of 400 to 600 per minute. The auricle is never emptied, the blood flowing into the ventricle unaided by auricular systole. The *a* waves are therefore absent from the venous pulse, and the *P* waves from the electrocardiogram; they are replaced in either record by numerous small fluctuations called *f* waves (Fig. 72, 4). The auriculo-ventricular connections are capable of transmitting only a fraction of the impulses arising in the auricular muscle. Those which do reach the ventricle are irregular in time, and induce contractions of the ventricle of variable strength. The pulse is, therefore, very irregular and usually rapid. Auricular fibrillation is seen very frequently when the heart, as a result of disease of the heart muscle, is weakening and performing its work with difficulty. The serious nature of the condition is not due to any direct effect upon the dynamics of the circulation resulting from the absence of auricular systole, but rather to the irregular and rapid excitation of the ventricular muscle. The drug most commonly used in the treatment of auricular fibrillation is digitalis, which acts chiefly by depressing the conductivity of the A-V bundle. The ventricle is therefore shielded from many of the impulses arising in the fibrillating auricles; the pulse usually becomes slower and more regular in consequence.

THE REGULATION OF THE HEART'S ACTION

The heart rate is more rapid in small than in large animals. The heart of the canary, for example, beats 1000 times per minute, whereas, the average heart rate of the elephant is 25 per minute. In adult man, at rest, the usual rate is about 70 per minute, but a rate of 75 or of 60 per minute is not unusual in perfectly healthy persons. Athletes have, as a rule, a slower heart rate than have persons leading a sedentary life; the pulse rate of some famous runners is from 50 to 60 per minute. The heart rate diminishes progressively from birth, when it is around 130 per minute, to adolescence. The heart is accelerated in *muscular exercise*, by *emotional excitement*, at high *environmental temperatures* and during *digestion*. Among abnormal conditions which cause an increase in cardiac rate are, *hemorrhage, surgical shock, fever, hyperthyroidism* and certain *cardiac disorders* (p. 137).

Tachycardia is a general term meaning increased heart rate. *Bradycardia* means an unusually slow rate of the heart.

The cardiac nerves. Though the heart will continue to beat rhythmically after all nervous connections have been cut, under the ordinary conditions of life, it is under the constant influence of nervous impulses, discharged from centers in the brain. These centers are influenced in turn by impulses conveyed to them from various parts of the body along *afferent nerves* (p. 378), as well as by impulses received from the higher centers of the brain. It is common knowledge that emotional disturbances, anger, fear, excitement, etc., exert a profound influence upon the pulse rate. The *efferent cardiac nerves*, i.e., the nerves which transmit impulses from the nervous centers to the heart, are the *vagus* and the *accelerator* (or *augmentor*) nerves (Pl. 4 A). Thus, through its nervous connections, the heart may undergo slowing or acceleration as a result of the stimulation of nerve endings situated in regions remote from the heart itself. These reflex mechanisms are dealt with in greater detail on page 142.

The **vagus nerves** arise, one on each side, from the medulla oblongata. The great majority of the fibers of which they are composed belong to the parasympathetic division of the involuntary nervous system. The vagus branches are very widely distributed, passing to the bronchi, lungs, stomach and small intestine, as well as to the heart. The fibers going to the heart separate from the main trunk of the nerve in the lower part of the neck. They terminate around nerve cells (ganglion cells) situated in the auricular muscle. The impulses are relayed by the axons of the ganglion cells to the sino-auricular and auriculo-ventricular nodes. The first link in this nervous path, i.e., the fiber from the medullary center (*cardio-inhibitory center*) to the ganglion cell, is called the preganglionic fiber; the second link, i.e., the axon of the ganglion cell, is called the postganglionic fiber. The right vagus is distributed to the S-A node; it affects the *rate of the heart* to a somewhat greater extent than does the left nerve. The left vagus is distributed chiefly to the A-V node; its effect upon auriculo-ventricular conduction is greater than that exerted by the nerve of the right side. (See below.) The distributions of the two nerves overlap to a considerable extent, however, both the S-A node and the A-V node, receiving fibers from both.

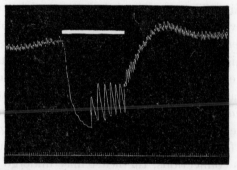

F IG. 73.   Effect of vagal stimulation upon heart rate and blood pressure. Heavy white line indicates duration of the stimulus.   Note the escape of the heart.   (After L. Hill.)

Action of the vagus nerves. The vagus is the inhibitory nerve of the heart. When it is stimulated, slowing or stoppage of the heart results. Diminished force of the beat usually accompanies the reduction in rate, though the first few beats immediately following the stimulus may be of greater amplitude than those preceding it. The blood pressure falls (Fig. 73). The vagus exerts no direct effect upon the ventricular muscle. Its action is upon the auricle, and the auriculo-ventricular bundle; stimulation of the vagus after section of the A-V bundle does not affect the ventricular rate. The excitability of the auricular muscle is reduced, and its refractory period shortened; the conductivity

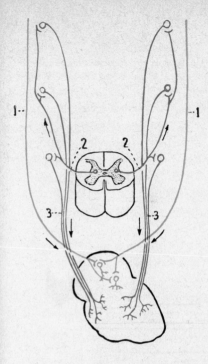

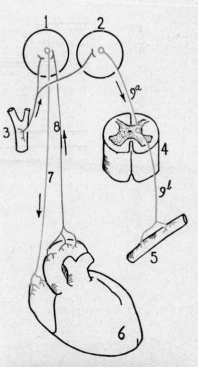

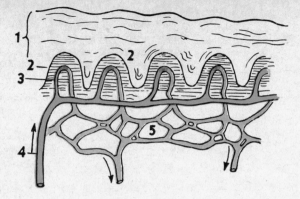

PLATE 5A

A diagram of the circulation through the skin. 1, epidermis; 2, papillae;
3, capillary loop; 4, terminal arteriole; 5, subpapillary venous plexus. The venous
limb of the capillary loop and the plexus are shown in the conventional blue color,
but actually the blood in these channels in health is little darker than arterial blood.

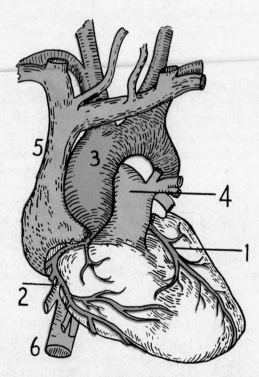

PLATE 5B

Showing the coronary arteries. 1, left coronary artery; 2, right coronary artery;
3, aorta; 4, pulmonary artery; 5, superior vena cava; 6, inferior vena cava.

of the auriculo-ventricular connections is depressed. The slowing of the heart following vagal stimulation is due, mainly, to lengthening of the diastolic period and, when the heart stops, it does so in the diastolic phase. For this reason, the vagus is sometimes called the diastolic nerve of the heart. The action of the vagus upon the heart resembles closely that caused by an excess of potassium (p. 117).

When the heart is arrested by vagal stimulation it very often commences to beat, though the stimulus is still being applied. That is to say, the heart breaks away from the vagal restraint. This is spoken of as the *"escape of the heart"* from vagal inhibition.

The tone of the vagus. When the physiologist says a nerve or muscle possesses tone he means that it exerts a continuous action. In this sense the cardiac vagus (or rather its center in the medulla) has tone; it exerts a constant restraint upon the action of the heart, sending a continuous stream of impulses along the vagus nerves which holds the heart in check. When this restraint is removed, as by cutting both vagus nerves, the rate of the heart increases very greatly. This method of demonstrating vagal tone cannot, of course, be used in man. Atropine, a drug which temporarily paralyzes the vagus, can, however, be given without danger. When a full dose of this drug is given, the heart rate is more than doubled (150 to 180 per minute).

The accelerator or augmentor nerves belong to the sympathetic division of the involuntary nervous system (p. 461). Like other pathways of the involuntary nervous system, the pathway for the accelerator impulses to the heart consists of preganglionic and postganglionic fibers. The preganglionic fibers are the axons of cells situated in the lateral horns of the cord in the upper five thoracic segments. The postganglionic fibers arise from the upper thoracic and the inferior, middle and superior cervical ganglia of the sympathetic cord; they pass to the heart by the inferior, middle and superior cardiac nerves (Fig. 72). Some fibers also pass to the heart from the first and second thoracic ganglia.

Stimulation of the accelerator nerves increases the rate of both auricles and ventricles and increases the force of their contractions. The nerves exert a direct action upon the ventricular muscle. They also increase A-V conduction. Like the vagus, the accelerators exert a continuous effect upon the cardiac rate, that is, they exercise a tonic effect. Consequently, when their influence is removed by excision of the sympathetic ganglia from which they arise, the heart slows down (see Plate 4 A).

Cardiac reflexes. The stimulation of practically any sensory (afferent) nerve in the body may cause a change in cardiac rate. In the frog, merely tapping the abdomen results in slowing of the heart, and it has been shown that in man, the stimulation of abdominal organs by manipulations during surgical operations causes changes in the heart rate. Afferent impulses arising in a diseased organ may also influence the rate of the heart. For example, cardiac inhibition may be caused by stimulation of the endings of the fifth nerve in the nose, as by some pungent odor or of afferent fibers in the lungs by irritant vapors. A similar effect may follow pressure upon the outer angle of the eye (*oculocardiac reflex*). In animals stimulation of a sensory nerve, such as the sciatic, is not infrequently followed by cardiac acceleration.

Among the afferent fibers which are most effective in bringing about reflex changes in heart rate are those contained within the vagus nerves themselves, for these nerves are made up of fibers which convey impulses *to* as well as *away from* the cardio-inhibitory center. The afferent vagal fibers end in the heart and in the arch of the aorta (see p. 153). The endings in the aortic arch, and in the left side of the heart are stimulated by a rise in arterial blood pressure; cardiac slowing results. Those on the right side of the heart are stimulated by a rise in the pressure of venous blood in the great veins and auricle; they cause acceleration of the heart by depressing the tone of the cardio-inhibitory center.

The **sinus nerve** is another afferent nerve which, when stimulated, causes reflex slowing of the heart. Its endings are situated in the walls of the carotid sinus (p. 153). The normal stimulus to these nerve endings is a rise in arterial blood pressure.

Marey's law states that the heart rate is inversely related to the arterial blood pressure, i.e., a rise or a fall in the arterial blood pressure causes, respectively, slowing or acceleration of the heart. These effects are brought about through (1) the afferent fibers of the vagus ending in the aorta and the left side of the heart, and (2) the sinus nerves. Since reflex changes in the caliber of the peripheral vessels are also brought about through these nerves, any further description of their effects will be postponed until we come to deal with the control of the blood vessels.

Bainbridge's reflex. This is the name given to the increase in heart rate which, as just mentioned, results from a rise in venous pressure. The reflex comes into play during muscular exercise when the venous return to the heart is increased. The rise in venous pressure which occurs when the ventricles become filled stimulates the afferent vagal endings in the right auricle. The heart rate is, in this way, automatically adjusted to the quantity of venous blood brought to it from the contracting muscles.

The sensory pathways from the heart. The heart, like other internal organs, is insensitive to the ordinary types of stimulus. Those stimuli, for example, which arouse the sensation of touch, heat, cold or pain, when applied to the skin, cause no sensation when applied to the heart. The heart may be touched, pinched or cut without any sensation being aroused. In disease, however, e.g., angina pectoris, severe pain may be experienced. The pain is felt over the front of the chest and down the left arm. The pain impulses travel by afferent sympathetic fibers in the middle and inferior cardiac nerves. None apparently are conveyed by the vagus. They enter the cord via the posterior roots of the upper 4 or 5 thoracic segments. Removal of the upper sympathetic ganglia, or the injection of alcohol around these ganglia, abolishes the conductivity of the pain fibers, and is sometimes resorted to for the relief of the severe, intractable pain of angina pectoris.

The action of certain drugs upon the heart. *Atropine*, as mentioned on p. 141, causes an increase in the heart rate by abolishing vagal tone. It acts by antagonizing the action of acetylcholine — the vagus substance (see below). *Muscarine*, a principle in poisonous mushrooms (amanita) slows or arrests the heart; thus, its action is similar to that following stimulation of the vagus. The effects of atropine and muscarine are, therefore, antagonistic. *Pilocarpine*, *physostigmine* (also called *eserine*), *choline* and its ester *acetylcholine*, have the same effect upon the heart as that of muscarine. *Nicotine* acts upon the ganglion (vagal) cells in the heart, first stimulating, and later paralyzing them; slowing of the heart followed by acceleration results. *Digitalis* depresses conduction in the auriculo-ventricular bundle, thus causing ventricular slowing. Large doses may cause complete dissociation of the auricles and ventricles — heart block.

The chemical (humoral) transmission of vagus and accelerator effects. Some few years ago, the astonishing and important discovery was made by Loewi, a German pharmacologist, that the vagus and accelerator nerves exert their actions upon the heart, not through the *direct* effect of nerve impulses, but through the intermediary of chemical substances. The terminals of the vagus in the heart produce *acetylcholine*, and the cardiac slowing or arrest, which results from vagal stimulation, is the result of the direct action of this substance upon the heart muscle. The production of the vagal substance or *Vagusstoff*, as Loewi called it, was demonstrated by the following experiment. Two frog hearts were set up as shown in Fig. 74. The perfusion fluid, after passing through the heart on the right (*donor heart*), then passes through the heart on the left (*recipient heart*). Now, when the vagus of the donor heart was stimulated for a time, inhibition of the recipient heart followed. The latter effect must have been due to a chemical substance

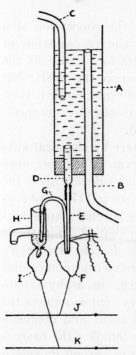

passing into the perfusion fluid during the vagal stimulation and being conveyed to the recipient heart. Subsequent experiments have left little doubt that the chemical mediator of the vagal effects is an ester of choline, namely, acetylcholine. Experiments of a similar nature have proved that an *adrenaline-like substance* is produced during stimulation of the accelerator nerves.

The vagal substance is quickly destroyed after its production. In order that a chemical shall serve as a mediator of vagal effects it is absolutely necessary that it be removed rapidly after it is produced. Otherwise it would continue to exert its effect and so cause prolonged slowing or even arrest of the heart. The destruction of acetylcholine is brought about by the action of an enzyme present in the heart muscle and in the blood. The enzyme is called *cholinesterase*. The action of physostigmine (eserine) upon

FIG. 74. The perfusion apparatus A is furnished with an overflow tube B, the height of which can be varied to allow alterations in the perfusion pressure. Fluid is delivered through the tube C. The fluid from A passes through the tube D to the inflow limb E of the double cannula which supplies the donor heart F. After irrigating the inside of the donor heart, the fluid passes by the outflow limb G to the glass cannulated tube H to which is attached the recipient heart I. This cannulated tube is provided with a lateral overflow, so that the hydrostatic pressure of the fluid supplied to the recipient heart remains constant. J and K are the levers to which the hearts F and I are respectively attached. (After Bain.)

the heart is, as mentioned above, similar to that of the vagus, or of acetylcholine itself. It has been shown that eserine acts simply by antagonizing the action of the cholinesterase. In other words, it prevents the destruction of acetylcholine which is being liberated constantly from the vagal endings and, as a consequence, enhances the tonic action of the vagus.

More recent work has shown that the conception of a chemical or humoral mechanism in the transmission of nervous effects has a much wider application. Not only the effects of the *vagus and sympathetic* upon the heart, but also those of other parasympathetic and sympathetic nerves, e.g., of the stomach, intestine, blood vessels, etc., are mediated by chemical materials (see p. 466).

The control of the action of the heart by chemical substances conveyed to it in the blood stream. The importance of the minerals *sodium*, *potassium* and *calcium* upon the action of the heart has been described (see p. 117). *Adrenaline*, the hormone of the medulla of the adrenal glands, acts upon the heart in a manner similar to that of sympathetic stimulation (see p. **346**). The *carbon dioxide* and *oxygen* pressures in the blood exert a powerful influence upon cardiac action. Excess of carbon dioxide (e.g., in asphyxia) increases the tone of the cardio-inhibitory center, reduces the rate of impulse formation in the S-A node, and depresses conduction in the auriculo-ventricular bundle; the heart is therefore slowed. When the pressure of carbon dioxide is such that a marked change in blood reaction toward the acid side occurs (e.g., to pH 7.0) heart block results. Reduction in the carbon dioxide pressure in the blood (as may be produced by prolonged forced breathing, p. 193) causes the reverse effects, namely, decrease in the tone of the cardio-inhibitory center, increased rate of impulse formation in the S-A node, and enhanced conduction in the A-V bundle.

A low *oxygen* pressure in the blood causes an increase in heart rate. If the oxygen lack is severe or prolonged, slow-

ing of the beat occurs, irregularities appear and the heart
fails. The heart muscle is unable to contract for long unless
the oxygen supply is adequate; it is much more susceptible
to oxygen lack (anoxia) than is skeletal muscle.

**The length of the muscle fiber in relation to the force of
the cardiac contraction.** It has been demonstrated experimentally that the well-nourished heart possesses great reserves of energy. For example, when the quantity of blood
entering the ventricles during their period of filling (diastole)
is increased several fold, the heart ejects the greater quantity
of blood without difficulty during the succeeding systole.
Again, when the arterial blood pressure is raised to double
the normal value, the left ventricle readily overcomes the
greater resistance and discharges its contents as easily, apparently, as it did at the lower pressure. Starling found
that the dog's heart was capable of discharging, per minute,
a weight of blood nearly 60 times that of the heart itself.
We have already seen that the minute volume of a robust
man, whose heart weighs about 300 grams, may amount to
over 35 liters (approximately 35 kilograms). How does the
heart gain the required energy for the performance of the
extra work? Now, it is well known that a skeletal muscle
contracts more forcibly if it is stretched by a weight, than
if it is permitted to contract unweighted. The degree of
stretch to which the muscle is subjected, i.e., the length
of the muscle fibers before excitation, determines the force of
the ensuing contraction. The cardiac muscle fiber behaves
in a similar manner. The greater the weight, within physiological limits, which is applied to the muscle during diastole
and, consequently, the longer the fiber, the more powerful
will be the following systole. In the case of the heart the
weight which stretches the muscle during diastole is, of
course, the mass of blood entering the ventricles. Thus,
automatically, does the heart gain the necessary energy to
perform the extra work entailed by an increased venous
return. In order to gain power to eject blood against a

raised arterial pressure, the heart does not completely empty itself for the first beat or two. The residual blood thus increases the diastolic volume of the heart, i.e., increases the length of the muscle fibers. From then on, the heart empties its chambers completely during systole.

The ability of the heart to do work above the ordinary requirements of the resting state of the body is called its *reserve power*. One might therefore, in a sense, compare the cardiac muscle fiber to an elastic band which, as we know, rebounds most powerfully when it is fully stretched. The behavior of the heart in this regard has been expressed by Starling in the following words: "The energy of the cardiac contraction is a simple function of the length of the muscle fibers of the ventricle at the end of diastole." This is known as Starling's law of the heart.

When, as a result of disease, the contractile power of the heart is reduced, it must dilate. In other words, it must increase the length of its fibers to a greater degree than does a healthy heart in order to perform the same amount of work. Thickening — *hypertrophy* — of the muscle fiber also occurs. Enlargement of the heart is therefore a sign of heart disease. Nevertheless, the enlargement in itself is beneficial, and may be looked upon as a compensatory process which enables a heart which is at a mechanical disadvantage (e.g., one with a valvular lesion) to discharge its functions. Indeed, the hypertrophied heart may have a reserve power almost as great as that of the normal heart. When the heart muscle itself is diseased, it may be so greatly weakened that it cannot even, at maximal dilatation, contract forcibly enough to maintain an efficient circulation. The signs of heart failure then ensue — breathlessness (dyspnea, p. 199), edema (p. 57) and the appearance of a bluish tint of the skin, especially of the lips, ears and finger tips (cyanosis, p. 202).

It is now generally accepted that a healthy heart cannot be "strained" by overwork. Athletics, even though of a strenuous nature, do not injure a normal heart.   On the other hand, if a person with valvular, coronary or other organic cardiac disease indulges in strenuous muscular exercise, serious injury may be inflicted upon the heart.

CONTROL OF THE BLOOD VESSELS

As already mentioned on p. 80, the walls of the arterioles are composed largely of smooth muscle fibers arranged in such a fashion that when they contract the vascular lumen is narrowed.   This muscle, in so far as its innervation is concerned, may be compared to the muscle of the heart.   One set of nerve fibers — *vasoconstrictors* — excite the muscle, that is, cause constriction of the arterioles.   The other set — *vasodilators* — inhibit the muscle, causing it to relax and so cause vascular dilatation.

The vasoconstrictor nerves belong to the sympathetic division of the involuntary nervous system.   They arise, in common with other sympathetic fibers (p. 432), from cells in the lateral horns of the gray matter of the spinal cord lying between the levels of the 1st thoracic and the 3rd

Fig. 75.   Showing effect upon arterial blood pressure of stimulating the great splanchnic nerve.   (After Macleod.)

lumbar segments.   The vasoconstrictor fibers to the vessels of the limbs, for the most part, are carried in the mixed spinal nerves, e.g., ulnar, sciatic, etc.   Those to the head and neck pass from the cervical ganglia of the sympathetic to the carotid arteries which they surround in a net-like (plexiform) manner.   These plexuses invest the vessels to their smallest branches, ultimately furnishing filaments to the arterioles.   The vasoconstrictor fibers to the abdomen pass to the vessels in three well-defined strands, the *greater*, the *lesser* and the *least splanchnic* nerves. The greater splanchnic nerve supplies the larger proportion of the arterioles of the abdomen; when stimulated, the wide-spread vasoconstriction which results causes a very pronounced rise in blood pressure (Fig. 75).

The vasodilator nerves may be grouped into three categories, (a) those which belong to the *sympathetic division* of the sympathetic nervous system, (b) those belonging to the *parasympathetic division* and (c) those which leave the central nervous system in the *posterior spinal nerve roots*. The sympathetic vasodilators arise from the thoracic and lumbar segments of the spinal cord and follow the same general course as the vasoconstrictors. They appear to be distributed almost exclusively to the vessels of the muscles and viscera.

Of the parasympathetic vasodilators, some leave the brain in the facial, glossopharyngeal and vagus nerves; others arise in the sacral part of the cord and are carried in the pelvic nerve (p. 462) to the vessels of the bladder, rectum and external genital organs. The vasodilators which leave the brain in the facial nerve enter its chorda tympani branch, and are ultimately distributed to the vessels of the tongue and salivary glands.

Vasodilator impulses conveyed along the pelvic nerve to the vessels of the penis or of the corresponding organ of the female — the clitoris — are responsible for the phenomenon of *erection* (p. 535).

The vasodilator fibers of the posterior spinal nerve roots appear to be distributed, mainly at any rate, to the skin of the limbs. There has been much discussion as to the nature of these nerves. When the posterior nerve roots supplying fibers to a limb are stimulated, the vessels may dilate. Many believe that the ordinary sensory fibers, of which the posterior roots are mainly if not entirely composed, must transmit the vasodilator impulses. That is to say, impulses pass to the vessels, apparently, over fibers which have been thought to be capable only of conveying impulses to the spinal cord, i.e., sensory impulses. According to this conception, the vasodilator impulses travel over the nerve in a direction opposite to that of the ordinary sensory impulses. For this reason they have been termed *antidromic* (G. *anti* = against, *dromos* = a running) vasodilator impulses. Other physiologists offer another explanation of the vasodilatation which follows stimulation of the posterior roots, claiming that *efferent* fibers are contained in the posterior roots, and that these alone are the transmitters of vasodilator impulses. The question remains unsettled.

The vasoconstrictor and vasodilator centers are situated in the medulla oblongata, in the floor of the 4th ventricle (see p. 451). The vasoconstrictor center is connected by tracts of fibers with the nerve cells in the lateral horns of the spinal cord which, as mentioned above, give rise to the vasoconstrictor fibers. These cells may be looked upon as constituting a spinal vasoconstrictor center. Centers controlling the vessels also probably exist at higher levels than the medulla, e.g., in the hypothalamus, and even in the cerebral cortex.

The vasoconstrictor center in the medulla and, though to a much less degree, the vasodilator center as well, possess tone. That is to say, impulses are constantly passing from the centers along the vasoconstrictor and vasodilator nerves. Under ordinary circumstances, vasoconstrictor tone predominates — the vessels being always slightly constricted. This tonic vasoconstrictor action is at once abolished if the spinal cord is cut across in the lower cervical region — the stream of impulses from the medullary center is thus interrupted. The blood vessels then dilate, the peripheral resistance, which is such an important factor in maintaining the arterial blood pressure, is greatly reduced and a profound fall in pressure results. Sectioning the splanchnic nerves, by depriving the abdominal vessels of tonic vasoconstrictor impulses, acts in a similar way to cause a fall in blood pressure.

Vascular reflexes. Variations in the caliber of the arterioles can be brought about by stimulating an afferent nerve, i.e., through reflex action. The impulses set up in the afferent nerve pass to the centers and are reflected along efferent nerves, vasoconstrictor or vasodilator, to the blood vessels. A rise or a fall in blood pressure, depending upon the afferent nerve which has been stimulated and the type of stimulus, may thus be induced. A reflex rise in blood pressure is called a *pressor* reflex, a reflex fall, a *depressor* reflex. Stimulation of practically any afferent nerve in the body may alter the calibers of the peripheral vessels. It is not always possible, however, to predict whether a pressor or a depressor reflex will result. A strong stimulus applied to an ordinary spinal sensory nerve is more likely to produce a rise in blood pressure. As a general rule, painful stimuli of various sorts result in a pressor, and mild pleasant types of stimulus, in a depressor response. In man, stimulation by cold, e.g., a draft, applied to a cutaneous area causes constriction of the vessels of the skin over parts of the body remote from the area to which the cold is applied, as well as of the vessels in the mucous membranes of the nose, throat and bronchi. Gentle stimulation of the skin (e.g., massage) causes, as a rule, vasodilatation. Warming the skin usually causes vasodilatation in areas of skin some distance from the warmed part, but if the temperature is raised to the point where a painful sensation is aroused, reflex vasoconstriction is more likely to result.

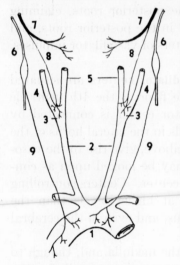

Fig. 76. Showing sinus and cardiac depressor (aortic) nerves. 1, arch of aorta; 2, common carotid; 3, carotid sinus; 4, internal carotid; 5, external carotid; 6, vagus nerve; 7, glossopharyngeal nerve; 8, sinus nerve, branch of the glossopharyngeal nerve.

The aortic and sinus nerves. There are two sets of afferent fibers which exert a very special controlling influence upon the circulation. When stimulated they cause slowing of the heart and vasodilatation and, in consequence of these effects, a fall in blood pressure. One set of such afferent fibers is contained in the vagus nerve. They terminate peripherally in the wall of the aorta and base of the heart. A rise in blood pressure, by stretching the aorta, stimulates the nerve terminals; impulses ascend to the cardiac and vasomotor centers in the medulla; impulses are discharged, in turn, down the efferent fibers of the vagus and the vasodilator nerves. The tonic vasoconstrictor impulses are, at the same time, reduced in frequency. The vasodilatation is therefore due to reduced vasoconstrictor tone as well as to increased tone of the vasodilators. Though, in man, these afferent (depressor) fibers are bound up in the vagus trunk with the efferent fibers, in certain animals, e.g., the rabbit, they are contained in a separate branch of the vagus, known as the *cardiac depressor* or *aortic* nerve (Fig. 76).

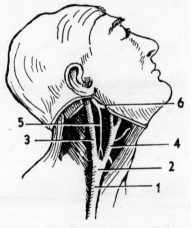

Fig. 77. Showing the carotid sinus region in man. 1, common carotid artery; 2, carotid sinus; 3, internal carotid; 4, external carotid; 5, sinus nerve; 6, glossopharyngeal nerve.

The other set of afferent fibers are contained in the *sinus nerve*. This nerve, when stimulated, brings about reflex effects upon the circulation. It is a branch of the glossopharyngeal nerve. Its terminals ramify in the wall of the *carotid sinus*, the term given to the slight enlargement of the common carotid artery at its bifurcation into the external and internal carotids (Fig. 77). The sinus nerve is stimulated by a rise in the pressure of blood within the carotid sinus. Reflex slowing of the heart, vasodilatation, and a fall in blood pressure follow. Mere compression of the sinus between the finger and thumb in an animal, or even pressure through the skin of the neck in a proportion of normal human subjects, will stimulate the nerve endings in the sinus wall and evoke the reflex. In certain rare instances the human carotid sinus is abnormally sensitive. In such persons the lightest pressure in the neighborhood of the sinus (as during shaving, or buttoning a collar) may cause marked slowing of the heart, and a profound fall in blood pressure. The fall in blood pressure may, by depriving the brain of an adequate supply of blood, cause syncope (fainting) or convulsions.

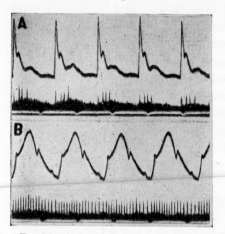

Fig. 78. A, upper tracing, blood pressure; lower curve, record of impulses from single fiber of the sinus nerve. Impulses discharged only during the systolic phase. B, upper tracing, blood pressure raised. Note the increase in the frequency of the impulses which are now discharged throughout the diastolic phase. (After Stella and Bronk.)

The maintenance of the arterial blood pressure within the normal limits is dependent to a large extent upon the activity of the sinus and aortic nerves. These nerves transmit at all times a stream of impulses to the cardiac and vasomotor centers, and thus exert continuously a depressing effect upon the blood pressure. Any marked rise in blood pressure increases the frequency of the afferent impulses and magnifies the depressor effect upon the medullary centers; the blood pressure is thus automatically reduced again. Any tendency for the blood pressure to fall is countered by an opposite effect, namely, reduction of the frequency of the impulses going to the center and, in consequence, cardiac acceleration and vasoconstriction (Fig. 78). The sinus and aortic nerves thus exert a governing or buffering effect upon the blood pressure, preventing it from fluctuating greatly in either direction. For this reason they are sometimes referred to as the "buffer nerves" of the circulation.

In hemorrhage, for example, the fall in blood pressure occasioned by the reduction in blood volume, diminishes the intensity of the stimulus normally applied to the sinus and aortic nerves, thus lowering the frequency of the afferent impulses impinging upon the centers. Reflex vasoconstriction and cardiac acceleration follow, which tend to restore the blood pressure to its normal level. The vasoconstriction seen in surgical shock, and the ability of the circulation to compensate for the effect of gravity and maintain the blood pressure when the erect posture is assumed, are mainly dependent upon the activity of the sinus and aortic nerves.

The reflex control of the heart and blood vessels is shown diagrammatically in Pl. 4 B.

SPECIAL FEATURES OF THE CIRCULATION IN CERTAIN PARTS

The capillary circulation. The capillaries are the smallest vessels of the circulatory system, measuring about a millimeter long, and having an average diameter of 10 to 15 microns. Their walls are composed of a single layer of endothelial cells, and are of such delicate construction that they are seen with the greatest difficulty, even by careful microscopical examination. The blood within the capillaries (the corpuscles being clearly seen through their walls) enables one to locate the position of these vessels. Here and there, peculiar spider-like cells can be seen in close relation to the capillary. The bodies of these cells possess several long slender processes which embrace the endothelial wall. They are called *Rouget cells* (see Fig. 44, p. 81).

Though, of course, the existence of small vessels between the arterial and venous systems was implicit in Harvey's theory of the circulation of the blood, it was not until some years after Harvey propounded his theory that the capillaries were actually demonstrated by the Italian anatomist Malpighi. It has been mentioned elsewhere (p. 81) that the whole purpose of the elaborate circulatory system is to drive blood through the capillaries, for it is through the walls of these vessels alone that oxygen and nutritive materials pass from the blood to the cells of the tissues, and carbon dioxide and waste materials from the tissues to the blood.

Each arteriole terminates in a group of about 20 capillaries. The capillaries are also under nervous control, receiving vasoconstrictor and vasodilator sympathetic fibers.

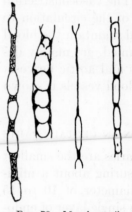

They receive, as well, vasodilator antidromic impulses, and, in certain parts of the body, vasodilator impulses are conveyed to them by parasympathetic fibers.

The capillaries show spontaneous movements, their calibers changing from time to time in accordance with the activity of the tissue (Fig. 79). In a resting muscle, for example, a large proportion of the capillaries are constricted, the channels being completely obliterated. Upon stimulation of the muscle large numbers open up, thus increasing the blood flow through the tissue several fold, and assuring an adequate oxygen supply for the contraction process.

FIG. 79. Muscle capillaries of guinea-pig injected during life with India ink, showing different degrees of constriction. Blank oval and circular areas indicate red corpuscles. (After Krogh.)

A number of chemical materials exert an influence upon capillary diameters. Carbon dioxide and lactic acid, produced during tissue activity, cause dilatation. Iodine, urethane, silver nitrate and histamine have a similar effect. Adrenaline and pituitrin cause constriction.

The most superficially placed capillaries of the human skin are in the form of hairpin-like loops running more or less at right angles to the skin surface with their convexities directed outwards. They lie just beneath the papillae of the skin. These loops may be seen when the skin at the base of the finger nail is examined with a strong light beneath the microscope (Pl. 5 A and Fig. 80). One limb of a capillary loop receives blood from the arterial side; the blood in the other limb, having given up a part of its oxygen load, is more venous in character. The venous limb drains into a plexus of capillary vessels lying beneath the bases of the papillae of the skin, and named the *subpapillary venous plexus*. It is the blood in this plexus, and not that in the capillary

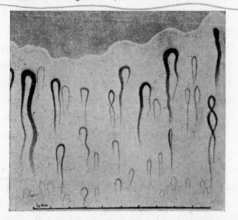

Fig. 80. Showing capillary loops in the human skin at the base of the finger nail. The divisions in the scale at the bottom of the illustration represent tenths of millimeters. (After Lewis.)

loops, which gives color to the skin. When the flow is rapid and the vessels of the plexus dilated, the skin is bright red in color. When the vessels are constricted the skin is pale. If the blood flow through the plexus becomes slowed, more oxygen is given up by the blood within the vessels, a greater proportion of the hemoglobin is in the reduced state and, in consequence, the skin acquires a bluish tint (see cyanosis, p. 202). This is seen most commonly in subjects with heart disease, the slowing then being due to failure of the heart pump. But slowing of the cutaneous blood flow, to a less degree, may occur in normal persons if exposed to cold. When the body is chilled the arterioles of the skin become constricted (an attempt on the part of the body to conserve heat, p. 305); as a result of the diversion of blood to deeper parts, the blood flow through the capillaries of the subpapillary venous plexus may be slowed to such an extent that a definitely blue tint is given to the skin, especially of the finger tips, ears and nose.

The blood supply to the heart, or coronary circulation. The heart of mammals possesses a well developed system of vessels — arteries, arterioles, capillaries and veins. The blood is delivered to the heart muscle by the *right* and *left coronary* arteries (Pl. 5 B) and, after passing through the small vessels, is drained into the right auricle by a large vein known as the *coronary sinus,* and by a number of smaller veins — *veins of Thebesius* — into the left auricle and the right and left ventricles. About 60 per cent of the blood escapes from the coronary system by the coronary sinus, the remainder by the veins of Thebesius. The coronary arteries arise from the aorta just beyond the attachments of the aortic valves.

Unlike any other organ or tissue of the body, the greatest flow of blood through the heart muscle takes place during the diastolic phase of the heart. During the ejection phase of ventricular systole the coronary blood flow is greatly reduced, for the cardiac muscle fibers when they contract compress the coronary vessels; the flow of blood is reduced through some vessels and completely arrested through others.

The mean blood pressure during the diastolic phase of the cardiac cycle is, therefore, the important factor in filling the coronary vessels and determining the magnitude of the coronary blood flow.

The coronary vessels receive fibers from both the vagus and the sympathetic nerves. The vagus causes vasoconstriction, the sympathetic vasodilatation. Adrenaline also causes dilatation of the coronary vessels; in animal experiments, a threefold increase in coronary blood flow has been obtained by the use of this substance.

Angina pectoris and coronary occlusion. The term angina pectoris means breast pain, and is used to denote an attack of intense pain felt in the region of the heart, and in many cases in the left shoulder and arm. It is due to the heart muscle being inadequately supplied with oxygen. The commonest cause is disease (arteriosclerosis) of the coronary vessels. The disease causes narrowing of the caliber of the arteries and, as a consequence, reduces the blood supply to the heart muscle. The attack most frequently follows some muscular effort or emotional excitement which increases the cardiac output. In other words, the heart is called upon to do work for the performance of which it is unable to obtain an adequate supply of oxygen. A drug such as amyl nitrite, which dilates the coronaries, is commonly given to arrest an attack.

Complete occlusion of a large branch of a coronary artery is not an uncommon event. The occlusion is usually the result of the clotting of blood within a vessel (*thrombosis*) which is the seat of arteriosclerosis. Coronary thrombosis, or occlusion of a large coronary branch from whatever cause, is accompanied by intense pain, nausea and vomiting, breathlessness and collapse. Death may occur almost instantly. If recovery takes place the area of heart muscle deprived of its blood supply dies (necrosis), and is replaced by scar tissue. The electrocardiogram taken shortly after an attack shows certain special features which are of the greatest value in diagnosis.

The pulmonary circulation. The blood passes from the right to the left side of the heart through the lungs. The same quantity of blood as is discharged in a given time by the right side of the heart, is received and discharged by the left. In other words, the quantity of blood passing through the lungs per minute is the same as that passing through the systemic circulation. The vessels of the pulmonary circuit, as of any other part, consist of arteries, arterioles, capillaries and veins. The main artery is called the *pul-*

monary. It contains *venous blood* received from the right ventricle. The main veins are four in number (two from each lung); they contain *arterial* (oxygenated) blood, which they deliver into the left auricle.

The capillaries of the lung differ from those of any other tissue in that they are separated from air only by the very delicate and incomplete membrane composing the walls of the pulmonary alveoli. The pulmonary capillaries can increase their capacity to a relatively great extent. Ordinarily the lungs contain from 7 to 10 per cent of the total amount of blood in the body, but under certain conditions they may contain 20 per cent of the blood volume. If, for example, there is some resistance on the left side of the heart (e.g., mitral stenosis or weakness of the left ventricle) while the right ventricle continues to contract forcibly, the pressure in the pulmonary circuit rises; the capillary bed becomes distended, and a much greater volume of blood is contained in the lungs. This is likely to cause breathlessness — a common symptom of heart disease.

The pressure in the pulmonary circulation is about $\frac{1}{6}$ of that in the systemic circulation. In the dog the mean pressure in the pulmonary artery is around 25 mm. Hg as compared with 130–150 in the aorta.

Variations in intrathoracic pressure occur during ordinary quiet respiration. The intrathoracic pressure amounts to about − 6 mm. Hg during inspiration, and about − 2.5 mm. Hg during expiration. More blood, therefore, is "sucked" into the great veins of the thorax and right auricle during inspiration than during expiration; more blood is discharged from the right heart into the pulmonary system during inspiration. The quantity of blood received and given out by the left side of the heart must, of course, vary with the quantity discharged by the right side. The variations in output of the left ventricle cause corresponding fluctuations in the systemic blood pressure. The increased discharge of the left ventricle and the rise in systemic blood pressure are not, however, synchronous with inspiration, but owing to the increased vascular capacity of the lungs themselves, caused by the inspiratory movement, are somewhat delayed. The rise in systemic blood pressure does not commence until near the end of inspiration, and reaches its maximum toward the end of expiration (see Fig. 81).

The pulmonary vessels are supplied with fibers from the sympathetic and the vagus. The former are mainly vasoconstrictor in action, the latter mainly vasodilator.

The hepatic circulation. The blood from the gastrointestinal tract and spleen is collected by the portal vein

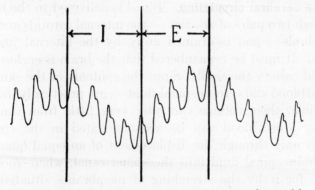

Fig. 81. Showing the effect of the respirations upon the arterial blood pressure. I, inspiration; E, expiration.

and conveyed to the liver. The blood from the small intestine contains materials derived from the food, e.g., glucose, amino-acids, as well as a proportion of the fat. The portal vein breaks up within the liver into numerous branches; its smallest subdivisions run between the lobules of the liver, and are called *interlobular veins*. These open into capillary-like vessels called *sinusoids*, lying between rows of liver cells (the *liver cords*). All the sinusoids of a liver lobule converge toward the center of the lobule where they drain into a *central vein*. The central veins drain in turn into a system of larger veins which ultimately join to form vessels called the *hepatic veins;* these open into the

inferior vena cava (see Pl. 3).   Thus the portal vein resembles an artery in that it breaks up into branches which
lead into capillary vessels.   It, therefore, lies between two
capillary beds, one in the walls of the gastro-intestinal tract
and spleen, the other in the liver.   The blood of the portal
vein has a pressure of only about 10 mm. Hg, a low content
of oxygen, and a high content of carbon dioxide.   But the
liver cells must receive well-oxygenated blood under high
pressure.   This is delivered through the hepatic artery — a
branch of the celiac artery which arises directly from the
abdominal aorta.

The cerebral circulation.   Blood is delivered to the brain
through two pairs of arteries — the internal carotids and the
vertebrals — and is drained away by the internal jugular
veins.   It must be remembered that the brain is enclosed in
a rigid case — the skull.   Since the contents of the skull —
brain, blood and cerebrospinal fluid — are practically incompressible, their volume can alter very little from time to
time.   More blood can be accommodated in the cranial
cavity only through the displacement of an equal quantity
of cerebrospinal fluid into the spinal canal, where room is
made for it by the stretching of membranes situated between the joints of the vertebrae.   Though the quantity of
blood within the skull changes comparatively little from time
to time, the *velocity* of the blood flow through the cerebral
vessels varies considerably.   The flow is determined largely
by the blood pressure in the rest of the body, a rise in pressure in the aorta increasing the cerebral blood flow, and vice
versa.   For example, when a person assumes the standing
position, the carotid sinus and aortic nerve mechanisms
come into play and prevent a fall in the pressure of blood in
the arteries going to the head, which otherwise would result
from the effect of gravity upon the circulation.   The brain is
thus assured of an adequate blood supply.

The flow through the brain is dependent also upon the
pressure gradient, i.e., upon the difference between the pres-

sures in the cerebral arteries and the cerebral veins. An increase in the pressure in the internal jugular veins (the pressure in the cerebral arteries being unchanged) will, therefore, tend to diminish the cerebral blood flow.

Variations in the blood flow through the cerebral vessels can occur, however, quite independently of the general blood pressure for, though denied for years, it is now recognized that these vessels are supplied with nerves, which can bring about active changes in vascular calibers. Though the systemic blood pressure remains unchanged, an increased cerebral blood flow can, therefore, be effected through intracranial vasodilatation. Constriction of the cerebral vessels, with a constant systemic pressure, will cause the opposite effect, namely, a reduction in the blood supply to the brain. The vasodilator fibers to the cerebral vessels are derived from the facial nerve, the vasoconstrictors from the sympathetic.

CHAPTER IV

RESPIRATION

Introductory. All living things, with a few exceptions, absorb oxygen. The oxygen combines with the carbon and hydrogen furnished by food material. Carbon dioxide (CO_2) and

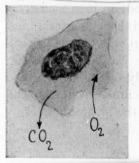

water (H_2O) are produced. These oxidations take place in the cells of the tissues; they generate heat and furnish the organism with energy for the performance of work (see Chapter VII). The carbon dioxide, so formed, is eliminated; the oxidation of the hydrogen constitutes an important source of body water (the water of metabolism). The exchange of gases (O_2 and CO_2) between an organism and its environment is termed *respiration*.

FIG. 82. Respiration of a unicellular organism (e.g., ameba).

In unicellular organisms and many multicellular forms of lower orders, the gaseous exchange takes place directly between the cells and their surroundings (see Fig. 82). Higher forms of animal life are composed of cells of which the great mass are removed from direct contact with the external environment. But the cells of such higher forms, like those of the most primitive, are bathed in fluid. This tissue fluid we may speak of as the *internal environment;* from it the cells absorb oxygen (as well as nutriment) and into it the cells discharge their waste materials, including carbon dioxide (Fig. 83). Through the medium of the blood-vascular system, oxygen is transported from the external to the internal environment; thus a steady supply of oxygen to the cells is secured. By the same means, carbon dioxide is carried from the tissue fluids. In air-breathing animals the exchange of gases between the blood and the external environment takes place in the lungs. This is called *external respiration*. In fish it is a function of the gills. The exchange of gases between the tissue cells and their fluid environment is termed *internal respiration*.

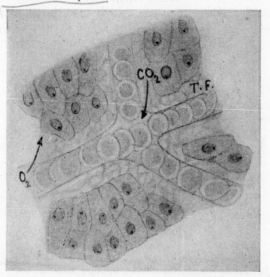

Fig. 83. Illustrating internal respiration. Capillary shown filled with red cells; T.F. = tissue fluid.

AN OUTLINE OF THE STRUCTURE OF THE RESPIRATORY ORGANS

The air passages. These are, the *nasal cavities,* the *pharynx, larynx, trachea, bronchi* and *bronchioles* (see Figs. 84 and 85). The interior of the nose is divided into two lateral halves by the nasal septum. From the lateral wall of each nasal cavity spring three spurs of bone called, respectively, the *inferior, middle* and *superior turbinates* (or *conchae*). These incompletely divide each side of the nose into three passages (the meatuses of the nose). Situated between the superior turbinate bone and the floor of the skull is a small recess containing the olfactory epithelium (see p. 520). The main air currents do not enter this recess, the meatuses of the nose alone serving as airways. The meatuses are lined with ciliated epithelium; the movements of the cilia are toward the exterior, thus mucus and dust or any other foreign particles which may enter the nose in the respired air are carried to the nostrils.

The nasal cavities open posteriorly into the *pharynx* which, therefore, serves as a common passage for the transmission

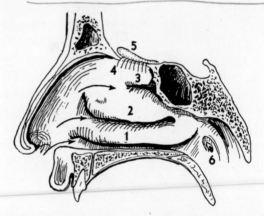

FIG. 84. The inner surface of the outer wall of the nose. 1, lower turbinate bone (concha); 2, middle turbinate bone; 3, upper turbinate bone; 4, olfactory nerves; 5, olfactory bulb; 6, opening of Eustachian tube. The arrows indicate the course taken by the air in breathing.

of air to the larynx, and of food from the mouth to the esophagus. During swallowing, the food has the right of way, the respirations being then inhibited.

The larynx is situated in the neck in front of the lower part of the pharynx and at the commencement of the trachea or windpipe. It contains the vocal cords, and will be described more fully later.

The trachea (human) is a tube about ½ inch in diameter and 4½ inches long, extending from the larynx to a little below the upper boundary of the chest; here it divides into two branches — the *right* and *left bronchi*. Each bronchus enters the corresponding lung and divides, like the limbs of a tree, into a number of smaller branches. The larger of these are

also called bronchi, but the finer terminal twigs are referred
to as *bronchioles*. It is, of course, imperative that this important airway be always kept open. The patency of the
trachea is ensured by the presence of a series of C-shaped
rings of cartilage which support its wall in front and at the
sides. The gaps in the cartilages posteriorly, as well as the
intervals between them, are bridged by a strong fibro-
elastic membrane. The trachea is lined by ciliated columnar
epithelial cells. The walls of the two main bronchi are constructed upon a plan almost identical with that of the
trachea, but the cartilage in the walls of the smaller bronchi
is in the form of thin isolated and irregular plates which become smaller and fewer in number with each successive
branching of the bronchial tree.

The bronchioles are about 1 mm. or less in diameter.
Their walls are composed of smooth muscle lined by mucous
membrane of the same character as that lining the trachea
and bronchi; cartilage is entirely lacking. The muscle fibers
of the bronchioles are arranged circularly. Their contraction,
therefore, causes narrowing of the bronchiolar lumen. In
asthmatic attacks marked bronchiolar constriction occurs,
and is responsible for the respiratory distress characteristic
of this condition. The muscle of the bronchioles receives its
nerve supply from both the vagus and the sympathetic;
the former is constrictor, the latter dilator in action.

The lungs. The left lung is divided by a fissure into two
lobes, an upper and a lower (see Fig. 85). Two fissures
divide the right lung into three lobes. The bronchi and
bronchioles possess no truly respiratory function; no interchange of gases can occur across their relatively thick walls.

The lung tissue proper consists of an immense number of
irregularly shaped *air spaces*. The terminal twigs of the
bronchial tree (*terminal bronchioles*) open each into one of
these air spaces. One of the latter with its several named
parts — *respiratory bronchiole, alveolar ducts, alveolar sacs*
and *pulmonary alveoli* — is illustrated diagrammatically in

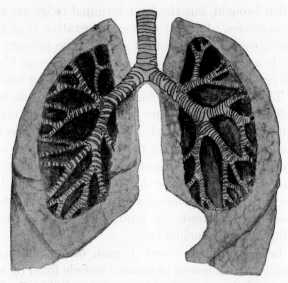

Fig. 85.   Showing trachea and bronchi.   Portion of the lung tissue removed to show branchings of the bronchial tree.

Fig. 86.   The pulmonary alveoli are seen as three or four outpouchings of the cavity of each alveolar sac.   A single layer of flat cells and a network of fine elastic fibers compose their walls; a rich network of blood capillaries surrounds them.   Thus the blood as it flows through the lungs is separated from the air in the alveoli by two membranes — the alveolar and capillary walls — so extremely thin that little hindrance is offered to the free exchange of the respiratory gases.   The number of pulmonary alveoli in both lungs has been estimated to be about 750,000,000.

THE MECHANICS OF RESPIRATION

The chest or thorax is a closed cavity, bounded laterally and behind by the ribs and the vertebral column, in front by the ribs and sternum (breast bone), below by a dome-shaped sheet of muscle (the diaphragm), which separates it from the abdominal cavity, and above by the upper ribs and the tissues of the neck.   The lungs, heart and great blood vessels almost completely fill the thorax.

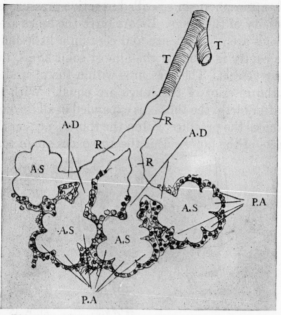

FIG. 86. Diagrammatic representation of a respiratory unit. A.D, alveolar ducts; A.S, air sacs; P.A, pulmonary alveoli; R, respiratory bronchiole; T, terminal bronchiole (muscular wall). Note the capillaries filled with red cells surrounding the alveoli.

The intrapleural pressure. The lungs are covered by a thin membrane called the *pleura*, which passes from each lung at its root (i.e., at the point where the main bronchus and pulmonary vessels enter it) on to the interior of the chest-wall and upper surface of the diaphragm. Thus, two membranous sacs, called the *pleural cavities*, are produced, one on each side of the chest, between the lungs and the thoracic boundaries. Since the pleura covering the lung and that lining the chest are in contact under all conditions of health, no actual space exists; these so-called cavities are potential ones only. In disease, however, air, fluid or blood may collect and separate the pleural layers.

The pressure between the layers of the pleura (*intrapleural pressure*) and indeed throughout the thorax generally (*intrathoracic pressure*) is below that of the atmosphere.

This sub-atmospheric or so-called negative pressure is due to the elasticity of the lungs. Before birth the lungs are airless, the air sacs are of small size and contain a little fluid. The thoracic cavity is filled by the almost solid lungs, the heart and great vessels. The pressures within the pleural cavities and in the interior of the lungs are equal. With the first breath after birth, the thorax is expanded in all its diameters. This reduces the pressure within the thorax, i.e., on the pleural aspects of the lungs. But the air spaces are in communi-

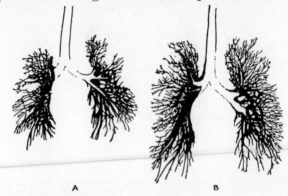

A   B

FIG. 87. Tracing of an X-ray photograph demonstrating elasticity of bronchial tree. A, full expiration; B, full inspiration. (After Macklin.)

cation with the outside air through the air passages. Atmospheric air, therefore, enters the lungs and, were the lung tissue inelastic, equalization of pressure between the atmosphere and the pleural cavities would result. But the bronchial tree and the lung substance itself are richly supplied with elastic tissue. When the lungs expand and fill the enlarged thoracic cavity the elastic tissue is put upon the stretch. The lungs in post-natal life are, therefore, constantly under tension and tending to recoil to their original dimensions. This pull of the elastic lungs away from the thoracic walls, though it cannot separate the layers of the pleura, creates a "negative" pressure.

Throughout life the intrapleural pressure undergoes rhythmical variations with the respiratory movements as a result of changes in the thoracic dimensions, and the consequent variations in the degree of stretching to which the lungs are subjected (see Fig. 87). The intrapleural (or intrathoracic) pressure is around − 6 mm. Hg during inspiration and − 2.5 mm. during expiration.

The respiratory movements — the intake and expulsion of air. The drawing of air into the lungs is called *inspiration*, and its expulsion *expiration*. The capacity of the thorax is enlarged during inspiration and reduced during expiration. These two movements alternate rhythmically at the rate of from 18 to 20 per minute. At the end of expiration the

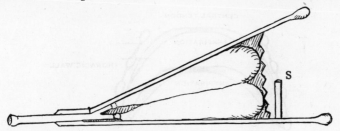

FIG. 88.   Description in text.

pressure of air within the lungs (*intrapulmonary pressure*) equals or nearly equals the atmospheric pressure. The inspiratory movement, as mentioned above, reduces the pressure upon the pleural surfaces of the lung. The air sacs are dilated thereby and the air within them is rarefied, i.e., reduced below that of the atmosphere. Air, therefore, flows into the lungs until the intrapulmonary pressure again almost equals that of the atmosphere. During expiration the intrapleural pressure is increased, the air sacs return to their previous dimensions and the intrapulmonary pressure rises above that of the atmosphere; air is therefore expelled from the lungs.

It should be emphasized that the lungs play a purely passive role in the respiratory movements. The changes in volume which they undergo, and to which the intake and expulsion of air are directly due, are brought about solely through changes in the capacity of the thoracic cavity. The inspiratory and expiratory movements of the thorax may be compared to the opening and closing of a fire bellows. A pair of bellows, which may be taken to represent the thorax, is shown in Fig. 88. Two elastic bags, contained within it and communicating with the outside air through the nozzle, correspond to the lungs and air passages. The space surrounding the bags is hermetically sealed. Opening the bellows ("inspiration") causes the bags to expand and fill with air; closure of the bellows ("expiration") to the stop S causes their partial deflation.

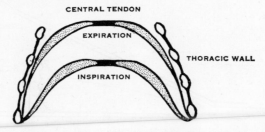

FIG. 89. Showing position of the diaphragm at the end of inspiration and expiration, respectively.

Having outlined the general principles underlying the ventilation of the lungs, the muscular mechanisms whereby the changes in thoracic capacity are brought about will be considered.

The enlargement of the thorax during inspiration. All diameters — vertical, antero-posterior and transverse — are increased during the inspiratory phase. Increase in the vertical diameter of the thorax is brought about by the descent of the *diaphragm*. This is a tendo-muscular sheet which separates the thoracic from the abdominal viscera. The muscle fibers arise from the spinal column and lower ribs and, arching upwards and inwards, are inserted into a central leaf-shaped tendon. This tendon forms the highest part of the diaphragm and is called the *central tendon of the diaphragm* (Fig. 89). The central tendon of the diaphragm

blends with the inferior surface of the pericardium; on either
side of the pericardium the diaphragm is in contact with the
bases of the lungs.   When the muscular fibers of the diaphragm contract the structure shows little change in shape,
but is seen under the X rays to move downwards as a whole
very much like the stroke of a piston.   The diaphragm is the
most important muscle of respiration, about 60 per cent of
the volume of the air inspired being due to its action.

The thorax is enlarged in its antero-posterior diameter by
the movement into a more horizontal position, of the 3rd, 4th,

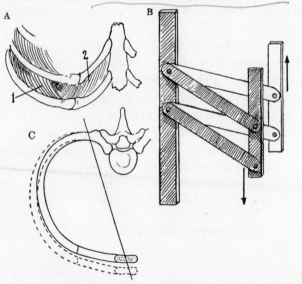

Fig. 90.   A, fourth and fifth ribs and section of sternum.   1, external intercostal
muscles; 2, internal intercostals.   B, diagram illustrating the action of the external
intercostals.   C, showing axis of rotation of ribs in bucket-handle movement.

5th and 6th pairs of ribs, which slope obliquely downwards
and forwards (Fig. 90 A and B).   This movement is brought
about by the contraction of the external intercostal muscles.
The fibers of the latter take a slanting direction across the
intercostal space from the lower border of one rib to the
upper border of the next rib below.   When the external intercostals contract, the anterior ends of the four pairs of ribs

are elevated and the sternum thrust forwards and upwards. Any downward pull exerted by the contracting fibers upon the upper of two adjacent ribs is antagonized by the pull of certain other muscles acting upon the ribs from above.

The part of the thorax bounded by the 7th, 8th, 9th and 10th ribs is increased in its transverse diameter by rotation of these ribs around an axis directed from the sternum obliquely backwards and a little outwards (Fig. 90 C). These ribs are bowed outwards and downwards, and their movement during inspiration has been compared to raising a bucket handle from its position of rest toward the horizontal plane.

Expiration is effected mainly in a passive manner. At the end of the inspiratory phase the intercostal muscles and the diaphragm relax. The walls of the thorax, by their own weight and the pull exerted upon them by the elastic lung (see Fig. 87), return to their original position. The relaxed diaphragm ascends, being drawn up by the "negative" intrathoracic pressure. Under certain circumstances contraction of the abdominal muscles occurs as part of the expiratory act. The pressure thereby exerted upon the abdominal viscera aids the ascent of the diaphragm.

ARTIFICIAL RESPIRATION

The tissues cannot survive for long without oxygen. The central nervous system is especially susceptible to oxygen deprivation, irreparable damage resulting if the oxygen supply is completely cut off for 10 minutes or so (e.g., by occlusion of the blood vessels). When the respirations are suspended, as in the apparently drowned, in asphyxiation with poisonous gases (e.g., carbon monoxide), or as a result of a strong electric shock, the tissues suffer less acutely from oxygen lack than when the blood supply is abruptly arrested, for in such conditions a considerable time may elapse before the oxygen store of the blood is completely exhausted. During this time, the tissues, though receiving a very limited

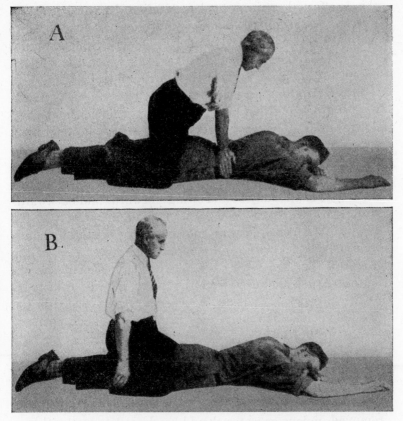

FIG. 91. Schafer's prone pressure method of artificial respiration (see text). A, expiration. B, inspiration. (After Wills Maclachlan.)

amount of oxygen, receive enough to sustain their vitality. So long as the heart continues to beat, the blood, of course, is circulating through the lungs, but since the lungs are no longer being ventilated by the respiratory movements oxygenation of the hemoglobin cannot occur. It is therefore imperative that artifical respiration be instituted before the heart muscle fails from lack of oxygen. Obviously, artificial respiration is useless after the blood has ceased to circulate.

The object of artificial respiration is to ventilate the air spaces of the lungs with fresh air. In most methods in use, this is effected, as in normal respiration, by causing rhythmical alterations in the dimensions of the chest cavity. Two methods will be described, namely, Schafer's, which requires no special apparatus, and Drinker's, in which the subject, except for his head, is enclosed in a chamber.

Schafer's prone pressure method. The subject is placed in the prone position (i.e., lying with abdomen and chest downwards). The head is turned to one side and laid upon the arm of the opposite side, which is bent at the elbow to form a suitable support. The other arm is fully extended in front of the face (see Fig. 91). The operator kneels astride the thighs of the subject and swings forwards and backwards with arms held rigid in a position of slight flexion at the elbows. With each forward movement the operator's hands come in contact with, and compress the lower part of the subject's thorax. With each backward movement the operator's hands are raised from the thorax which recoils to its resting position. Thus air, which had been expelled in the first movement, is replaced by inspired air. The operator makes about 16 double movements per minute.

Artificial respiration should be continued until natural breathing returns or until a physician has examined the patient and pronounced him dead. As soon as artificial respiration has been started all possible obstructions should be removed, mucus or water should be cleared from the throat and all clothing about the neck, chest or abdomen loosened.

The Drinker mechanical method. This method is used when artificial respiration must be carried out for long periods — days, weeks or even months — owing to paralysis of the respiratory muscles. Such an emergency is most likely to arise as a result of infantile paralysis (anterior poliomyelitis). The patient lies upon a bed within a hermetically closed steel cabinet, his head alone being outside. A flexible collar is fitted around his neck, so as to prevent the leakage of air (Fig. 92). A motor-driven pump causes alternate variations in the air pressure within the chamber.

Reduction in air pressure below that of the atmosphere causes expansion of the chest (inspiration). The next moment the pressure within the chamber becomes atmospheric, the chest returns to the resting position and expiration occurs. Portholes for tending the patient are provided in the walls of the apparatus. The patient is kept continuously in the chamber until respiratory muscles which have not been paralyzed, or unparalyzed fibers within the affected muscles (e.g., diaphragm or intercostals), have developed sufficient strength to carry out, unaided, the movements required for adequate ventilation of the lungs.

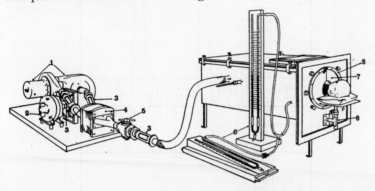

Fig. 92. Drinker's mechanical method of artificial respiration.   1, pumps; 2, motor; 3, vents; 4, alternate; 5, valve; 6, manometers; 7, external shutters; 8, adjustment for head rest; 9, adjustable ring to hold collar in place. (After Shaw and Drinker.)

In cases of apparent drowning or gas poisoning it is usually of great benefit to add oxygen to the inspired air. Carbon dioxide in a concentration of about 7 per cent is also frequently employed, the object being to stimulate the respiratory center (p. 191) and bring on natural breathing. Oxygen and carbon dioxide are also used in patients suffering from pneumonia and other conditions in which, though the patient is able to breathe, the blood is being imperfectly oxygenated.

THE SUBDIVISIONS OF THE LUNG AIR

Only about $\frac{1}{10}$ of the total air capacity of the lungs is inspired and expired in ordinary quiet breathing; this, which amounts to about 500 cc., is called the *tidal air*. In an inspiration of maximum depth, six times this amount, namely, 3000 cc., can be inhaled. This is termed the *complemental air*. If one empties his lungs as completely as possible

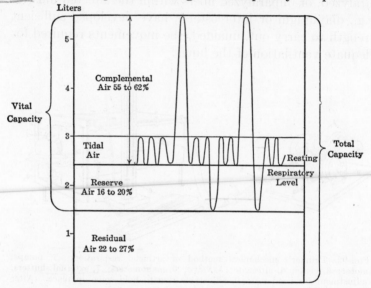

Fig. 93. Diagram showing subdivisions of the lung air.
(Modified from Christie.)

(forced expiration) after an ordinary expiration, about 1000 cc. of air can be expelled from the lungs. This air, which can be expelled by an extra effort, is called the *reserve* (or *supplemental*) *air*. The lungs cannot, of course, be emptied completely for they are kept in the partially expanded state by the subatmospheric pressure within the pleural cavities. Even after the most forcible expiration, from 1000 to 1500 cc. of air remain in the lungs. This large volume of air can be expelled only after death by opening the thoracic cavity, thus establishing communication between the pleural cavities and the atmosphere; it is called the *residual air* (see table 5 and Fig. 93). But, the lungs, even after their removal from the body, contain air entrapped within the air sacs. This part of the residual air is termed the *minimal air.* To it the lung tissue owes its buoyancy when put into water. The lungs of a still-born child, since they are unexpanded, sink in water. This fact is the basis of an important medico-legal test in cases of suspected infanticide, by means of which it is possible to determine whether or not an infant had been born alive.

The maximum quantity of air which can be expired after the deepest possible inspiration, i.e., the sum of the complemental and reserve airs, is called the *vital capacity.* Athletes and other persons in good physical condition have, in general, greater vital capacities than those who lead a sedentary life or are debilitated. The vital capacity is, therefore, used as a criterion of physical fitness. In health it bears a relationship to the surface area of the body, amounting to 2500 cc. per square meter of body surface for the average man, 2000 cc. for women and 2800

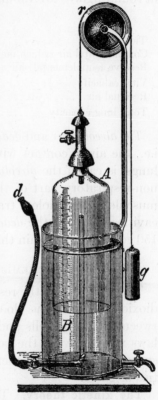

FIG. 94. Spirometer. *A*, graduated glass bell; *B*, water; *d*, mouthpiece; *g*, counter weight; *r*, pulley. (After Reichert.)

cc. for athletes. For a man of average build (1.7 square meters of body surface) it amounts, therefore, to $(1.7 \times 2500 =)$ 4250 cc. Certain diseases of the lungs, chest and heart reduce the vital capacity below the normal standard for the individual.

The vital capacity is measured by having the subject inspire fully, and then empty his lungs as completely as possible into an instrument called a *spirometer* (see Fig. 94).

The average values of the main subdivisions of the lung air in round figures are tabulated below.

TABLE 5

Tidal air...	500 cc.
Complemental air (which includes tidal air)......	3000 cc.
Reserve (supplemental) air.....................	1000 cc.
Vital capacity.................................	4000 cc.
Residual air..................................	1200 cc.
Total lung capacity..........................	5200 cc.

The alveolar air and *dead space air*. The air in the air sacs i.e., the air in contact with the true respiratory part of the lungs, is called the *alveolar* air. The space enclosed by the non-respiratory part of the lungs, namely, the bronchi and muscular bronchioles, trachea, larynx, pharynx and nasal cavities, is called the *dead space;* it has a capacity of about 150 cc. The air within this space is called the *dead space air.*

THE CHEMISTRY OF RESPIRATION

The exchange of the respiratory gases (oxygen and carbon dioxide) between the blood and the air in the lungs, and between the tissue cells and the blood, follows those physical laws which govern the behavior of gases in general. Some space will be devoted, therefore, to an account of the properties of gases.

The kinetic theory. The behavior of a gas is explained upon the theory that its molecules are in ceaseless motion. They move at high velocity and if unobstructed in any way become separated from one another by immeasurable distances. A gas, therefore, is capable of expanding to infinite dimensions, its molecular concentration diminishing proportionately as it expands. When confined, the gas molecules strike numberless blows upon the walls of the container. The pressure exerted by a gas is attributed to this ceaseless molecular bombardment. It follows, therefore, that the greater the number of molecules within a given space (i.e., the higher their concentration), the higher will be the gas pressure.

If two samples of the same gas but of different molecular concentrations be brought together, rapid and even distribution of the molecules takes place between the two samples, with consequent equalization of the pressure throughout any space in which the gas is confined (see Fig. 95). The final pressure has a value somewhere between the pressures of the separate samples. Gas molecules are

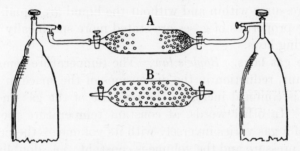

Fig. 95. Illustrating the diffusion of gases. The two gas storage cylinders contain the same kind of gas at unequal pressures. In the cylinder on the left the gas is at the lower pressure. When samples of gas from each cylinder are allowed to enter the glass chamber A, the molecules, as indicated by the small circles, intermingle freely and become evenly distributed (as in B) with consequent equalization of pressure throughout.

therefore said to move from a point of higher to one of lower pressure.

When two dissimilar gases either at the same or at different pressures are brought together, each behaves as though it were the only kind present. The molecules of each gas become evenly dispersed throughout the space, its molecular concentration and, in consequence, its pressure becoming everywhere equal. After mixing, the molecular concentrations of the two gases may differ widely from one another for, as just mentioned, they behave quite independently of one another, their final concentrations depending upon the original concentrations of the respective samples. In order to realize the speed with which dispersion of the molecules occurs, one has only to recall how quickly some odorous or pungent gas permeates the atmosphere. The process whereby samples of the same gas at different pressures, or of different gases at the same or unequal pressures are mixed, is called *diffusion*.

Though the molecular movements are much slower, liquids and solids in solution behave in the same way. For example, a basin of water in which a bottle of red ink is opened carefully, so as to avoid mechanical mixing, becomes, after a time, of a uniform color throughout. Molecules of gases also diffuse into liquids in contact with them until the gas pressures within and without the liquid are equal.

The properties of gases are stated more specifically in the following laws.

The gas laws. *Boyle's law.* The temperature remaining constant, reduction in the dimensions of the space in which a gas is confined increases the pressure of the gas and vice versa. In other words, at constant temperature the pressure of a gas varies inversely with its volume — the product of the pressure and the volume is constant; i.e., doubling the pressure reduces the volume by half.

Charles' (or *Gay-Lussac's*) *law.* For each rise in temperature of 1° C. a gas kept at constant pressure expands by $\frac{1}{273}$ of its volume at 0° C. The volume of a gas at constant pressure is, therefore, proportional to its absolute temperature (− 273° C).

Dalton's law of partial pressures. A quantity of gas when mixed with other gases exerts the same pressure as it would exert were the other gases not present. The total pressure of a mixture of gases is, therefore, the sum of the pressures of the individual gases in the mixture, each gas exerting a pressure proportional to its percentage in the mixture. For example, the atmosphere (dry) at sea level has a pressure of 760 mm. Hg; it contains 20.96 per cent of oxygen. The pressure exerted by oxygen, in the air at sea level is, therefore,

$$\frac{20.96}{100} \times 760 = 159.2 \text{ mm. Hg.}$$

Henry's law of the solution of gases. The temperature remaining constant, the quantity of gas which goes into solution in any given liquid is proportional to the partial pressure of the gas. For example, water when exposed to the atmosphere absorbs the constituent gases — oxygen, nitrogen and carbon dioxide — in quantities proportional to the pressure which each exerts in the air mixture. The partial pressure of each gas in the water will be the same as its partial pressure in the atmosphere. The liquid is then said to be equilibrated with the gas.

The compositions and partial pressures of the gases in atmospheric, expired and alveolar airs.

Atmospheric air contains 20.96 per cent of oxygen, 79.00 per cent of nitrogen and 0.04 per cent of carbon dioxide. It also contains minute amounts of the rare gas argon. The approximate partial pressures of these gases in atmospheric (i.e., in inspired air) are, therefore, 159, 596 and 0.30 mm. Hg, respectively. In expired air the pressure of oxygen is lower (since its percentage is lower) and that of carbon dioxide higher, than in inspired air. In the alveolar air the oxygen pressure is lower again, and the carbon dioxide pressure higher (see tables 6 and 7). Thus, the pressure of oxygen declines from inspired air to alveolar air, and that of carbon dioxide from alveolar air to inspired air. Nitrogen is an inert gas so far as respiration is concerned, i.e., it is neither retained in the body (like oxygen) nor produced (like carbon dioxide). The difference between the pressure of nitrogen in the expired and alveolar airs, on the one hand, and in the inspired air, on the other (see table 7), is due simply to changes in the pressures of the other gases and to the water vapor added to the air in the lungs, for it should be remembered that the *total* pressure of expired air or of alveolar air must be the same as that of the atmosphere.

The partial pressure of water vapor in the air of the lungs amounts to about 47 mm. Hg. The value for the barometric pressure, less 47, must therefore be used in calculating the partial pressure of one or other gas in the expired or alveolar airs from its percentage. For example, if the expired air contains 16.3 per cent of oxygen and the barometer registers 760 mm., then the partial pressure of oxygen is

$$\frac{16.3 \times (760 - 47)}{100} = 116.2 \text{ mm. Hg.}$$

TABLE 6

Volumes per cent of gases in dry, inspired, expired and alveolar airs (average figures)

	Volumes per cent		
	Inspired (atmospheric) air	Expired air	Alveolar air
Oxygen..................	20.96	16.3	14.2
Carbon dioxide.............	0.04	4.0	5.5
Nitrogen (and argon).......	79.00	79.7	80.3
Totals.................	100.00	100.0	100.0

TABLE 7

Partial pressures of gases in inspired, expired and alveolar airs (average figures). Barometer reading 760 mm. Hg.

	Partial pressures		
	Inspired air mm. Hg	Expired air mm. Hg	Alveolar air mm. Hg
Oxygen	159.2	116.2	101.0
Carbon dioxide	0.3	28.5	40.0
Nitrogen	596.5	568.3	572.0
Water vapor	4.0	47.0	47.0
Totals	760.0	760.0	760.0

The diffusion of gases between the atmosphere and the lung air. It has been pointed out that the lungs are not filled with fresh air during inspiration nor are they ever com-

pletely emptied (p. 178). The tidal air amounts to only
about one-sixth of the total quantity of air contained in the
lungs, under ordinary circumstances. The ventilation of the
air sacs is brought about largely through diffusion, that is,
the movement of gas molecules from a point of higher to one
of lower pressure; though a certain degree of mechanical
mixing also occurs as a result of the respiratory movements,
especially during the elastic recoil of the lungs at the end of
inspiration. Oxygen diffuses into the alveolar air from the
fresh air drawn into the respiratory passages (dead space)
during inspiration, and carbon dioxide diffuses from the
alveolar air into the air of the dead space. During expiration a part of the air (about 500 cc. of the total 2500 or
3000 cc. in the lungs) is forced from the air sacs. About
350 cc. of this is expelled to the outside together with about
150 cc. which had filled the respiratory passages. The last
150 cc. of alveolar air replaces that which has been swept
from the dead space. At the next inspiration the column
of air which was in the dead space is drawn back again into
the air sacs, together with 350 cc. or so of atmospheric air.
Another 150 cc. of atmospheric air fills the dead space.

The depth to which fresh air is drawn into the air sacs
varies, of course, with the quantity of air inspired. In very
shallow breathing, atmospheric air may little more than fill
the dead space, whereas in deep breathing it penetrates beyond the respiratory bronchioles (p. 169).

**The exchange of gases between the alveolar air and the
blood.** Each minute during bodily rest some three or four
liters of blood are delivered to the lungs by the pulmonary
artery. In traversing the capillaries of the lungs the red
blood corpuscles are separated from the alveolar air by the
exquisitely thin and highly permeable membranes forming
the alveolar and capillary walls. In their passage through
the capillaries which surround the alveoli, the red cells are
for the most part in a single file. Thus, a thin film of blood,
having an area calculated at about 1000 square feet, is ex-

TABLE 8

Pressures of oxygen and carbon dioxide in arterial and in mixed
venous blood (averages).   Compare with table 7.

	Pressures		
	Arterial blood	Mixed venous blood	Difference [1]
	mm. Hg	mm. Hg	
Oxygen..............	100	40	60
Carbon dioxide........	40	46	6

posed to the alveolar air. The blood coming to the lungs (i.e.,
the mixed venous blood from all parts of the body), having
given up a part of its oxygen load to the tissues, and having
received therefrom a somewhat smaller volume of carbon
dioxide, has therefore a relatively low pressure of the former
gas and a relatively high pressure of the latter.   The capillary blood and the alveolar air (which at the end of inspiration has a relatively high pressure of oxygen and a low
pressure of carbon dioxide) come rapidly into gaseous equilibrium, oxygen diffusing from alveolar air to blood and carbon dioxide from blood to alveolar air.   The blood leaving
the lungs (arterial blood) therefore contains more oxygen
and less carbon dioxide than does venous blood; the oxygen
and carbon dioxide pressures show corresponding differences,
the oxygen pressure being around 100 mm. Hg in arterial
and 40 mm. in venous blood; the carbon dioxide pressures
are about 40 and 46 mm. Hg, respectively.

The volumes per cent (i.e., the number of cubic centimeters
of gas in 100 cubic centimeters of blood) and the pressures
of oxygen and carbon dioxide in arterial and in mixed venous
blood are given in Tables 8 and 9.

The gaseous exchanges in the tissues. The gaseous exchanges taking place in the tissues (internal respiration) are

[1] Carbon dioxide is much more diffusible (30 times) than oxygen, so that
rapid diffusion of the former gas takes place at a smaller pressure difference.

TABLE 9

Volumes per cent of oxygen and carbon dioxide in arterial
and in mixed venous blood (averages)

| | Volumes per cent | | |
	Arterial blood	Mixed venous blood	Difference
Oxygen...............	19	12.5	6.5
Carbon dioxide........	52	58	6.0

the reverse of those in the lungs (external respiration). The oxygen pressure in the tissues is low, the carbon dioxide pressure high. The blood in passing through the systemic capillaries gives up from 5 to 7 volumes per cent of oxygen (depending upon the particular type of tissue and its activity at the time) and absorbs from 4 to 7 volumes per cent of carbon dioxide.

The transport of the respiratory gases in the blood. *Oxygen transport.* When human blood is fully oxygenated (as after exposing it to the atmosphere, which at sea level has an oxygen pressure of about 160 mm. Hg), each 100 cc. contains 20 cc. of oxygen. This is the maximum quantity of oxygen which the blood will absorb, and it is then said to be fully saturated with the gas. Twenty volumes per cent is, therefore, the *oxygen capacity* of human blood. The blood does not, however, become fully saturated with oxygen in passing through the lungs. Arterial blood contains only about 19 volumes per cent of oxygen. In other words, it is only 95 per cent saturated. Of the 19 volumes in every 100 cc. of blood 18.76 volumes are in combination with hemoglobin. The remaining 0.24 volume per cent is in simple solution in the plasma. Whole blood, owing to its content of hemoglobin, can absorb, therefore, 80 times more oxygen than can an equivalent quantity of plasma.

Hemoglobin nearly saturated with oxygen is called *oxy-*

hemoglobin. The oxygen is bound very loosely to the hemoglobin; the latter is said to be *oxygenated* rather than *oxidized*, for a true oxide is not formed. Hemoglobin which has given up its oxygen is called *reduced hemoglobin*. If hemoglobin formed a stable compound with oxygen, i.e., if it formed an oxide which did not readily part with its oxygen, it would serve no useful purpose in respiration, for the unloading of oxygen to the tissues is quite as important as its rapid absorption by the blood in the lungs. The combination of oxygen with hemoglobin in the lungs and the dissociation of oxygen in the tissues proceed at nearly equal velocities. The quantity of oxygen which will combine or be held in combination with hemoglobin is dependent upon the partial pressure of oxygen in the plasma (i.e., the oxygen in simple solution). The pressure of oxygen in the plasma varies in turn with the pressure of oxygen in the alveolar air, on the one hand, and in the tissue fluids and cells, on the other. For example, in passing through the lungs the plasma comes into equilibrium with the alveolar air which has an oxygen pressure of around 100 mm. Hg. The hemoglobin, therefore, becomes nearly saturated with oxygen. In the tissue fluids the oxygen pressure is relatively low, and still lower in the cells. Oxygen diffuses, therefore, from the plasma to the tissue fluids and from the latter to the cells. The lowered oxygen pressure of the plasma thus occasioned, causes the liberation of oxygen from the hemoglobin.

The oxygen dissociation curve of hemoglobin. The relationship between the oxygen saturation of hemoglobin and the partial pressure of oxygen to which it is exposed can be shown by placing samples of blood in a series of cylindrical glass containers (called *tonometers*) and introducing air mixtures of known oxygen pressures. The glass vessels are rotated in a water bath at body temperature; the blood is thus spread in a thin film over their interiors, and allowed to come into gaseous equilibrium with the atmosphere to which it is exposed. The percentage saturation of each of the blood samples is then determined and plotted as shown in Fig. 96. Percentage saturation is indicated along the upright lines (ordinates), oxygen pressures along the horizontal lines (abscissae). The curve plotted in this way is called the *oxygen dissociation curve of hemoglobin*. It is important to notice the peculiar shape of this curve. It tends to flatten

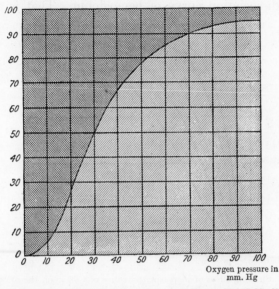

Fig. 96. The oxygen dissociation curve of hemoglobin. *Heavy Shading*, reduced hemoglobin, *light shading*, oxyhemoglobin. Percentage saturation of hemoglobin with oxygen along vertical lines (ordinates); oxygen pressure in mm. Hg along horizontal lines (abscissae). (After Barcroft.)

out at oxygen pressures above 70 mm. Hg. At 100 mm. Hg, which is the oxygen pressure in the alveolar air, the hemoglobin is 95 per cent saturated. Raising the oxygen pressure above 100 mm. Hg can therefore cause little increase in the quantity of oxygen absorbed; and a fall in oxygen pressure down to 50 or 60 mm. Hg causes little reduction in the oxygen saturation.

The slope of the lower part of the curve (i.e., at the lower oxygen pressures) is much steeper. This means that any given reduction in oxygen pressure causes the release of a relatively large quantity of oxygen from the hemoglobin. In other words, in passing through the tissues, where the oxygen pressure is low, very free dissociation of oxyhemoglobin occurs.

Two factors, namely, a *rise in temperature* and an increase in *hydrogen ion concentration,* cause a shift to the right of the oxygen dissociation curve of hemoglobin. That is to say,

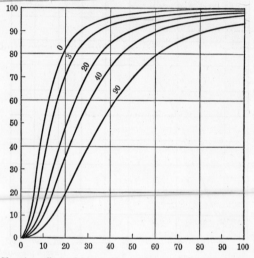

Fig. 97. Showing effect of increasing pressures of CO_2 upon the oxygen dissociation curve of hemoglobin (Bohr effect). (After Barcroft.) Percentage saturation of hemoglobin along upright lines (ordinates); oxygen pressure in mm. Hg along horizontal lines (abscissae).

each of these factors reduces the quantity of oxygen which hemoglobin will hold at any given oxygen pressure. Therefore, during increased tissue activity (e.g., muscular contraction) the local rise in temperature, and the increase in hydrogen ion concentration resulting from carbon dioxide and lactic acid production, cause a greater load of oxygen (per unit quantity of blood) to be delivered to the tissues. The influence of carbon dioxide pressure variations upon the form of the oxygen dissociation curve of hemoglobin is illustrated in Fig. 97. This is known as the Bohr effect.

Carbon dioxide transport. Arterial blood contains from 44

to 52 volumes per cent of carbon dioxide, venous blood from 50 to 58 volumes per cent. A small part of this, namely, about 2.5 volumes per cent (or from 4 to 5 per cent of the total) is in simple solution in the plasma. A further 4 or 5 volumes per cent (8 to 10 per cent of the total) is combined *directly* with hemoglobin. The compound is called *carbohemoglobin*. The rest of the carbon dioxide is carried in the plasma as sodium bicarbonate. The chloride shift mechanism through which the sodium bicarbonate is formed when carbon dioxide enters the blood from the tissues has already been explained (p. 68). After a study of this mechanism it will be realized that though only a small part of the carbon dioxide is carried in the blood actually combined with hemoglobin, the latter serves in an indirect way, i.e., by giving up its alkali, for the carriage of over 85 per cent of the total carbon dioxide. For this reason the quantity of carbon dioxide which can be absorbed by plasma from which the red cells have been separated by centrifuging (so-called *separated plasma*), is only a small fraction of that which the plasma in whole blood (*"true plasma"*) will absorb.

THE CONTROL OF RESPIRATION

Respiration is essentially an involuntary act, that is, it is carried out automatically and without thought. Nevertheless, it is to a certain extent under voluntary control. One can, for example, cease breathing for a time, or can vary the rate or the rhythm of the respirations (as in speaking or singing). The respirations are also controlled through an effort of the will or semi-automatically during swallowing, coughing, sucking, etc., and are altered by emotional states. But the respiratory movements are essentially automatic in nature. The breathing cannot be suspended voluntarily for more than 45 seconds or so. At the end of this time one is compelled to take a breath.

The automatic, involuntary character of the respiratory movements is due to the rhythmical discharge of impulses from a group of nerve cells situated in the lower part of the floor of the 4th ventricle, in the medulla oblongata. These constitute the *respiratory center*. Destruction of this region causes complete and permanent arrest of respiration. The impulses originating in the center are conducted down the spinal cord to the anterior horn cells of the 3rd, 4th and 5th cervical segments. The *phrenic nerve* which supplies the chief muscle of respiration, namely the diaphragm, arises from these spinal segments. Impulses also descend to the motor neurons in the 3rd, 4th, 5th and 6th thoracic segments, supplying fibers to the intercostal muscles.

The frequency of the impulses discharged from the respiratory center varies rhythmically with (and is the cause of) the respiratory movements, rising to a maximum during inspiration and falling to a minimum during expiration; impulse discharge may cease entirely during expiration.

The respiratory center, though fundamentally automatic in its action, is influenced by chemical and reflex factors. These will be considered separately.

Chemical factors. *Carbon dioxide* stimulates the respirations, any rise in its partial pressure in the arterial blood resulting in increased frequency and depth of the respirations. Under ordinary circumstances, the carbon dioxide pressure in the alveolar air, as in the arterial blood, remains remarkably constant at around 40 mm. Hg, for the slightest rise suffices to increase the pulmonary ventilation. The excess gas is thus removed and the pressure restored, automatically, to the normal level. Professor J. S. Haldane and his associates found that an increase of only 0.2 per cent in the carbon dioxide of the alveolar air (a rise in partial pressure of 1.5 mm. Hg) doubled the volume of the air breathed per minute. The effect of carbon dioxide upon the respirations may be demonstrated by having a subject breathe an air mixture containing a high percentage (5 or 6 per cent) of carbon dioxide (Fig. 98). The respirations become rapid and violent, even though the mixture contains over 90 per cent of oxygen. Conversely, if a subject increases his pulmonary ventilation by breathing quickly, and as deeply as possible for a minute or so, carbon dioxide is "pumped" out of his blood. When the forced voluntary effort (*forced breathing*) ceases, spontaneous respiratory movements are not resumed for a period of from 40 to 60 seconds. This interval of suspended respiration, during which there is no desire to breathe, is called *apnea* (literally, no breathing; see Fig. 99). With longer periods of forced breathing, the apneic period may be extended to 2 minutes or more.

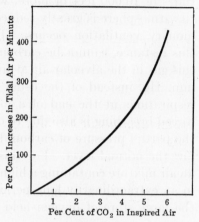

FIG. 98. Showing effect upon the pulmonary ventilation of increasing the CO_2 percentage in the inspired air. (After Scott, redrawn and modified.)

If the subject repeats the experiment, but instead of breathing ordinary air, breathes an air mixture containing a higher concentration (4–5 per cent) of carbon dioxide and a normal percentage of oxygen, apnea does not occur. The cessation

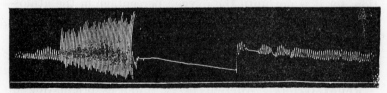

FIG. 99. Forced breathing for a period of two minutes is followed by apnea lasting for three minutes. This is succeeded by periodic breathing of the Cheyne-Stokes type which persists for a minute or so before normal breathing is resumed. (After Douglas and Haldane.)

of breathing following hyperventilation of the lungs is due therefore, to the removal of carbon dioxide from the blood, and not to its being overcharged with oxygen. A reduction in the carbon dioxide pressure of the alveolar air by about 0.2 per cent is sufficient to induce a short period of apnea.

A low partial pressure of oxygen in the arterial blood. The effect upon the respirations of oxygen want is seen at altitudes of 10,000 feet or more, where the oxygen pressure of the atmosphere is greatly reduced. Marked increase in pulmonary ventilation occurs. The respiratory stimulus, in this instance, cannot be carbon dioxide, for the pressure of this gas in the alveolar air at high altitudes may be only 30 mm. Hg, instead of the usual 40 mm. The return of the respirations at the end of a long apneic period caused by forced breathing is also due to oxygen want, for at this time the partial pressure of carbon dioxide in the blood is still below the normal level. For this reason, forced breathing of an air mixture containing a high percentage of oxygen results in an extraordinarily long period of apnea (10–15 minutes), the large store of oxygen held in the lungs postponing the onset of oxygen want.

The stimulating effect which oxygen want exerts upon the respiratory center is now believed to be an indirect one, namely, through the stimulation of the chemoreceptors in the carotid body (p. 78). The *direct* effect of anoxia upon the center is of a depressing rather than of a stimulating nature. Under ordinary circumstances, however, oxygen want is not even an indirect factor in the control of respiration, for it is not until the oxygen percentage in the atmosphere reaches a very low level (12–14 per cent) that any noticeable effect upon respiration is produced. When one holds the breath, for example, the uncontrollable desire to breathe is due to the accumulation of carbon dioxide.

Reflex factors. Afferent nerve impulses originating in almost any part of the body may influence the activity of the respiratory center. The sharp inspiration which follows a painful stimulus, the inhibition of inspiration during swallowing (p. 237) or when sensory endings in the nasal mucosa are stimulated (as by some pungent odor), and the increased rate and depth of breathing caused by the stimulation of cutaneous nerves by a cold or a hot bath, are a few familiar examples illustrating the effects of afferent nerve stimulation upon the respiratory movements.

The activity of the respiratory center is also influenced by proprioceptive impulses arising in the respiratory muscles, as well as by impulses discharged from the higher (psychic) centers of the brain. Various changes in respiratory rate, depth and rhythm may be brought about through emotional and mental factors. The spasmodic breathing of laughter, the sobbing respirations in grief, the slow shallow breathing during attention, suspense or apprehension and the rapid respirations in excitement or fear, may be cited.

An outstanding reflex effect upon the rate and depth of breathing is brought about through impulses originating in afferent endings of the *vagus* situated in the lungs themselves. The adequate stimulus for the vagal endings is inflation of the lungs. Thus, at the end of inspiration, distension of the air sacs causes a stream of impulses to be discharged to the respiratory center. These depress the activity of the center, that is, the frequency of the impulses discharged down the phrenic and other *efferent* respiratory nerves, is reduced; or the efferent discharges may cease entirely. Expiration which, as we have seen, is brought about mainly in a passive manner, therefore follows. The arrest of inspiration brought about in this way, with the consequent onset of expiration, is called the *Hering-Breuer reflex*. Section of the vagus nerves in experimental animals, by interrupting the afferent impulses from the lungs, results in slowing and deepening of the respirations — the inspiratory phase being prolonged.

The carotid sinus (p. 153) *and carotid body* under certain special circumstances, but probably not in ordinary conditions, play a role in respiratory control. The walls of the sinus contain receptors which when stimulated mechanically (pressure) discharge impulses to the respiratory center as well as to the cardio-inhibitory and vasomotor centers. Thus, distension of the sinus by a rise in blood pressure causes slowing of the respirations, or even complete respiratory arrest (apnea) for a short time. A fall in blood

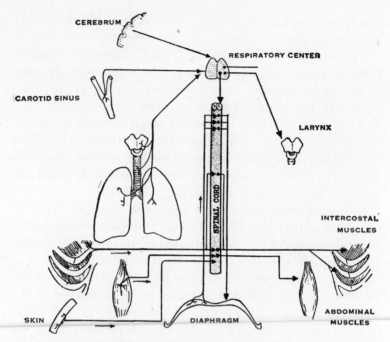

FIG. 100. Diagram summarizing the nervous factors in the control of respiration. (Modified from Best and Taylor, *The Physiological Basis of Medical Practice*.)

pressure has the reverse effect, namely, increased pulmonary ventilation. These effects must come into play only under very unusual and special circumstances.

The carotid body is a small structure lying in close relation to the carotid sinus. It contains cells which have the specialized function of responding to chemical stimuli. These chemoreceptors, as they are called, are stimulated by a rise in the carbon dioxide tension of the arterial blood, by an increase in hydrogen ion concentration or by oxygen lack. The impulses set up by the stimulation of these chemoreceptors and discharged along the sinus nerve to the respiratory center result in an increase in the rate and depth of breathing. A rise in the carbon dioxide pressure exerts a similar, though less pronounced, effect (see Fig. 100).

As mentioned on page 194, it is only when oxygen want reaches an extreme degree that the chemoreceptors of the carotid body are stimulated. The same applies to carbon dioxide excess. The sinus mechanism, therefore, plays a very minor role in the control of *normal* respiration.

PHYSIOLOGICAL MODIFICATIONS OF RESPIRATION

Laughing consists of a deep inspiration followed by a series of short spasmodic expirations. The characteristic sound is caused by the vibrations of the vocal cords which are held tense in the path of the outgoing air. In *crying* the respiratory movements are very similar.

Coughing is a reflex act. It is caused, usually, by stimulation of sensory endings of the vagus nerve in the mucosa of the larynx or trachea; but it may result from the excitation of afferent vagal endings in the lungs or pleura. The act comprises a short inspiration, followed immediately by closure of the opening of the larynx (glottis), and a forcible expiratory effort. A high pressure is thus created within the lungs and lower air passages. The glottis then opens suddenly, allowing the air to escape in a blast. Thus, any irritating material which may be present in the larynx is expelled.

Sneezing, like coughing, consists of a short inspiration, followed by a forcible expiration, but the glottis remains open. During the first part of the expiratory effort the way into the mouth is blocked by the elevation of the tongue against the soft palate, the blast of air being thus directed through the nose. Later, the resistance offered by the tongue is removed, the air then escaping through the mouth. The sneezing reflex is initiated by irritation of the nasal endings of the trigeminal nerve.

Yawning is usually an indication of fatigue, sleepiness or simply of boredom. It may also be induced by seeing someone else yawn. It is primarily of psychic origin. A yawn comprises a deep inspiration with the mouth open to its full extent. *Sighing* consists of a prolonged expiration.

Hyperpnea is the term applied to any increase in pulmonary ventilation, due to an increase either in the rate or in the depth of breathing, or of both.

ABNORMAL TYPES OF RESPIRATION

Periodic breathing is the term given to certain types of abnormal respiratory rhythm (see Fig. 101). The best known of these is called *Cheyne-Stokes breathing*, after two physicians of the last century who described it as a character- istic feature of certain diseases. This type of breathing is marked by periods of rapid and deep respiration (hyper- pneic periods) alternating with intervals of complete cessa- tion of respiration (apneic periods). At the beginning of the hyperpneic periods the respirations are slow and shallow, but they quickly increase to a maximum rate and depth, and

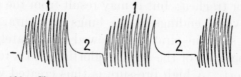

FIG. 101. Cheyne-Stokes breathing. 1, hyperpneic periods; 2, apneic periods. (After Waller.)

then, becoming smaller and smaller again, cease. The apneic periods are due to the removal of carbon dioxide from the blood during the preceding periods of hyperpnea. The latter are due, in turn, to oxygen lack and the accumulation of carbon dioxide during the apneic periods. The respiratory center, apparently, has lost some stabilizing factor which normally prevents it from responding too vigorously to changes in the gaseous composition of the blood. Like a machine without a fly-wheel, the action of the center is un- even, relatively small changes in gas pressures causing a too sudden and unduly great respiratory effect.

Cheyne-Stokes breathing is seen in advanced kidney dis- ease, in cases of raised intracranial pressure and in poisoning by narcotics. But periodic breathing of a similar type occurs under certain physiological conditions, e.g., in animals during hibernation and sometimes in children during sleep. It is also seen when the respirations are returning after the period of apnea caused by forced breathing, or it may occur at high altitudes.

Dyspnea, or difficult breathing, is seen in a number of diseased conditions. The breathlessness in heart disease, during muscular exercise or in acidosis, and the respiratory distress of asthma, pneumonia and other pulmonary conditions, and at high altitudes, are examples. In acidosis the respirations are increased in an effort to maintain the $\dfrac{H_2CO_3}{NaHCO_3}$ ratio at its normal value by reducing the numerator of the equation, i.e., by "blowing off" carbon dioxide from the blood (p. 67). The dyspnea of heart disease, anemia and pneumonia, and at high altitudes, is caused by an inadequate supply of oxygen to the tissues. Dyspnea may occur in a healthy subject as a result of strenuous muscular exercise. A rise in metabolism, from whatever cause, brings about an increase in the pulmonary ventilation, since larger amounts of carbon dioxide are then produced. Muscular exercise, even of a mild grade, causes, therefore, some degree of hyperpnea, yet no difficulty in breathing is experienced by a healthy subject until the severity of the exercise and, in consequence, the hyperpnea, becomes extreme. The degree of hyperpnea at which respiratory distress is experienced varies widely in different individuals according to their physical state. As compared with untrained persons, athletes are able to increase their pulmonary ventilation to a much greater extent before any difficulty in breathing (i.e., dyspnea) is experienced.

OXYGEN WANT — ANOXIA

A failure of the tissues to gain an adequate supply of oxygen is referred to as *oxygen want* or *anoxia*. Anoxia is classified according to its cause into the following four groups — *anoxic, stagnant, anemic* and *histotoxic*.

Anoxic anoxia. This term applies to any type of anoxia caused by defective oxygenation of the blood in the lungs, whether as a result of a low oxygen tension in the atmosphere, as at high altitudes and in vitiated atmospheres (e.g., in mines), or to some interference with breathing, e.g., obstruction of the respiratory passages, asthma, pneumonia, etc.

Mountain sickness. The unpleasant and sometimes serious effects of the anoxia of high altitudes are referred to as mountain sickness. At a height of 14,000 feet above sea level the atmospheric pressure is around 450 mm. Hg. The partial pressure of oxygen, being reduced proportionately, amounts to $\left(\dfrac{20.96}{100} \times 450 = \right)$ 94 mm. Hg, as compared with 160 mm. at sea level. The oxygen pressure in the alveolar air and arterial blood is, therefore, only from 55 to 60 mm. Hg. The oxygen saturation of the hemoglobin is considerably below normal, and the symptoms and signs of anoxia are apparent. These include headache, nausea and vomiting, dyspnea and cyanosis. Emotional outbursts, e.g., laughing or crying, quarrelsomeness or hilarity are common. There is often a sense of exhilaration, or an exhibition of foolhardiness, boisterousness or stubbornness. If a person remains for a time at the high altitude these effects gradually disappear; he becomes acclimatized. The acclimatization process consists of a rise in the red cell count (see Fig. 22, p. 25), and adjustments in the circulatory and respiratory mechanisms. Natives of high mountains have a red cell count of from 6,500,000 to 8,500,000, depending upon the altitude at which they live. The capacity of the chest is greater than the normal for a man of the same height residing at sea level. In rapid ascents to high altitudes (40,000 to 50,000 feet), as in a balloon or an airplane, consciousness is lost rapidly unless the balloonist or aviator can receive oxygen inhalations from a storage cylinder.

Stagnant anoxia is due to slowing of the circulation. The reduced velocity of the blood in the capillaries permits the hemoglobin to give up a greater fraction of its total oxygen load than normally. The venous blood contains, therefore, a proportionately larger amount of reduced hemoglobin. When the blood remains long in the capillaries, though a larger quantity of oxygen is abstracted from it, the greater part of the gas is delivered at low pressure. The tissues, therefore, receive less oxygen in a given time than when the blood flow is rapid.

Anemic anoxia is the type resulting from a reduced oxygen-carrying capacity of the blood. This form of anoxia includes that due to carbon monoxide poisoning as well as to that resulting from anemia.

Carbon monoxide poisoning. Carbon monoxide combines with hemoglobin to form COHb, a relatively stable compound, i.e., one which dissociates very slowly. Any hemoglobin in this form cannot take up oxygen, and is therefore dispossessed of any respiratory function. Carbon monoxide acts as poison for this reason only. The subject poisoned by the gas is deprived of the use of part of his hemoglobin just as surely as if it had been lost from the body, and the tissues, in consequence, cannot be supplied adequately with oxygen.

Hemoglobin has a very great affinity for carbon monoxide, and this is why it is so especially dangerous. When blood is exposed to an atmosphere containing equal concentrations of carbon monoxide and oxygen it absorbs 300 parts of the former gas for every one part of the latter. In other words, the hemoglobin becomes almost completely saturated with carbon monoxide to the exclusion of oxygen. As a result of the preference shown by hemoglobin for carbon monoxide, a concentration of as little as 0.2 per cent in an atmosphere otherwise normal in composition will cause death if breathed for a few minutes. As in the anoxia of mountain sickness, so in that due to carbon monoxide poisoning, the subject often becomes stubborn, perverse or unruly. Though he is not unaware of his danger he may, owing to some fanciful idea, make no attempt to escape, and may even resist efforts of others to bring him into fresh air. This is another dangerous feature associated with exposure to this gas.

Histotoxic anoxia. In this type the oxidative processes of the tissues are depressed or abolished by a poison such as cyanide. The oxygen-carrying capacity of the blood is not affected, but, since cellular oxidations are greatly reduced or in abeyance, the usual amount of oxygen is not removed from the blood in the capillaries. The venous blood, therefore, has a high oxygen saturation, and is arterial in color. Cyanide poisoning is treated by injections of solutions of methylene blue. This dye stuff converts part of the hemoglobin to methemoglobin. The latter combines with the cyanide to produce a relatively innocuous compound, cyanmethemoglobin. However, since cyanide poisoning is so rapidly fatal, there is rarely an opportunity for applying this or any other method of resuscitation.

Cyanosis is the name given to the blue tint of the skin caused by an unusually high concentration of reduced hemoglobin in the blood of the capillaries composing the subpapillary venous plexus (p. 157). The blueness is usually most pronounced in the skin of the lips, ears and finger tips. It is the visible sign of anoxia, either of the anoxic or stagnant type. That is, the blood either does not receive a full load of oxygen in the lungs or it gives up an unusually large proportion of its oxygen to the tissues. In both these instances, the capillary blood will have an abnormally high concentration of reduced hemoglobin, which is darker in color than oxyhemoglobin. Blood contains some 15 grams of hemoglobin per 100 cc. In the cutaneous capillaries of a normal person about 2.5 grams of this is reduced hemoglobin, the remaining 12.5 grams is oxyhemoglobin. When, as a result of either of the two types of anoxia just mentioned, the concentration of reduced hemoglobin in the capillary blood increases to 5 grams per 100 cc., cyanosis appears.

The anemic and histotoxic types of anoxia do not cause cyanosis. In the first of these, though the hemoglobin is diminished in amount, what there is of it is as fully saturated with oxygen as in health. Furthermore, a person with a very severe anemia (hemoglobin less than 5 grams per 100 cc. of blood) obviously cannot become cyanosed under any circumstances, for even though all his hemoglobin should be in the reduced form, it would not be in sufficiently high concentration to cause any discoloration of the skin. On the other hand, a person whose blood had an abnormally high concentration of hemoglobin (25 to 30 grams per 100 cc., as in polycythemia) becomes cyanosed with a relatively mild degree of anoxia.

In the histotoxic type the capillary blood actually contains a *lower* concentration of reduced hemoglobin than in health, for, as a result of poisoning of the respiratory function of the cells of the tissues, the oxygen in the blood is not utilized.

THE VOICE

The mode of production of the human voice, with its varied tones, its range of pitch and its volume, has long aroused the interest of physiologists. As an instrument of sound, the voice-box or larynx, with the cavities of the mouth, throat, trachea and lungs, may be compared to the pipe of an organ. A reed and the column of air in the organ pipe are set into vibration by an air blast. In a somewhat similar manner the vocal cords within the larynx are thrown into vibration by air expelled from the lungs. The nose, mouth, throat and chest serve as resonating chambers. Certain notes can be played by the organist which imitate the human voice in a truly remarkable way.

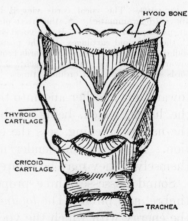

FIG. 102. The larynx and upper rings of the trachea. The *hyoid* is a small bone lying near the root of the tongue. The *thyroid* cartilage forms the front and side walls of the larynx. The *cricoid* is a circle of cartilage shaped like a signet ring, lying between the larynx above and the trachea below.

The larynx (Fig. 102) lies at the upper end of the trachea,

its walls being formed of cartilage and lined with mucous membrane; the vocal cords are two thin-edged bands or membranes lying within it. The cords run from before backwards, being attached behind to two small cartilaginous bodies (the *arytenoid cartilages*) and fixed in front to the wall of the larynx. By the contraction of small muscles attached to them the arytenoid cartilages can be rotated when necessary. By this means the vocal cords can be swung away from one another, that is, outwards against the

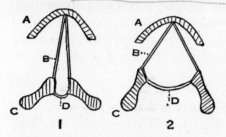

FIG. 103. The vocal cords viewed from above (diagrammatic). A, the front of the larynx (thyroid cartilage). B, the vocal cords. C, the arytenoid cartilages. D, the posterior wall of the larynx. 1, shows the cords brought toward the mid-line during speech; 2, the cords swung outward at ordinary times.

walls of the larynx (Fig. 103), or inwards toward one another until only a small chink remains between them. At ordinary times the cords lie against the wall of the larynx, and the gap separating them is wide, and no sound is produced during the passage of the breath. During speech they are brought toward one another and into the current of air expelled from the lungs, which, being unable to escape except through the narrow opening, sets the edges of the cords into vibration. By means of slender muscles running in the cords themselves they may be tightened or slackened.

Sound possesses three properties — loudness, quality or timbre, and pitch. The *loudness* of the voice depends upon the energy with which the vocal cords vibrate; the greater the pressure under which the air is expired, and the greater the movements made by the cords, the louder will be the sound. The *pitch* is determined primarily by the length and tightness of the cords, and also by the frequency of their vibrations. In children and women the cords are short, and the voice is high-pitched. In men the cords are longer, and the voice is deeper. All of us can adjust the tension and to some extent the length of our vocal cords and so alter the pitch of the voice, but trained singers have developed this ability to the greatest degree. The *quality* or *timbre* of our voices depends on the number and intensity of the overtones or harmonics which are produced, and these in turn depend upon the shape and capacity of the resonating chambers — the mouth, the trachea and the chest. Training of the voice consists very largely in modification of the mouth and throat cavities so that the sound produced in the larynx receives

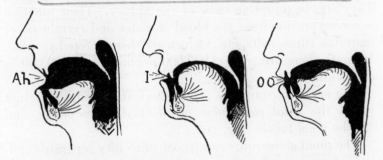

Fig. 104. Showing the positions of the lips and tongue and the shape of the mouth cavity when pronouncing Ah, I and OO.

the greatest possible number of these harmonics or supplementary tones.

In speech the musical sounds produced by the vibration of the vocal cords are modified by the numerous changes which may be made in the size and shape of the air passages — the pharynx and the mouth. The vowel sounds, *a, e, i, o, u,* are formed in the lower air passages, and the mouth cavity assumes positions which are characteristic for each vowel (Fig. 104). When we whisper these sounds may be produced simply by placing the mouth in the required position, that is, without vibration of the vocal cords. The consonants are formed by interrupting to different degrees the expired air in various parts of the vocal pathway.

CHAPTER V

THE PHYSIOLOGY OF THE KIDNEY.
MICTURITION

The structure of the kidney. The kidney is composed of a large number of microscopical structures called *nephrons*. They are the excreting units of the kidney. Their function is the separation from the blood of water and certain other materials (urea, salts, etc.,) which are then excreted as urine. In man, there are some 2,000,000 nephrons — 1,000,000 in each kidney.

The nephron comprises (1) a spherical, vascular structure called the *renal glomerulus* or *Malpighian corpuscle*, and (2) the *renal tubule* (Fig. 105).

The renal glomerulus consists of some fifty separate capillaries bent into short loops to form a compact mass called the *glomerular tuft*. The upper end of each renal tubule is expanded into a structure known as Bowman's capsule. The cavity of Bowman's capsule is crescentic in cross section, owing to the encroachment, by pressure from without, of the capillary tuft. The walls of the capsule are formed of a thin membrane composed of a single layer of flat cells which, therefore, serves also as a covering for the glomerulus. This membrane and the equally thin walls of the capillaries separate the blood from the cavity of Bowman's capsule.

The renal tubule drains Bowman's capsule and, for purposes of description, can be divided into three parts. The first third or so is tortuous, and lies in close relation to the glomerulus; it is known as the *proximal convoluted tubule*. The walls of this portion of the tubule are composed of a single layer of columnar epithelial cells. The free borders of the cells show fine perpendicular striations which give

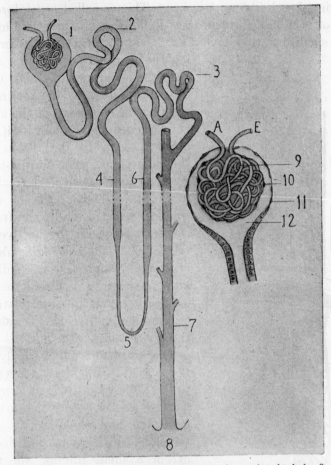

Fig. 105. The nephron. 1, glomerulus; 2, proximal convoluted tubule; 3, distal convoluted tubule; 4, descending limb of Henle's loop; 5, Henle's loop; 6, ascending limb; 7, collecting tubule; 8, pelvis of kidney. Enlarged drawing of glomerulus on the right; 9, tuft of capillaries; 10, layer of Bowman's capsule covering capillaries; 11, outer wall of Bowman's capsule; 12, cavity of Bowman's capsule; A, afferent arteriole; E, efferent arteriole.

them a brush-like appearance. This so-called *brush border* is not seen elsewhere in the tubule, though the cells lining the small intestine have a similar appearance. After forming the proximal convoluted tubule, the nephron straightens out and descends for a distance through the substance of the kidney; then, turning upon itself, it ascends again to the region of the glomerulus. The hairpin-like bend, so formed, is called *Henle's loop;* the straight parts of the tubule leading to and away from the bend are called, respectively, the *descending* and *ascending limbs* of Henle's loop. The ascending limb passes into a second tortuous section lying in close relation to the glomerulus; this is called the *distal convoluted tubule.*

FIG. 106. Diagram of the renal circulation. A, artery; E, efferent vessel; G, glomerulus; P, network of vessels surrounding the tubule and draining into the vein V.

The blood and nerve supply of the kidney. Blood is delivered to the kidney by the *renal artery*, a short thick vessel which arises from the abdominal aorta. All the blood which enters the kidney, except a small fraction for the nourishment of the covering and connective tissue of the organ, passes through the glomeruli. The capillaries of each glomerular tuft are derived from a single arteriole called the *afferent vessel*. Converging again, the capillaries form a single effluent channel, known as the *efferent vessel* (Fig. 106). This is also of arteriolar construction. There is considerable disparity in size between the diameters of the two glomerular arterioles, the efferent vessel being the smaller. This arrangement makes for a relatively high pressure within the capillary loops. Furthermore, variations in glomerular capillary pressure can be brought about through changes in the relative diameters of the two vessels. Dilatation of the afferent arteriole or constriction of the efferent, the caliber of the other vessel in each instance remaining the same, causes a rise in the capillary blood pressure. Constriction of the afferent or dilatation of the efferent vessel will produce the reverse effect.

The blood, after traversing the glomerulus, is distributed to the rest of the nephron through branches of the efferent vessels which terminate in a capillary network surrounding the tubules.

The *nerves* of the kidney are derived from the *vagus* and *splanchnic (sympathetic)* nerves. These nerves have no secretory action, for the kidney continues to perform its functions in a normal manner after it has been completely denervated.

The composition of the urine. The chief urinary constituents in grams per liter of urine are given in the following table.

I. *Inorganic constituents*

	Grams per liter
Chloride expressed as $NaCl$	9.0
Phosphorus expressed as P_2O_5	2.0
Total sulphur expressed as SO_3	1.5
Sodium expressed as Na_2O	4.0
Potassium expressed as K_2O	2.0
Calcium expressed as CaO	0.2
Magnesium expressed as MgO	0.2
Iron	0.003

II. *Nitrogenous constituents*

Urea
   25.0 grams containing approximately   10.0 grams nitrogen
Ammonia
   0.6 gram containing approximately   0.4 gram nitrogen

Uric acid
    0.6 gram containing approximately   0.2 gram nitrogen
Creatinine
    1.5 gram containing approximately   0.5 gram nitrogen
    Undetermined nitrogen................ 0.6 gram
    Total.............................. 11.7 grams nitrogen

Urea is derived mainly from the breakdown in the body of food protein; it, therefore, varies considerably with the quantity of protein in the diet. On a low protein intake, it may be less than a sixth of the value given in the above table. The creatinine, on the other hand, is derived mainly from the disintegration of body tissue; its excretion is, therefore, almost uninfluenced by the protein level of the diet.

The uric acid is derived from purines (p. 294) taken in the food, as well as from the purines of body tissue. Ammonia is formed in the kidney itself from a part of the urea carried to it in the blood. The color of the urine is due to a pigment called *urochrome*. Normal urine does not contain glucose, except occasionally after meals; minute amounts may then appear.

The reaction and specific gravity of the urine. The urine is definitely acid. The average pH is around 6.0, but the reaction varies considerably with the nature of the diet. Most fruits reduce the acidity of the urine, for they contain the salts of organic acids; the acid is oxidized, leaving the alkali, which is excreted. Starvation increases the urinary acidity, because sulphuric and phosphoric acids are formed from body protein, and acetoacetic and β-hydroxybutyric acids from body fat. A high protein diet also increases the quantity of acid excretion. Herbivorous animals, on the other hand, excrete an alkaline urine except when fasting, the urine then becoming acid. In diseases associated with the production of large amounts of organic acids in the body, e.g., acetoacetic and β-hydroxybutyric acids in diabetes, the urine is more strongly acid than normally.

The normal acidity of the urine is a manifestation of one of the most important functions performed by the kidney, namely, the maintenance of the alkalinity of the blood and body fluids. Blood coming to the kidney has a pH of around 7.4; the urine, as just mentioned, has an average pH of 6.0. The kidney separates acid from basic substances, retaining the latter within the body and excreting the former. This conservation of the body's base is brought about in part by the conversion in the kidney of the alkaline phosphate of the blood (Na_2HPO_4) into the acid phosphate (NaH_2PO_4). For example, the concentrations of the alkaline and acid phosphates in plasma are as 4 to 1, whereas, in urine they are as 1 to 9. Another way in which the kidney conserves fixed base (chiefly sodium) to the body is by the formation of ammonia. The ammonia then combines with acids brought to the kidney, which excretes them as ammonium salts.

The specific gravity of the urine ranges under ordinary circumstances between 1.020 and 1.032. In health the specific gravity swings readily in one or other direction, in response to variations in the intake of fluid. For example, when a normal person drinks a large quantity of water, the urine which he passes within the next couple of hours is very dilute; the specific gravity may be as low as 1.001 or 1.002. On the other hand, after abstaining from fluids for some time, the specific gravity of the urine rises to 1.030 or higher. In the later stages of kidney disease the specific gravity of the urine is low under all circumstances. It remains almost fixed around a value of 1.010, in spite of wide variations in the fluid intake.

The volume of the urine. In man, from 1000 to 1500 cc. of urine are formed in 24 hours. The volume varies, of course, with the amount of fluid drunk and with that lost through other channels — skin, lungs and bowels. It is reduced, therefore, in hot weather or as a result of diarrhea or vomiting. The products of protein metabolism, especially urea, increase urine production; the volume of the urine is greater, therefore, upon a high than upon a low protein diet. Urine formation is reduced during sleep, but the total excretion of urinary solids, e.g., urea, uric acids, phosphate, etc., is about the same during the night as during a day period of equal length. The urine passed after rising in the morning is, therefore, more concentrated than ordinary day urine. A decided rise in the volume of the night urine, as a persistent phenomenon, is called *nycturia*. It is a sign of chronic renal disease. Muscular exercise, especially of a strenuous nature, reduces the urine volume.

The formation of urine. Though the renal corpuscle was described by the Italian anatomist, Marcello Malpighi, in the seventeenth century (1666), it was not until nearly 200 years later (1842) that the English anatomist and surgeon, Sir William Bowman, recognized the functional significance of this structure, and of the capsule which is known by his name. From his studies of the structure of the glomerulus Bowman concluded that it served simply as a filter to remove water and salts from the plasma. Though others have contended that the layer of Bowman's capsule covering the capillaries of the glomerular tuft actually *secreted* these urinary constituents, the former view is now generally accepted. The glomerular membrane acts in a purely passive manner, its cells, unlike those of a true gland, possessing no secretory function.

Filtration through the glomerulus. Let us now consider the filtration process in greater detail. Filtration through a membrane may be defined as the separation, by gravity or pressure, of liquid and such materials as can pass through the membrane from other materials to which it is impermeable. Water, salts and other substances of relatively small molecular size, enter Bowman's capsule, but the glomerular membrane is impermeable to the blood cells and the plasma proteins. The driving force separating the plasma constituents is the difference between the pressure of blood in the glomerular capillaries, which amounts to about 70 mm. Hg, and the pressure in Bowman's capsule, which is in the neighborhood of 5 mm. Hg. But, the plasma proteins, since the glomerular membrane is impermeable to them, exert an osmotic pressure (see p. 26) which opposes the blood pressure. This force acts to hold water and dissolved substances within the vessels, and must be overcome by the hydraulic force of the blood in the glomerular capillaries. The capillary blood pressure must be higher, therefore, than the osmotic pressure of the plasma colloids (proteins), in order for filtration to occur. The osmotic pressure of the plasma proteins is around 25 mm. Hg. Therefore, the actual driving force, or effective filtration pressure, in millimeters of mercury is:

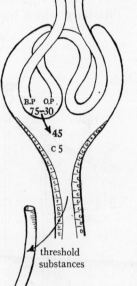

$$70 \ - \ 25 \ - \ 5 \ = \ 40$$

| Blood pressure | Osmotic pressure | Pressure in capsule | Effective filtration pressure |

(see also Fig. 107).

Fig. 107. Diagram illustrating the factors governing glomerular filtration. B.P, blood pressure in glomerular capillaries; O.P, osmotic pressure of plasma; C, pressure in Bowman's capsule. Figures indicate mm. Hg; short arrow represents the passage of fluid and dissolved substances into Bowman's capsule, the driving force being $70 - 25 = 45$ mm. Hg.

The theory of glomerular function just outlined has been confirmed in every detail by experiment. For example, a rise in blood pressure within the glomerular capillaries, without any change occurring in osmotic or capsular pressure, causes an increase in the amount of urine formed. Lowering the osmotic pressure while the blood pressure is kept constant, as by the intravenous injection of a saline solution (which of course dilutes the proteins), also increases the flow of urine. On the other hand, raising the pressure in Bowman's capsule by blocking the ureter reduces the flow of urine, and when the capsular pressure just about equals the amount by which the blood pressure exceeds the plasma osmotic pressure (which would be 45 mm. Hg in the example given above), urine formation ceases.

A crucial experiment was performed by Dr. Richards of Pittsburg which has finally dispelled all doubt that the glomerulus acts as a filter. He obtained a sample of fluid as it was produced by the glomerulus of the kidney of a living frog, by inserting a fine glass pipette into Bowman's capsule (Fig. 108). This fluid was found to contain glucose, chloride and all the other constituents of plasma except the proteins. It was alkaline in reaction. In other words, it was a filtrate — simply *deproteinized* plasma.

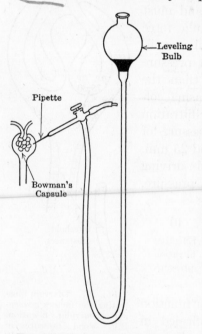

Fig. 108. Illustrating Richards' method of obtaining a sample of glomerular filtrate.

The concentrating function of the tubules. The urine is much more concentrated than the filtrate, that is, it contains a higher percentage of total solids, and has a much smaller volume. The quantity of filtrate formed by the human kidneys in 24 hours amounts to from 75 to 100 liters, whereas the quantity of urine secreted in the same time is only from 1 to 1½ liters. Obviously, a large volume of water — from 98 to 99 per cent of that filtered through the glomerulus — must have been reabsorbed from the tubules into the blood stream. Furthermore, glucose is present in the filtrate, but is absent, as a rule, from the urine. Glucose, then, must be reabsorbed, so too must sodium chloride, for Richards, in the experiment mentioned above, found it in the filtrate but not in the urine. Materials such as urea, phosphates and uric acid are reabsorbed to only a small extent, while other waste products, such as creatinine and sulphates, are not absorbed at all. Glucose and the essential salts, since they do not escape into the urine in considerable quantities unless their concentrations in the plasma are abnormally high, are called *high threshold substances*. Those substances which are reabsorbed to a minor extent (urea, phosphate and uric acid) are called *low threshold substances*, while those (creatinine and sulphates) which are not absorbed at all are called *non-threshold substances* (see table 10).

TABLE 10
(After Cushny)

	Blood plasma	Urine	Change in concentration in kidney
	per cent	per cent	
Water....................	90–93	95	
Proteins, fats, and other colloids.	7–9		
Glucose....................	0.1		
Na....................	0.30	0.35	1
Cl....................	0.37	0.6	2
Urea....................	0.03	2	60
Uric acid....................	0.004	0.05	12
K....................	0.020	0.15	7
NH$_4$....................	0.001 (?)	0.04	40
Ca....................	0.008	0 015	2
Mg....................	0.0025	0.006	2
PO$_4$....................	0.009	0.15	16
SO$_4$....................	0.002	0.18	90
Creatinine....................	0.001 (?)	0.075	75

The proximal convoluted tubule is responsible for the reabsorption of glucose and some 20 per cent of the water. The ascending limb of Henle's loop and the distal convoluted tubule reabsorb chloride, and the remainder of the water. The fluid undergoes no further change after it has passed through the distal convoluted tubule. It then passes as urine along the system of collecting tubules, and is delivered into the pelvis of the kidney, whence it is conveyed by the ureter to the urinary bladder.

The tubules, in some species at any rate, have also a secretory function, adding urea, uric acid and other substances to the filtrate.

Diuresis. Increased flow of urine is called *diuresis*, and drugs which cause such an effect are known as *diuretics*. This group of drugs includes *caffeine* (of coffee), *theobromine* (of cocoa), *theophylline* (of tea), *urea* and various salts, e.g., *potassium nitrate, potassium citrate, ammonium chloride, sodium sulphate* and certain *mercury compounds*.

It is evident from the outline of the mechanism of renal excretion just given that there are two ways in which a greater flow of urine could be produced, namely, by increasing glomerular filtration or by diminishing tubular reabsorption. Caffeine, theobromine and theophylline cause more capillary loops to open up and thus increase the total filtering surface of the kidney. Sodium sulphate and the mercurial diuretics diminish reabsorption.

Summary of the chief functions of the kidney. 1. The kidney maintains the normal composition of the plasma through the elimination of excess water and the waste products of protein and purine metabolism, e.g., urea, creatinine, sulphates, uric acid, etc., retaining at the same time the essential constituents of the blood, e.g., cells, proteins, glucose and inorganic salts.

2. The kidney plays a prominent role in the regulation of the acid base balance of the body, through (a) the production of ammonia which, being then excreted in combination with fixed acids (ammonium salts) conserves the body's store of alkali, and (b) through the conversion of alkaline phosphate to the acid salt (Na_2HPO_4 to NaH_2PO_4).

Impairment of renal function. In *nephritis*, the commonest type of kidney disease, a proportion of the renal glomeruli are the seat of an acute or chronic inflammatory process. Some or all of the capillary loops in the diseased glomeruli are destroyed and, as a consequence, the filtering surface of the kidney is reduced. When the glomerular destruction is extensive, serious impairment of renal function results. The reader will recall that the tubules are supplied with blood which has previously traversed the glomerular capillaries. It follows, therefore, that glomerular damage must inevitably interfere with the nourishment of the tubules, with consequent impairment of their power to concentrate the filtrate. It has been mentioned that the specific gravity of the urine in chronic nephritis cannot be raised above 1.010 or so.

The chief manifestations of kidney disease are (1) the retention in the blood of nitrogenous waste products, e.g., urea, uric acid, creatinine, as well as of phosphates and sulphates, (2) impaired excretion of water, (3) protein, casts and perhaps blood in the urine, (4) edema, (5) high blood pressure and (6) acidosis, in the later stages of the disease.

In severe nephritis the concentration in the plasma of urea and the other wastes mentioned above may be several times greater than in health. The difficulty in the excretion of water is shown by giving the subject a quart or so of water to drink and measuring the urine output hourly for a few hours thereafter. The normal person excretes all the ingested water within from 2 to 4 hours, but when the kidneys are seriously damaged only a part of the water is excreted by the end of 4 hours.

Normal urine is free from protein, but in kidney disease large quantities may appear. It is derived from the plasma. The diseased glomerular membrane permits the passage of serum albumin and smaller quantities of serum globulin (whose molecule is larger than that of albumin); fibrinogen, on the other hand, which has a larger molecule than those of the other plasma proteins, does not escape into the urine. When the loss of protein in the urine is excessive its concentration in the plasma is reduced. The osmotic pressure of the latter falls in consequence, and edema results (see p. 57).

MICTURITION OR THE VOIDING OF URINE

The tubules of the kidney empty through a number of short ducts into a funnel-shaped membranous structure called *the pelvis (basin) of the kidney.* A narrow duct containing smooth muscle in its walls and called the *ureter,* conveys the urine from the kidney pelvis to the *urinary bladder.* The urine is propelled along the ureter by peristaltic contractions; it enters the bladder in jets which occur at the rate of from 1 to 5 per minute.

The urinary bladder serves as a reservoir for the urine. It is a hollow muscular organ lined by modified stratified epithelium. It has a maximum capacity of from a half to one pint. The most dependent part of the bladder leads into the *urethra,* through which the urine is passed to the exterior. This junction of the bladder with the urethra is guarded by a collection of circularly arranged smooth muscle fibers, called the *internal vesical sphincter.* A little above and behind the urethral opening the bladder wall is pierced obliquely by the ureters. The triangular area of the bladder wall marked off by the urethra and the two ureteral openings is called the *trigone.* The muscle forming the rest of the bladder wall is called the *detrusor muscle.* The caliber of the first inch or so of the male urethra is controlled by striated muscle, which is generally referred to as the *external vesical sphincter.*

Evacuation of the bladder. As urine gradually collects within the bladder the pressure within it shows very little change, for a time, the tone of the detrusor muscle adapting readily to the increased volume (see postural tone, p. 227). Not until the urine volume is between 200 and 300 cc. does any noticeable rise in internal pressure result (Fig. 109). Rhythmical contractions of the detrusor muscle then occur in response to the tension exerted upon the muscle fibers. The contractions are weak at first, but gradually gaining strength as the urine volume increases culminate in a strong reflex contraction of the bladder wall, accompanied by relaxation of the internal sphincter and trigone.

The act of micturition, though dependent upon reflex mechanisms, is, in the adult, very largely under voluntary control. The reflex contractions of the detrusor can be inhibited, and contractions of the internal sphincter induced, by an effort of the will. Thus, the reflex mechanisms can

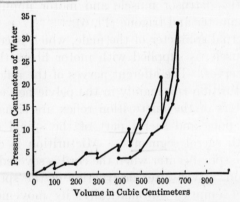

Fig. 109. Curve of pressure changes in the human bladder during filling (*upper curve*) and emptying (*lower curve*). Note that the internal pressure shows little permanent increase until the volume of fluid amounts to more than 200 cc. (Denny-Brown and Robertson.)

be restrained until an opportunity for voiding the urine presents itself. The restraint is then removed, and the contractions of the bladder wall which ensue are reinforced by voluntary nerve impulses transmitted along the motor nerves supplying the detrusor muscle. A rise in intraabdominal pressure, due to contractions of the abdominal muscles and fixation of the diaphragm in the inspiratory position, usually precedes and accompanies the act of micturition. However, a voluntary movement of this character is not essential, the bladder mechanism being capable itself of expelling the urine.

The motor fibers to the detrusor muscle, and the inhibitory fibers to the internal sphincter and trigone, are derived from the parasympathetic division of the autonomic nervous system through the pelvic nerves (2nd, 3rd and 4th sacral segments). These fibers are peculiar in that, as indicated above, they transmit voluntary as well as involuntary impulses to the detrusor muscle.

The sympathetic division of the autonomic nervous system exerts an opposite effect upon the movements of the bladder. Through the hypogastric nerves it transmits inhibitory impulses to the detrusor muscle and motor impulses to the internal sphincter and trigone (Pl. 6).

The external sphincter of the male, which is composed of striated muscle, is supplied with motor fibers through the pudendal nerves. The afferent nerves of the reflex arc governing micturition run mainly in the pelvic nerves.

The centers of the micturition reflex are situated in the mid-brain, pons and sacral part of the spinal cord (2nd, 3rd and 4th sacral segments). Micturition is carried out through the spinal center when the cord is severed above the sacral region. Even after destruction of the spinal center, the bladder empties automatically, its movements being then brought about through the nerve plexuses in close relation to the bladder wall.

CHAPTER VI

DIGESTION

Introductory. The alimentary or digestive tract comprises the *mouth, pharynx, esophagus* (or *gullet*), *stomach* and *intestines.* The pharynx receives the food from the mouth and transfers it to the esophagus, along which it is conveyed to the stomach. The stomach evacuates its contents into the small intestine which discharges, in turn, into the large intestine (see Fig. 110). A descriptive outline of the structure of each part of the digestive tract, in so far as a knowledge of structure is necessary for an understanding of function, will be given in the section dealing with the physiology of that particular part.

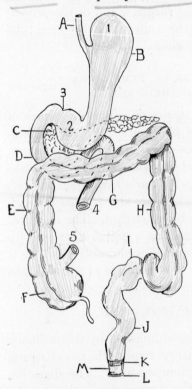

The processes taking place within the alimentary tract whereby the food is prepared for absorption into the blood stream are all included under the term *digestion.* These processes are both

FIG. 110. Diagram of gastro-intestinal tract. A, esophagus; B, stomach; C, pancreas; D, duodenum; E, ascending colon; F, cecum; G, transverse colon; H, descending colon; I, pelvic colon; J, rectum; K, internal anal sphincter; L, external anal sphincter; M, anal canal; 1, fundus; 2, pyloric part; 3, pylorus; 4, cut end of jejunum; 5, opening of ileum into cecum. Coils of small intestine between 4 and 5 excised.

mechanical (e.g., mastication, swallowing and the movements of the stomach and intestines) and chemical. Digestion in the different parts of the alimentary tract will be described in order, commencing with the mouth. In each instance, a description of the chemical changes which the food undergoes during the digestive process, and of the nervous and hormonal mechanisms controlling secretion of the digestive juices, will be followed by an account of the movements of the part under discussion. First of all, a general account of *ferments* or *enzymes*, and of the *properties of smooth muscle*, of which the walls of the digestive tube are largely composed, must be given.

FERMENTS OR ENZYMES (G. *ZYMĒ* = YEAST OR LEAVEN) AND THEIR ACTION

These substances, e.g., the *ptyalin* of saliva, the *pepsin* of gastric juice and the *trypsin* of pancreatic juice, are responsible for the chemical changes which the food undergoes during digestion. The chemical changes comprise the breaking up of the large molecules of carbohydrates, proteins or fats into smaller molecules which are able to pass through the intestinal mucosa into the blood stream. The chemical process is called hydrolysis since, as a preparatory step to the splitting of the larger molecules, a molecule of water is taken up. Thus, the cleavage of a molecule of maltose into two of glucose is represented in the following equation:

$$C_{12}H_{22}O_{11} + H_2O = C_6H_{12}O_6 + C_6H_{12}O_6 \quad glucose$$

Such reactions, in order to be accomplished by the ordinary chemical methods of the laboratory, require the use of strong reagents, and usually a high temperature. The digestive ferments act at a relatively low temperature (that of the body), and without the aid of strong chemicals.

It is not only the chemical reactions involved in digestion that are dependent upon enzyme action. These substances are concerned in the great majority of chemical reactions which occur in the tissues of both animals and plants, and upon which the properties of living matter depend. Enzymes, or at least the great majority of them, are protein in nature. Though produced by living cells, they do not require the presence of cells in order to act. The enzyme of yeast, for example, when expressed from the yeast cells, is capable of exerting its usual effect — the conversion of sugar to alcohol.

Several theories have been put forward to explain the manner in which enzymes act, but none can be said to have been definitely established. However, many facts are known concerning the action of enzymes which indicate that they belong to the group of substances known as *catalysts*. Now, a catalyst increases the velocity of a chemical reaction, but does not actually initiate the reaction. Nor does a catalyst become altered or form a part of the product of the reaction. Catalytic action has been compared by Sir William Bayliss to the effect which a drop of oil exerts upon the speed of a metal weight moving down a glass incline. The oil hastens, but does not initiate, the movement of the weight, nor does it combine with the metal or the glass, or undergo any chemical change whatever. To take a specific instance of catalytic action; when acetic acid and ethyl alcohol are mixed, ethyl acetate is formed slowly, but the velocity of the reaction is greatly increased by the addition of a very small amount of hydrochloric acid. Thus:

$$HCl + CH_3COOH + C_2H_5OH \rightleftharpoons CH_3COOC_2H_5 + HOH$$

hydro-chloric acid	acetic acid	ethyl alcohol	ethyl acetate	water

It will be seen from this equation that the hydrochloric acid does not enter into the reaction. The latter, as shown by the arrows, is reversible. That is, the combination of acetic acid with ethyl alcohol to form ethyl acetate is accompanied by a reaction in the opposite direction, namely, the breakdown of ethyl acetate into acetic acid and ethyl alcohol. When the velocities of these two opposing reactions are equal, a state of equilibrium has been reached. If the concentration of ethyl acetate is raised the velocity of the reaction on the left is increased, i.e., the reaction shifts to the left until equilibrium is reached again; if the concentrations of acetic acid and ethyl alcohol are raised, the reaction shifts to the right.[1] The hydrochloric acid increases the velocity of the reaction in either direction; it is an *inorganic catalyst*. Enzymes act in the same way; they are therefore *organic catalysts*, i.e., catalysts formed by living organisms. It should be pointed out that both types of catalyst exert their effects in very low concentrations; a small quantity of ptyalin, for example, will convert a relatively large quantity of starch to maltose; "a little leaven leaveneth the whole lump."

Enzymes differ in one important respect from most of the inorganic catalysts in being absolutely specific in their actions. Ptyalin, for example, acts upon starch, but has no effect whatsoever upon proteins or fats; pepsin converts protein to proteoses and peptones, but has no action upon the other two types of foodstuff.

Conditions which influence the action of enzymes. 1. Enzymes act with maximum efficiency at a certain temperature (*optimum temperature*). Lowering the temperature below, or raising it above this level, slows the reaction. The digestive and other enzymes of animals act best around the temperature of the body. A high degree of heat (above 60° C.) permanently abolishes their action.

2. *Hydrogen ion concentration.* The optimum pH for the different enzymes varies widely. For pepsin it is around 1.5, for pancreatic amylase about 7.0. The former enzyme is inactive in an alkaline medium, the latter in a strongly acid medium.

3. *Inorganic salts.* Enzyme action is profoundly affected

[1] These facts are embodied in the *Law of mass action* which states that "the velocity of a chemical reaction is proportional to the concentrations of the reacting substances."

by certain ions, notably chloride which is necessary for the activation of the amylases. Magnesium accelerates greatly the action of phosphatase and trypsin is activated by calcium. Iron is essential for the action of certain respiratory enzymes in the tissues. Substances such as these, which activate or enhance the action of enzymes, are called *co-enzymes*.

4. *Poisons*. Mercury, gold, copper and several other heavy metals exert a strongly toxic effect owing, apparently, to their combining with the enzyme. Cyanides abolish the action of oxidizing enzymes of the tissues (p. 202). Fluorides, bromine, iodine and chloroform are also toxic for some enzymes.

5. *The products of the enzyme reaction.* It has been mentioned (p. 223) that a chemical reaction comprises two processes — decomposition and synthesis — proceeding simultaneously. As the equilibrium point is approached the velocity of the reaction gradually diminishes. For example, in the conversion of starch to maltose by ptyalin, the reaction proceeds rapidly at first, but as the concentration of maltose increases the velocity of the opposing or synthetic reaction — maltose to starch — increases. At a certain stage the quantity of starch broken down in a given time just balances the quantity resynthesized. In other words, the enzyme reaction, to all intents and purposes, ceases as a result of the accumulation of its own products. If more substrate (starch) is added the reaction starts again and continues until equilibrium is again reached.

Nomenclature. The material upon which an enzyme acts is called the *substrate*, and it is now the practice to derive the name of the enzyme by adding the suffix *"ase"* to the name of its substrate. For example, an enzyme which hydrolyzes starch is called an *amylase* (L. *amylum* = starch), one which acts upon protein a *proteinase* and on fat a *lipase* (G. *lipos* = fat). *Amyolytic* (starch-splitting), *proteolytic* (protein-splitting) and *lipolytic* (fat-splitting) are corresponding terms used to denote the respective actions of these three types of enzymes. In some instances the name of the enzyme is coined by suffixing *"ase"* to the name of the reaction which it brings about. Thus an enzyme which causes de-aminations (p. 291) is called a *deaminase*, and an oxidizing enzyme an *oxidase*.

Names were given to certain digestive enzymes before the system of terminology just outlined had come into use. The ferment of the saliva, for example, has long been known as *ptyalin*. *Pepsin* of the gastric juice, and *trypsin* (protein-splitting enzymes), *amylopsin* (starch-splitting enzyme) and *steapsin* (fat-splitting enzyme) given to the ferments of pancreatic juice are also old-established names. Corresponding terms in the new system are *salivary amylase*, *gastric proteinase*, and *pancreatic proteinase*, *amylase* and *lipase*.

The physiological properties of smooth (non-striated) muscle. Smooth muscle differs from skeletal muscle in the following respects: (a) slower, more sluggish contraction, (b) greater extensibility, (c) the exhibition of a sustained contraction or tonus for long periods, even though separated from the central nervous system, (d) the power of rhythmical contraction, (e) the possession of a double autonomic inner-vation (parasympathetic and sympathetic), (f) greater sensitivity to thermal and chemical influences and to certain types of mechanical stimulation, such as stretching, but a lower excitability to electrical stimulation.

Tonus of smooth muscle may be defined as the steady sus-tained contraction through which the muscle offers resistance to a stretching force. The rhythmical contractions are super-imposed upon the tonus state which may vary independently of the rhythmical contractions themselves. The tonic con-traction of smooth muscle is associated with a negligible expenditure of energy. It is relatively insusceptible to fatigue; heat production and electrical changes are not detectable; and a rise or fall in the degree of tonus is not accompanied by a corresponding change in oxygen con-sumption.

Certain hollow organs such as the stomach and urinary bladder and, to a less degree, the intestines, have the remarkable ability to enlarge when their contents are considerably increased without showing any rise in internal pressure. The tone of the muscle composing the walls of these organs adjusts automatically to the distending force. This *postural tone*, as it is called, is very difficult to explain. It is possible that, in the stomach at any rate, the individual

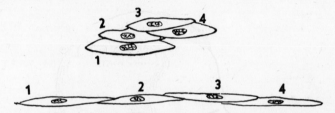

Fig. 111. Diagram to illustrate the manner in which muscle fibers may slide over one another and increase the capacity of a hollow organ. The *upper group* of four muscle cells (1 to 4) is from a hollow organ whose walls are contracted and its cavity almost obliterated; the *lower group* are the same muscle fibers when the organ is full. (Redrawn from Grützner.)

fibers which are disposed in layers, instead of being lengthened by the stretching force, simply slide over one another, the wall of the organ thus being increased in area, but reduced in thickness. This could occur with little strain being placed upon the fibers themselves (Fig. 111).

DIGESTION IN THE MOUTH

The structure of the salivary glands. Saliva is secreted by three pairs of glands, the *submaxillary, sublingual* and *parotid glands*. The submaxillary glands are situated beneath the floor of the mouth in close relation, one on either side, with the inner aspect of the lower jaw (mandible). The submaxillary secretion reaches the cavity of the mouth through the *duct of Wharton*, which opens beneath the tongue. The sublingual glands also lie below the floor of the mouth, but nearer the mid-line. Each pours its secretion into the mouth beneath the tongue through a number of small ducts

— *ducts of Rivinus* and of *Bartholin*. The parotid gland lies below the ear, behind and overlapping the vertical part of the mandible. Its duct — the *duct of Stenson* — opens upon the inner aspect of the cheek opposite the second upper molar tooth (see Fig. 112).

The salivary glands are composed of cells arranged in small groups around a central cavity called the *alveolus* or *acinus*. The alveoli are drained by fine ducts which join with those

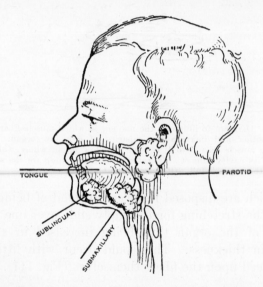

FIG. 112. Showing the salivary glands of one side.

from neighboring alveoli to form larger channels. Through the successive junctions of smaller ducts and the formation of larger ones, the secretion is directed into the main secretory duct or ducts (Fig. 113). This alveolar arrangement of the cells and the system of ducts of the salivary glands suggest a bunch of grapes. To these and other glands (e.g., the pancreas), showing a similar pattern, the term *racemose* (L. *racemus* = a bunch of grapes) is, therefore, applied.

The cells of the salivary glands are of two types, *serous* and *mucous*. The secretion of the former type is thin and

watery; that of the latter type contains mucin, and is
therefore thicker and more viscous. The parotid gland is
composed entirely of se-
rous cells, whereas the cells
of the sublingual gland
are predominantly of the
mucous type, serous cells
being scarce. The sub-
maxillary gland contains
both serous and mucous
cells in about equal pro-
portions, the two types
being seen in many in-
stances in the wall of the
same alveolus. The se-
rous cells are then found
on the outer side of the
mucous cells which, there-

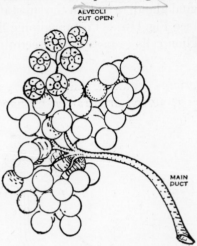

FIG. 113. Plan of a racemose gland (diagrammatic).

fore, lie between them and the alveolar cavity. The
serous cells have a somewhat crescentic shape and are
for this reason called *demilunes* (Fig. 114).

The control of salivary secretion. The salivary glands
are under the control of the autonomic (involuntary) nervous

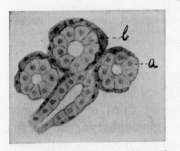

FIG. 114. Section of sublingual gland. *a*, serous cells; *b*, mucous cells (demilunes).

system, receiving fibers from
both its parasympathetic and
sympathetic divisions. The
parasympathetic fibers to the
submaxillary and sublingual
glands arise from a center —
the *superior salivary center* —
in the pons; they leave the brain
in the facial nerve and are conveyed in the *chorda tympani*
branch of the latter nerve to the

cavity of the mouth. Here they join the *lingual nerve* which
transmits them to the floor of the mouth where, separating

again from the lingual fibers they make connections with ganglion cells situated in close relationship with the sublingual gland, or within the substance of the submaxillary gland (see Fig. 115). Postganglionic fibers — the axons of the ganglion cells — pass to the secreting cells.

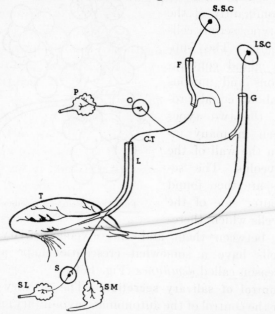

Fig. 115. Diagram of the nerve supply of the salivary glands. C.T, chorda tympani nerve; F, facial nerve; G, glossopharyngeal nerve; I.S.C, inferior salivary center; L, lingual nerve; O, otic ganglion; P, parotid gland; S, submaxillary ganglion; T, tongue; SL, sublingual gland; SM, submaxillary gland; S.S.C, superior salivary center.

The chorda tympani nerve also carries vasodilator fibers (p. 150) to the glands and taste fibers to the anterior two-thirds of the tongue. The posterior third of the tongue receives taste fibers through the glossopharyngeal nerve. The submaxillary and sublingual glands receive as well secretory and vasoconstrictor fibers from the sympathetic plexus investing the neighboring branches of the external carotid artery. The parotid gland derives secretory and vasodilator parasympathetic fibers through the tympanic branch of the glossopharyngeal nerve. These fibers arise from a group of cells in the upper part of the medulla oblongata called the *inferior salivary center*. Vasoconstrictor fibers to the parotid are derived from the sympathetic.

Stimulation of either the parasympathetic (chorda tympani) fibers or the sympathetic fibers to the submaxillary or sublingual gland causes a secretion of saliva. The secretion resulting from parasympathetic stimulation is, in most animals, profuse and watery in consistency; sympathetic stimulation, on the contrary, causes a scanty secretion of a thick mucinous juice. Apparently, then, the parasympathetic fibers innervate the serous cells, and the sympathetic the mucous cells. Stimulation of the parasympathetic fibers to the parotid gland causes likewise a profuse watery secretion, whereas no secretion follows stimulation of the sympathetic.

Under natural conditions, the secretion of saliva is a reflex phenomenon brought about usually by the stimulation of the taste fibers in the mouth. But stimulation of the ordinary sensory nerves in the mucosa of the mouth, i.e., those fibers conveying sensations of touch, pain and temperature, evokes a flow of saliva. We are all familiar with the salivation which results from moving some tasteless object around in the mouth, or from the manipulations of the dentist. Indeed, secretion of saliva may follow stimulation of almost any afferent nerve in the body. In animals stimulation of the central cut end of the sciatic nerve excites salivary secretion and, in man, irritation of the nerves of the stomach or esophagus, in diseased states, is not uncommonly a cause of troublesome salivation.

Salivary reflexes are of two types. The one caused by the introduction of material into the mouth is called an *unconditioned reflex*. But it is well known that salivation very often results from the sight, smell or even the thought of food. We often hear a person say that his "mouth waters" when he sees or smells appetizing food. The response following such forms of stimulation is called a *conditioned reflex*. The unconditioned reflex is inborn; it can be elicited immediately after birth. The conditioned reflex, on the contrary, depends upon experience. In order for it to become established, an association, upon some previous occasion, must have been formed in the mind between sensations received through the nerves of taste and those gained through some other sense organ, e.g., eye, nose, ear, etc. We need say no more here of this type of reflex; it will be considered in more detail in chapter X.

The characters, quantity and composition of saliva. Normal human saliva as collected from the mouth (i.e., mixed saliva, containing secretions of all six glands, as well as the secretion of the small mucous glands scattered diffusely over the mucosa of the mouth) is slightly acid in reaction, varying between pH 6.35 and 6.85. Its specific gravity is between 1.002 and 1.008. The average adult secretes from 1200 cc. to 1500 cc. of saliva in 24 hours. The composition of saliva is given in the following table.

TABLE 11

I. *Salts* (approximately 0.2 per cent)
   Sodium and potassium chloride
   Sodium bicarbonate
   Acid and alkaline sodium phosphates
   Calcium carbonate and calcium phosphate
   Potassium sulphocyanate
II. *Gases*
   Carbon dioxide and oxygen
III. *Organic substances*
   Ptyalin (salivary amylase)
   Maltase
   Serum albumin
   Serum globulin
   Urea
   Mucin, mainly in the submaxillary and sublingual secretions

The functions of saliva. 1. *Digestive*. The enzyme of the saliva — *ptyalin* — acts upon starch. The starch molecule is split into smaller molecules of the disaccharide, maltose. The rapid passage of the food through the mouth precludes the possibility that it is acted upon here to any appreciable extent by the saliva. Whether starchy food, after its thorough impregnation with saliva, undergoes any important degree of digestion in the stomach has been debated. Ptyalin is active in an alkaline, neutral or faintly acid medium, but is inactivated by strong acid. It was thought, therefore, that the highly acid gastric juice would prevent or soon terminate salivary digestion. It has been shown, however, that the latter part of the meal, which usually contains the carbohydrate, may remain in the fundus of the stomach, and thus be protected for some time, from the acidifying action of the gastric juice, by a layer of food ingested previously. For this reason it is likely that, under favorable circumstances, the salivary digestion of starch may proceed for a considerable period after food has reached the stomach.

If boiled starch be placed in a test tube with mixed human saliva and kept at body temperature, a slow conversion of the starch into maltose takes place. The chemical change occurs in a series of stages which may be distinguished by the manner in which the product of each stage reacts with iodine. Iodine gives a characteristic blue color with boiled starch. A short time after the saliva has commenced to act, a physical change may be seen to have occurred in the starch. It loses its opalescent appearance and becomes *soluble*, though it still gives the blue color with iodine. After a short time this soluble starch becomes partially broken down, being converted into a dextrin which, since it gives a red color with iodine, is known as *erythrodextrin*. Small amounts of maltose may also be detected at this stage. Still later, no color reaction occurs upon the addition of iodine; a colorless product — *achroodextrin* — has been formed. Finally, the starch is entirely converted into maltose and isomaltose. In the final stage, traces of glucose may also appear, due to the presence of an enzyme *maltase* present in saliva in low concentration. The following scheme illustrates the action of ptyalin:

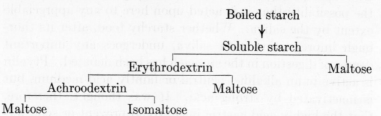

Ptyalin has no action upon cellulose, and for this reason the starch must be cooked in order to rupture the cellulose envelope surrounding the starch grains.

2. *Preparation of the food for swallowing by altering its consistency.* This is one of the most important functions of the saliva; the food is moistened, thus enabling it to be rolled into a plastic mass, and given a lubricant coating. Claude Bernard showed that a horse with a parotid fistula had the utmost difficulty in swallowing dry hay or oats.

3. *Solvent action.* Taste is a chemical sense (p. 517). All solid substances, therefore, in order that they shall stimulate the taste buds, must be dissolved in the saliva.

4. *Cleansing action.* The constant flow of saliva exerts a very necessary cleansing effect. The mouth and teeth are rinsed and kept comparatively free from food debris, shed epithelial cells, foreign particles, etc.; in this way the saliva inhibits the growth of bacteria by removing material which may serve as culture media. In order to realize how important its function is in this regard one has but to consider the foul condition of the mouth that occurs in certain fevers, when the salivary secretion is suppressed. Then, decomposing organic material, swarming with bacteria, collects upon the teeth and lips, and must be removed by artifical means.

5. *Moistening and lubricating action.* The saliva, by moistening and lubricating the soft parts of the mouth and

lips, keeps them pliable and resilient for the purposes of articulation. Frequent sips of water are almost essential for some public speakers in whom, as a result of evaporation from the mouth during speech, the supply of saliva is insufficient.

6. *Excretory.* Many substances, both organic and inorganic, are excreted in the saliva. Drugs such as mercury, potassium, iodide, lead, etc., when introduced into the body, are excreted, in part, by the saliva. Severe inflammation of the oral mucosa (stomatitis) may be caused by the excretion through this route of excessive amounts of mercury. The blue line on the gum margins, in lead poisoning, is due to the metal having been excreted in the saliva and deposited as the sulphide. The sulphur is provided by organic material contained in the tartar formed on the bases of the teeth. For this reason the discoloration of the gum does not occur where teeth are absent. In chronic nephritis the saliva contains a high percentage of urea; sugar sometimes appears in severe diabetes; and in parathyroid overdosage the calcium concentration of the saliva is elevated. Several types of microörganisms, some intensely virulent, e.g., the virus of hydrophobia, are excreted in the saliva.

Mastication. This act comprises the movements of the lower jaw, tongue, lips and cheeks, whereby the food is reduced to a soft mass which can be easily swallowed. The incisor and canine teeth are used chiefly for tearing the food and breaking it up into small pieces, the molars for grinding it. The movements of the tongue, lips and cheeks move the food about in the mouth, apply pressure or suction to it, and introduce fresh material between the jaws. The whole mass thus becomes thoroughly impregnated with saliva. The jaw movements are brought about by the contractions of temporal, masseter and pterygoid muscles, all of which are supplied by the third division of the trigeminal nerve.

Swallowing or deglutition. The act of swallowing is usually described in three stages. In the *first stage* the masticated food mass or *bolus*, as it is called, is placed upon the tongue, which is then drawn sharply backward by the action of muscles attached to its base. The food is thus projected into the pharynx. The opening into the pharynx, which is called the *fauces*, is limited on either side by two muscular

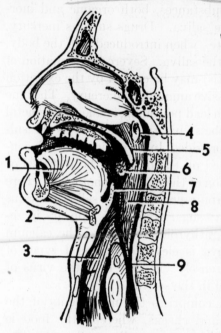

pillars (the *pillars of the fauces*). As a result of the backward movement of the tongue, which at the same time presses against the hard palate, a pressure of 20 centimeters of water is created in the posterior part of the mouth and pharynx. The first stage of swallowing is a voluntary act.

In the *second stage* the food passes through the pharynx. This stage is very brief. The muscles of the pharyngeal wall (*constrictors of the pharynx*) contract and, gripping or squeezing the food, force it into the esophagus. There are, however, three other paths which the food might take —

FIG. 116. The mouth, nose, pharynx, larynx and the commencement of the esophagus, as exposed by a section a little to the left of the median plane of the head. 1, tongue; 2, hyoid bone; 3, larynx; 4, opening of Eustachian tube; 5, soft palate; 6, tonsil; 7, epiglottis; 8, pharynx; 9, esophagus.

into the nose, into the larynx, or back again into the mouth (see Fig. 116). The food is prevented from entering the nose by the elevation of the soft palate; the posterior edge of the latter is brought against the posterior pharyngeal wall, thus separating the pharynx from the posterior entrance to the nasal cavities. This movement rarely fails to take place at the proper time in normal persons, but in the paralysis of the palate which sometimes follows diphtheria, the passage of liquids into the nose during swallowing is a common occurrence. The base of the tongue, which continues to be held in position against the fauces, and the approximation of the pillars of the fauces themselves, effectively block communication with the cavity of the mouth. Elevation of the larynx, which brings its opening under the shelter of the epiglottis and base of the tongue, prevents the food from entering the air passages. This upward movement of the larynx is an essential part of the swallowing act. When, as a result of disease, the larynx is fixed, swallowing becomes very difficult or impossible. When the movement is not accurately timed with the pharyngeal movements, food enters the larynx and excites the coughing reflex. Everyone at some time or another has experienced this accident.

A short inspiration (inspiration of swallowing) occurs at the commencement of the first stage; this is followed by complete inhibition of respiration, which persists until the end of the second stage.

The third stage is occupied in the passage of the food down the esophagus into the stomach. In man, the upper part of the esophagus is composed of striated muscle, the lower part of smooth muscle. The food is carried through the tube by a peristaltic contraction (p. 268) of the muscular wall, its passage being much more rapid through the upper striated portion of the tube than through the lower part. The esophagus of the dog is composed throughout of striated muscle, which accounts for the amazing rapidity with which this animal can swallow food. In the lower end of the esophagus, i.e., where it opens into the stomach, the muscle fibers are condensed to form the *cardiac sphincter*.[1] The sphincter at ordinary times is contracted; but it relaxes upon the approach of the food, which is then swept into the stomach by

---

[1] A sphincter is a circular band of muscle which, acting like a purse string when it contracts, serves to narrow the entrance to, or outlet from certain hollow organs.

the peristaltic wave. The second and third stages of the swallowing act are entirely reflex in nature, i.e., involuntary. The reflex is initiated by the passage of the food through the fauces. Afferent nerve endings are stimulated by the contact of the food with the mucosa in the region of the fauces and pharynx. Of course, we can swallow at will, even though no food is in the mouth. It might be thought, therefore, that it was not correct to speak of the second and third stages of swallowing as being involuntary. But when one wishes to swallow, food or (if the mouth is empty) a little saliva, by a movement of the tongue, is passed backwards, to act as a stimulus. Swallowing then occurs automatically.

Innervation of the swallowing reflex. The afferent fibers of the reflex are contained in the branches of the trigeminal, glossopharyngeal and vagus nerves supplying the mucous membrane in the region of the fauces, tonsil and pharynx. Temporarily abolishing the function of the nerve endings in these regions, by the application of a local anesthetic (e.g., cocaine) to the mucous membrane, renders swallowing impossible for the time. The chief swallowing *center* is situated in the medulla oblongata, in the neighborhood of the nucleus of the vagus. The efferent fibers travel to the various muscles taking part in the act, by the *hypoglossal* (to the muscles of the tongue), the *trigeminal* (to the mylohyoid muscle in the floor of the mouth) and the *glossopharyngeal* and *vagus* nerves to the muscles of the pharynx and esophagus.

The cardiac sphincter receives inhibitory fibers from the vagus and excitatory fibers from the sympathetic. It sometimes happens, though rarely, that the innervation of the sphincter becomes disordered, the sympathetic being overactive (or the vagus underactive). The muscle, as a result, remains tonically contracted during swallowing, and thus prevents the easy entrance of food into the stomach. Difficulty in swallowing is experienced, and the esophagus for some distance above the obstruction becomes distended by retained food. This condition is called *cardiospasm.*

DIGESTION IN THE STOMACH

General description of the stomach. The walls of the stomach are composed of smooth muscle fibers arranged in three layers — *longitudinal, circular* and *oblique* — in this order from without inwards. The mucous membrane is covered by columnar epithelium, and contains the gastric glands. When empty, the stomach is a narrow tubular organ; its mucosa is thrown into numerous longitudinal folds called *rugae.* Its contour varies somewhat in different persons, but most commonly bears a general resemblance to the letter J (see Fig. 117). The vertical part of the J is called the *body;* the upper part of the body is expanded into a domed chamber by a bubble of gas, and is called the *fundus.* The fundus lies in contact with the diaphragm which intervenes between it and the heart. The region of the stomach corresponding to the hook of the J is named the *pyloric part (pars pylorica).* An annular band of muscle, the *pyloric sphincter,* surrounds the opening between the pyloric part and the *duodenum* (first 10 inches or so of the small intestine). The walls of the empty stomach, except in the region of the fundus, are in contact, but the food after passing through the cardia presses steadily downwards, separating the gastric walls. As the organ distends it becomes pear-shaped; its rugae become flatter, and, with increasing distension, disappear. The capacity of the human stomach is from one to one and a half quarts.

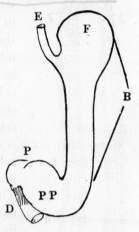

Fig. 117.   Diagram of the stomach. B, body of stomach; D, duodenum; E, esophagus; F, fundus of stomach; P, pylorus; PP, pars pylorica.

The gastric glands secrete the gastric juice. They are scattered diffusely in large numbers throughout the gastric mucosa. The total number of glands in the human stomach is around 35,000,000. They are minute tubular or flask-like

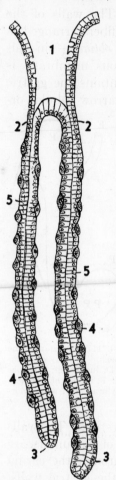

structures which open, each one separately, into a small pit upon the inner surface of the stomach. The cells forming the walls of the glands are continuous with the epithelium covering the gastric mucosa, but differ from the latter both structurally and functionally. The glands in the fundus and the rest of the body of the stomach differ, in so far as their cellular structure is concerned, from those in the lower part (pyloric region). The cells of the glands of the body of the stomach are of three types, (a) *mucous cells*, (b) *chief* or *zymogenic cells* and (c) *parietal* or *border cells*. The mucous cells are situated in the narrow superficial part of the gland tubule called the neck. They secrete mucus (Fig. 118). The chief or zymogenic cells form a continuous lining for the deeper part or body of the gland tubule. These cells secrete the ferments of the gastric juice. The parietal or border cells do not form a continuous layer, but lie here and there along the tubule to the outer side of the chief cells. They produce the hydrochloric acid of the juice.

Fig. 118. Glands from fundus of stomach. 1, pit on mucous surface of stomach; 2, neck of gland; 3, bottom (fundus) of gland; 4, parietal cells; 5, chief cells.

The glands of the pyloric region contain only mucus-secreting cells; chief cells and parietal cells are absent. The mucosa for a small area near the cardia also contains glands of this type.

The composition of gastric juice. The *gastric juice* contains *ferments*, *mucin* and *hydrochloric acid*.

An analysis of human gastric juice is given in the following table (modified from Carlson).

Acidity   Free HCl, 0.50 to 0.60 per cent
           Total acidity, 0.45 to 0.60 per cent
           pH, 0.9 to 1.5
Solids   Organic, including mucin and the various ferments, 0.42 to 0.46 per cent
           Inorganic, 0.13 to 0.14 per cent
Specific gravity, 1.006 to 1.009
Total nitrogen, 0.051 to 0.075 per cent

The ferments are *pepsin, rennin* and *lipase*. The pepsin acts upon protein. The protein molecule, as we shall see (p. 288), is constituted of large groups of amino-acids linked together. Pepsin splits the molecule into smaller amino-acid groups. These, the first cleavage products of the digestion of protein, are called *proteoses* and *peptones*. The attack made upon protein by pepsin ceases at this stage.

When the mucosa of the body of the stomach is extracted with an alkaline solution, the extract possesses little or no proteolytic activity, but becomes active upon acidification. It is, therefore, sometimes stated that pepsin is secreted as an inactive precursor which differs chemically from active pepsin, and is referred to as *pepsinogen*. A simpler and more correct explanation of the observation that an alkaline extract of the gastric mucosa is inactive is based upon the fact that pepsin, like other enzymes, acts best at a certain pH (*optimum pH*), and becomes inactive if any great change from this reaction occurs. The optimum pH for the action of pepsin is around 1.5, which is the reaction of pure gastric juice.

The concentration of hydrochloric acid in gastric juice, as the latter is secreted by the glands, is from 0.5% to 0.6%. The contents of the stomach have rarely, however, an acidity as high as this, for the juice, after it reaches the cavity of the stomach, becomes diluted by other fluids, e.g., saliva, mucus from the lining epithelium, the alkaline secretion of the pyloric glands, and food residues. The hydrochloric acid is formed by the parietal cells and is apparently secreted as such into the gland tubules, and not, as was once thought, in the form of a precursor which is converted to hydrochloric acid after reaching the lumina of the tubules, or the cavity of the stomach.   Indeed, it is a truly remarkable fact that the cells *do* form and secrete a mineral acid of such high concentration.   Also, why do not the pepsin and hydrochloric acid of the gastric juice digest the stomach itself?   This is a conundrum which has received no satisfactory solution.   It is no answer to this question to say that the stomach is living tissue, and so can protect itself, for, if the leg of a living frog is inserted into the stomach of a dog it undergoes digestion about as readily as if it were a piece of beef.

The hydrochloric acid is formed from the sodium chloride of the blood, but, though several theories have been advanced, the manner in which the gland cells accomplish this chemical feat is not clearly understood.

Rennin coagulates milk, producing a flocculent mass called the *curd*, and a clear fluid known as *whey*.   This action has been made use of from time immemorial in cheese-making, the rennin being extracted from calves' stomachs.   The curdling or clotting of milk presents a certain resemblance to the clotting of blood.   As a result of the action of rennin the soluble milk protein, *caseinogen*, is converted into an insoluble product, and, as in the conversion of fibrinogen to fibrin by thrombin, calcium is necessary for this reaction. The role played by calcium is not, however, the same in both instances.   In the clotting of milk the rennin first splits the caseinogen into two substances — *whey protein* and *para-casein* — both of which are soluble.   The latter protein then combines with calcium to form *calcium paracasein* which is insoluble.   The calcium paracasein is then digested by pepsin.

The *lipase* of gastric juice has a very weak fat-splitting action and in the adult is of little practical importance.   It acts only upon fats which are in very fine emulsion, e.g., cream and egg-yolk.   It may be of more value to the infant.

Mucin belongs to the class of glycoproteins (p. 290).   It is present in pure gastric juice. It is secreted by the cells in the necks of the glands in the body of the stomach, as well as by the pyloric glands. The secretion of the surface epithelium of the stomach (goblet cells, p. 9) also contains a high percentage of mucin. This latter secretion is a slimy fluid which tends to cling to the surface of the mucosa. It thus serves to protect the mucosa from injury by coarse particles of food and, to a certain extent, from the action of the pepsin-hydrochloric acid. It may be mentioned in this regard that mucin is capable of combining with a relatively large amount of hydrochloric acid, and of inhibiting peptic activity. Preparations of mucin obtained from pig's stomach have been used recently in the treatment of gastric and duodenal ulcers with the object of protecting the surface of the ulcer from the action of the highly acid gastric juice.

The secretion of gastric juice. The gastric glands receive secretory fibers through the vagus nerves. When these nerves are stimulated, the glands secrete a highly acid juice rich in pepsin. Sympathetic fibers can also be traced to the gastric glands, but their action is less well known; it seems, however, that they innervate the pyloric glands, causing a secretion of an alkaline juice consisting largely of mucus.

It is now customary to speak of three phases of gastric digestion: (1) *pyschic* or *cephalic*, (2) *gastric* and (3) *intestinal*.

The psychic or cephalic phase. It was first shown by the Russian physiologist, Ivan Pavlov, that gastric juice is secreted while food is being chewed, and before any has entered the stomach. The more appetizing the food, the greater is its effect upon gastric secretion. Pavlov therefore spoke of the secretion caused in this manner as the *appetite juice.* The secretion under such circumstances is, of course, purely reflex in nature. The afferent fibers of the reflex are in the nerves of taste, the efferent fibers in the vagus nerves. The effect cannot be produced after the vagus nerves have been sectioned.

Pavlov demonstrated this reflex in dogs by what he termed "sham feeding." An animal was first prepared by dividing the esophagus in the neck, bringing the lower end of the upper segment through the neck wound and fixing it there by sutures (Fig. 119). The animal, prepared in this way, relishes its food just as does any normal dog, but the food cannot enter the stomach; it simply falls from the open esophagus after it has been swallowed. Nevertheless, a flow

of gastric juice results. The juice secreted by the stomach can be collected from an opening made through the abdominal wall into the stomach, and measured. It can then be analyzed for its peptic and acid concentrations, if desired; or a miniature stomach can be fashioned as shown in Fig. 120.

FIG. 119. Showing esophagal fistula made for "sham feeding" experiments.

The psychic secretion of gastric juice has been clearly demonstrated many times in man. In Dr. Carlson's laboratory in Chicago, a man was investigated whose esophagus was impassable as a result of an injury received in childhood. A permanent opening had been made through the wall of the abdomen into the stomach. Through this opening — termed a *gastric fistula* — the man, like Pavlov's dogs, could be "sham fed," though in his case the food was spat out after it had been chewed. It was found that food for which this subject had a particular fondness caused the greatest secretion of juice (Fig. 121). In some instances the mere sight or smell of food called forth a secretion. That is to say, a conditioned reflex (p. 467) can be established for gastric as well as for salivary secretion.

The psychic secretion of gastric juice has also been demonstrated in persons during hypnosis. A suggestion made to the subject that he was eating some tempting piece of food stimulated secretion. On the other hand, psychic

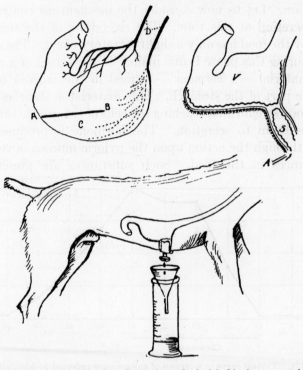

Fig. 120. *Upper drawings* show Pavlov's method of fashioning a gastric pouch or miniature stomach. A horizontal incision *A–B* is made which causes minimal injury to the gastric nerves and blood supply. *D*, vagus nerves. The flap (*C*) is turned down and the pouch (*S*) isolated from the main cavity of the stomach (*V*) as shown in the right-hand sketch. A, abdominal wall (Pavlov). The *lower drawing* illustrates the manner in which pure gastric juice can be collected from the miniature stomach while digestion is proceeding in the main part of the stomach.

influences, e.g., worry, fear and anxiety, can inhibit gastric secretion, as may also bad odors or an unattractive appearance of the meal. Pavlov sums up these facts, which obviously are of great practical importance, in the sentence, "Appetite spells gastric juice." Macbeth at the banquet expresses the same thought when he says, "Let good digestion wait on appetite, and health on both."

The gastric phase. This refers to the secretion of gastric juice which occurs after the food has entered the stomach; it continues for a much longer period than does the psychic secretion. Let us now consider the mechanisms controlling the secretion at this time. The stretching of the stomach wall by the food has only a slight secretory effect. The secretion during this phase is due mainly to the action of a chemical material — a *hormone* — formed in the mucosa of the pyloric part of the stomach. This material is absorbed into the blood stream and, reaching the cells of the gastric tubules, excites them to secretion. The hormone is produced, in turn, through the action upon the pyloric mucosa of certain substances in the food. Such substances are present in

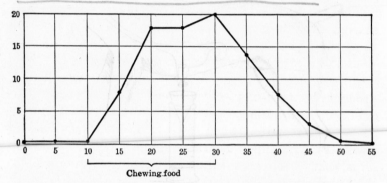

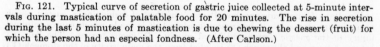

Chewing food

Fig. 121. Typical curve of secretion of gastric juice collected at 5-minute intervals during mastication of palatable food for 20 minutes. The rise in secretion during the last 5 minutes of mastication is due to chewing the dessert (fruit) for which the person had an especial fondness. (After Carlson.)

aqueous extracts of meats and vegetables (e.g., soups and beef extracts); they are therefore given the general name of *extractives.* The products of protein digestion — *proteoses* and *peptones* — and certain other materials act in a similar fashion.

When evidence for its existence was first obtained, the gastric hormone was named *gastrin;* its chemical nature was unknown. Extracts of the pyloric mucosa, obtained from an animal after a meal of meat or of other substances rich in extractives, contained the hormone. This was shown by the fact that when such extracts were injected into the veins of an animal, a profuse secretion of gastric juice resulted.

It is now generally conceded, however, that the hormone in pyloric extracts, i.e., gastrin, is not a specific and hitherto unknown substance, but is simply histamine, which is found in other tissues as well as in the gastric mucous membrane. The discovery that histamine and gastrin are identical does not necessarily lead to the conclusion that there is no other gastric hormone. On the contrary, a considerable body of evidence suggests that a gastric hormone quite distinct from histamine is formed in the gastric mucosa during digestion. But so far this hormone has not been obtained by extraction.

The intestinal phase. After the food materials have reached the intestine, certain of their constituents (split products of protein digestion, meat extracts, etc.) continue to exert an excitatory effect upon gastric secretion. Little is known concerning the manner in which this effect is brought about; it may be dependent upon the formation or liberation of a hormone from the intestinal mucosa, for an extract of the latter, when injected intravenously, has an excitatory effect upon gastric secretion. Another possibility is, that certain constituents of the food are absorbed into the blood stream and act *directly* as excitants of the gland cells.

The effects of different foods and of certain chemicals and drugs upon the secretion of gastric juice. The hydrochloric acid in the gastric contents is in part *combined* with food and mucus; the remainder is *free*. The combined acid and the free acid together are referred to as the *total acid*.

In man the activity of the gastric glands is investigated by giving a meal of toast and weak tea — the so-called *test meal* — and removing samples of the stomach contents every 15 minutes during a subsequent two-hour period. The samples are analyzed, the percentages of *total* and *free acid* determined, and a curve plotted (see Fig. 122). Meat, since it is rich in extractives, stimulates the glands more powerfully than does carbohydrate. Fats have an inhibitory effect upon gastric secretion, as well as upon the movements of the stomach. A meal containing a high proportion of fat takes a relatively long time to leave the stomach. Fat also exerts an inhibitory effect upon gastric secretion and motility, after it has reached the duodenum. The latter effect is attributed to a chemical substance (a *chalone*, p. 328) formed in the intestinal mucosa; this substance has been named *enterogastrone*.

Among chemicals which stimulate gastric secretion the most powerful are *histamine* and *alcohol*. *Atropine* by its action upon the vagus endings temporarily suppresses secretion. *Alkalies* such as sodium bicarbonate in repeated small doses excite the gastric glands, but a single large dose has, as a rule, an inhibitory effect.

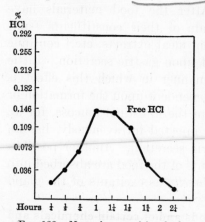

%
HCl
0.292
0.255
0.219
0.182
0.146
0.109
0.073
0.036

Free HCl

Hours   ⅛ ¼ ½ 1 1¼ 1½ 1¾ 2 2¼

Fig. 122.   Normal curve of free hydrochloric acid in the gastric contents following a test meal.

Abnormalities in gastric secretion. When no secretion of acid occurs after a test meal the condition is called *gastric anacidity* or *achlorhydria*. About 4 per cent of perfectly healthy and otherwise normal persons show this peculiarity. There may be a complete absence of peptic secretion as well; when such is the case the condition is called *achylia gastrica*. Gastric anacidity is also seen in a number of diseased states, e.g., *cancer of the stomach, pernicious anemia, chronic inflammation of the stomach, chronic arthritis, gall-bladder disease*, etc.

In some instances the gastric glands, though failing to secrete when stimulated by a test meal, respond to histamine; the anacidity is then called *false* or *apparent*. In other instances, even a powerful stimulus, such as histamine or alcohol, is ineffective. This *absolute* failure of acid secretion is called *true anacidity*. An abnormally high acidity of the gastric contents is called *gastric hyperacidity* or *hyper-chlorhydria*. In this condition the acidity of the gastric juice, as it leaves the gland tubules, is not higher than usual (0.5 to 0.6%), but owing to a high rate of secretion or to failure of the juice to be neutralized after it has reached the cavity of the stomach, the percentages of total and free acid are much above the normal values. Under normal circumstances the acidity of the gastric contents rises after a test meal, reaching a maximum in an hour or so and then declining (see chart, Fig. 122). The return of the curve to the resting level is due to several factors — reduced rate of secretion by the glands, emptying of the stomach, neutralization by mucus and probably also, to some extent, by the regurgitation of alkaline juices from the duodenum. Hyperchlorhydria is due to failure of one or other or all of these factors; the curve of gastric acidity rises above the normal maximum, and in many instances does not return to the resting level within the normal time. The condition is seen in a large proportion of cases of gastric and duodenal ulcer; indeed it is now generally agreed that hyperacidity is the chief cause of these conditions.

In *duodenal ulcer*, for example, ulceration occurs where the gastric juice, after issuing from the pylorus, first comes into contact with the intestinal mucosa. Treatment of gastric or duodenal ulcer is, therefore, directed toward reducing the acidity of the gastric contents. This is accomplished by giving alkalies and restricting the diet in respect to meat and other materials rich in extractives and substituting foods, e.g., milk, cream and carbohydrates, which either inhibit or exert no pronounced stimulating action upon acid secretion.

A high gastric acidity is also seen when the pylorus is obstructed and, as a consequence, gastric evacuation is delayed. The distension of the stomach which results from pyloric obstruction also acts as a stimulus to secretion.

The innervation of the stomach. The stomach is supplied by the *vagus* and *sympathetic* nerves. The vagus is motor in action, i.e., it raises the tone and increases the force of the contractions of the gastric muscle; the sympathetic is inhibitory. The vagus and sympathetic are also motor and inhibitory, respectively, to the pyloric sphincter.

Movements and emptying of the stomach. The upper half or so of the body of the stomach does not show active movements, but is the seat of a steady tonic contraction. When digestion is proceeding, peristaltic contractions commence about the middle of the body of the stomach and,

passing downwards (i.e., toward the pylorus), become progressively more powerful (Fig. 123). The pyloric part is, therefore, the more actively motile region, the motility becoming more and more marked as the digestive processes progress. These movements serve to mix the food thoroughly with the gastric juice and to break up food masses that have been softened by the digestive juices. When the food has reached a consist-

Fig. 123. Drawing of X-ray of stomach showing peristalsis.

ency suitable for discharge into the duodenum it is propelled through the pylorus by the descending waves of peristalsis.

The pyloric sphincter is relaxed most of the time. It is only when a peristaltic wave reaches it that its fibers contract and close the pyloric orifice. The pyloric opening varies in diameter from time to time, however, being wider during the later stages of digestion than at the beginning. Thus the stronger peristaltic contractions and the greater diameter of the pyloric opening when gastric digestion is nearing completion, facilitate the evacuation of the stomach. It should be emphasized that the consistency of the food is one of the most important factors determining the time after swallowing at which it leaves the stomach. Fluids, for example, commence to leave it almost immediately after entering.

Solid food in the stomach must first be reduced to a fluid or semifluid state, and those articles of diet which are most readily softened and liquefied, e.g., carbohydrates, leave before meats, which require a longer time for their digestion. Fats are evacuated most slowly, for, as already mentioned, they inhibit gastric secretion and motility. They also, for this reason, retard the evacuation of other types of food. An ordinary mixed meal is usually completely evacuated within from 3 to 4½ hours.

The stomach contents, after they have reached a semifluid consistency suitable for discharge into the duodenum, are referred to as the *chyme*. This is an old word meaning juice, and arose from the belief that digestion in the stomach was essentially a mechanical process, the nutritive juices being expressed from the food through the pressure exerted by the contractions of the stomach. That the food underwent chemical changes in the stomach was not realized until the French scientist René Réaumur (1683–1757) and the Italian priest and scientist Lazaro Spallanzani (1729–1799) carried out their ingenious experiments. Réaumur gave a kite and other animals small perforated metal tubes filled with meat. He found, upon recovering the tubes, that the meat, though thus protected from any mechanical action of the stomach, was partially dissolved. He also showed that gastric juice would digest meat in a test tube. Spallanzani performed similar experiments upon animals and upon himself. He swallowed perforated wooden tubes filled with food, and showed that, though the containers were unbroken, after passing through the alimentary tract, the food had become dissolved. He also found that gastric juice, obtained by making himself vomit, had the power to dissolve meat *in vitro*.

In the early part of the nineteenth century (1819) Dr. William Beaumont, an American army surgeon, was offered a unique opportunity to study the digestive processes in the human stomach. A French Canadian coureur de bois, Alexis

St. Martin, while at Fort Mackinac on Lake Michigan, received a severe wound in the abdomen from the accidental discharge of a musket. Part of the wall of the stomach was destroyed. Under Beaumont's care the man recovered, but the wound through the abdominal wall and stomach failed to close completely. Through this opening Beaumont was able to observe the changes taking place in the food during the different stages of digestion, and performed a number of simple experiments which served to clarify many aspects of gastric physiology.

The experiments of these pioneers upon the chemical features of digestion obscured for a time the importance of mechanical factors. The pendulum swung too far. But to-day, the mechanical factors are recognized as playing a leading role in gastric digestion. Abnormalities of the motor mechanisms of the stomach are much more often the cause of digestive disorders than are disturbances of chemical processes. Persons in whom gastric secretion is entirely lacking (*achylia gastrica*) may enjoy perfect health, and suffer no digestive discomfort whatsoever. On the other hand, disorders of the movements of the stomach, e.g., too slow or too rapid evacuation of the food, or spasm of the pylorus or of the cardiac sphincter, frequently give rise to severe gastric symptoms.

Vomiting is usually preceded by nausea. The ejection of the stomach contents is accomplished in the following manner. A strong contraction occurs in the pyloric part of the stomach, together with relaxation of the body of the stomach and the cardiac sphincter. Accompanying or immediately following these movements the abdominal muscles contract forcibly, and the diaphragm descends. Thus the stomach is compressed and its contents, being prevented from passing downwards by the firm contraction of the pyloric region, are forced through the relaxed cardia into the esophagus. The latter relaxes throughout its length, which permits the free passage upwards of the stomach contents. The larynx is raised at the same time and its opening closed, thus preventing the passage of material into the air passages. The stomach, it will be noted, is emptied *passively*, that is, from pressure applied from without. There is no evidence, in the adult at any rate, that an ascending peristaltic contraction of the gastric wall is instrumental in ejecting the stomach contents into the esophagus. In the young infant, however, a reverse peristaltic movement of this nature probably does occur.

Vomiting is a reflex act and may follow irritation of nerve endings (vagus or sympathetic) in the stomach or duodenum. But the stimulation of afferent fibers, especially those transmitting pain impulses, in almost any organ of the body may induce vomiting. The vomiting due to disease of the appendix or gall-bladder, or to some painful injury, is well known. Afferent impulses arising in a failing heart may also cause vomiting, or the act may be induced by psychic influences — anxiety, fear or disgust. Sea-sickness is due to the stimulation of nerve endings in the semicircular canals of the ear (p. 512). Nausea or vomiting not uncommonly results from eye strain, the afferent impulses initiating the reflex arising in the eye muscles.

Drugs and other substances used in medicine for the induction of vomiting are called *emetics*. Among those which act upon the nerve endings in the gastric or duodenal wall are *antimony tartrate* (tartar emetic), *copper* and *zinc sulphates*, and *salt or mustard and water*. Certain other emetics, such as *apomorphine*, act upon the *vomiting center* in the medulla oblongata. It is generally believed, however, that the vomiting which follows the administration of emetics of the latter type is also essentially reflex in nature. The drug acts, apparently, by raising the excitability of the center, that is, the threshold of the center to stimulation is lowered, so that impulses from various parts of the body, which normally make no impression upon it, become effective. The vomiting resulting from metabolic disturbances, e.g., in pregnancy or nephritis, or that associated with general bodily fatigue, is explained in a similar way.

The intestinal tract is divided for the purpose of description into two parts — the *small intestine* and the *large intestine*. The small intestine, though of smaller diameter, is much longer than the large intestine (see Fig. 110). In man its length is about 21 feet. The first 10 inches or so are called the *duodenum* (twelve finger breadths). The rest of the small intestine is divided rather arbitrarily into an upper portion (about $\frac{2}{5}$) called the *jejunum*, and a lower somewhat narrower portion (about $\frac{3}{5}$) called the *ileum*. The small intestine from the duodenum onwards is attached to the posterior abdominal wall by a fan-shaped membrane called the *mesentery* which conveys the vessels and nerves to the bowel.

The *large intestine* extends from the end of the ileum to the anus. It is about 5 feet long, in man, and consists of the *cecum, colon, rectum* and *anal canal*. The cecum is the sac-like dilatation at the commencement of the large intestine; it lies in the lower right-hand part of the abdominal cavity. The ileum opens into its upper end and the *vermiform appendix* arises from its lower blind end. The colon is divided for descriptive purposes into the *ascending, transverse, descending* and *pelvic colons*. These are shown in Fig. 110. The bends of the colon in the regions of the liver (i.e., at the junction of the ascending and transverse colons) and spleen (at the junction of the transverse and descending colons) are called, respectively, the *hepatic* and *splenic flexures*. The pelvic colon, the rectum and the anal canal lie in the pelvis. The *internal anal sphincter* is situated at the lower end of the rectum. The *external anal sphincter* guards the lower aperture of the anal canal. The latter opening is called the *anal orifice* or *anus*.

The *pancreas* is a racemose gland. It is an elongated structure lying across the posterior wall of the abdomen; its right-hand broad part, called the *head*, fits into the curve of the duodenum (Fig. 124). Its body and tail are directed toward the left. The cells which form its external secretion — the *pancreatic juice* — have an alveolar arrangement resembling that seen in the salivary gland. The alveoli are drained by a system of ducts. In the human subject the main pancreatic duct (duct of Wirsung) pierces the duodenal wall obliquely, and joins the common bile duct to form a small chamber — the *ampulla of Vater*. The ampulla opens into the duodenum

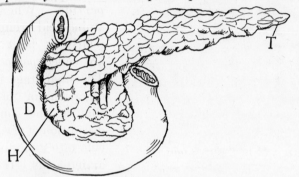

FIG. 124.   Diagram showing the relation of the pancreas to the duodenum.
H, head of pancreas;   T, tail;   D, duodenum.

about $3\frac{1}{2}$ inches below the pylorus. The pancreas contains, besides the cells which form the pancreatic juice, other rounded groups of cells called the *islands of Langerhans*. These lie between the alveoli, and are responsible for the production of insulin (p. 299).

When the gland is resting (as in a fasting animal) the alveolar cells, like the serous cells of the salivary glands, contain numerous granules; these furnish the enzyme of the juice. During secretion the cells discharge their zymogen granules into the alveolar cavity, their cytoplasm, except perhaps for a narrow zone bordering the alveolar cavity, then appearing quite clear (see Fig. 125).

The pancreatic juice. Composition. The pancreatic juice is alkaline in reaction, due to its content of *sodium carbon-*

ate and *bicarbonate*. Its principal ferments are *trypsin* (*pancreatic protease*), *amylopsin* (*pancreatic amylase*), *steapsin* (*pancreatic lipase*) and *rennin*.

Trypsin acts upon the proteoses and peptones formed in the peptic digestion of protein. This ferment is also capable of attacking any protein which has escaped gastric digestion, and converting it to proteoses and peptones. Trypsin breaks

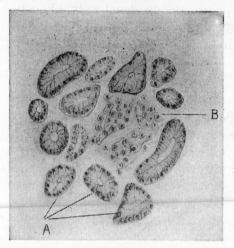

the peptone molecule into smaller groups of amino-acids, named *peptids*. When the amino-acid groups are relatively large they are called *polypeptids*. The final stage in the digestion of protein, that is, the complete disruption of the molecule into its individual amino-acids, is brought about by the erepsin (peptidases) of the intestinal juice. But, the protein molecule can

Fig. 125. Section of pancreas. A, alveolar cells which secrete pancreatic juice. B, islands of Langerhans, responsible for insulin production.

be broken down to groups of four amino-acids (*tetrapeptids*) and three (*tripeptids*) or even two (*dipeptids*) amino-acids during tryptic digestion.

Juice collected directly from the pancreatic duct has very little power to digest protein; but, if allowed to come into contact with the intestinal mucosa, it at once becomes active. The inactive material in the juice is called *trypsinogen;* its activation to trypsin is dependent upon a constituent of the intestinal juice, named *enterokinase* (p. 259). Trypsinogen is also activated by calcium.

Trypsin can act only in an alkaline medium, the optimum pH being around 8.5.

Amylopsin or pancreatic amylase (also called *pancreatic*

diastase) has an action similar to that of the ptyalin in saliva (p. 233), converting starch into maltose. But pancreatic juice has a more powerful starch-splitting action than has saliva; it is also afforded a longer time in which to act. As compared with saliva, pancreatic juice is, therefore, of much greater importance in the digestion of starch. The pancreatic juice contains also some *maltase* which converts a part of the maltose to glucose.

Steapsin, or *pancreatic lipase*, splits fats into their constituents — fatty acids and glycerine (glycerol). If the intestinal contents are alkaline in reaction, the liberated fatty acids combine with alkali to form soaps. The action of the steapsin upon the fat, *tristearin*, is shown in the following equation:

$$C_3H_5(C_{17}H_{35}COO)_3 + 3H_2O = C_3H_5(OH)_3 + 3C_{17}H_{35}COOH$$

tristearin $\qquad\qquad\qquad$ glycerine $\qquad$ stearic acid

$$C_{17}H_{35}COOH + NaOH = C_{17}H_{35}COONa + H_2O$$

stearic acid $\qquad\qquad$ sodium stearate
(soap)

Soap formation in the intestine probably occurs to a very limited extent, for soaps can form only in an alkaline medium; any which may have formed become precipitated again when the medium is acidified. The intestinal contents are slightly acid in reaction except when the pancreatic secretion is at its height. Even then, it is only the duodenal contents which are rendered slightly alkaline, the contents of the rest of the intestinal tract remaining acid.

The optimum pH for the action of pancreatic lipase is around 8.0.

The secretion of pancreatic juice. The secretion of pancreatic juice is brought about by a hormone formed in the mucosa of the small intestine. The existence of this hormone was demonstrated in 1902 by Bayliss and Starling. They found that a hydrochloric acid extract of the duodenal

mucosa, when injected intravenously, caused the secretion
of pancreatic juice. The intravenous injection of the acid
by itself was ineffective. On the other hand, the introduction of hydrochloric acid into a loop of bowel the nerves
of which had been sectioned, and thus isolated from all
connections with the pancreas except through the blood
stream, was followed by a secretion of pancreatic juice. It
was therefore concluded that in the normal course of digestion the acid chyme, after reaching the duodenum, acted

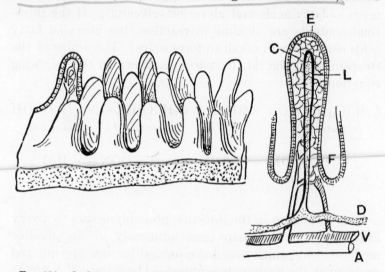

Fig. 126. *On left*, a group of intestinal villi (magnified). *On right*, section of
a villus. A, small artery; C, capillary network; D, lymphatic; E, surface epithelium; F, crypt of Lieberkühn; L, lacteal; V, small vein.

upon the duodenal mucosa to cause the formation and absorption into the blood stream of a hormone which excited
the pancreatic cells. The hormone was named *secretin*.
Later work has shown that extracts of the intestinal mucosa
made with solvents other than acid, namely, water or alcohol,
are active. It has also been demonstrated that bile introduced into the duodenum causes secretin to be absorbed
into the blood stream and induces, in consequence, a secretion of pancreatic juice.

The secretion of pancreatic juice is also brought about through nerve impulses. Stimulation of the vagus nerve causes the secretion of a juice very rich in digestive ferments; rapid exhaustion of the zymogen granules results. Secretin, on the other hand, appears to be responsible mainly for the secretion of the water and inorganic constituents of the juice. It was shown several years ago by Pavlov that psychic factors, the taste and smell of food, were capable of evoking a secretion of pancreatic juice. These reflex secretory effects were particularly well shown by feeding experiments in dogs. However, the psychic or cephalic element plays a much less prominent role in pancreatic than in gastric secretion.

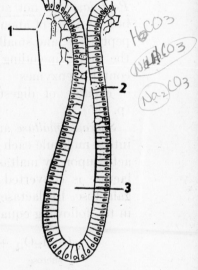

FIG. 127. Microscopical appearance of a crypt of Lieberkühn (semidiagrammatic). 1, villus; 2, goblet cell; 3, cavity of crypt.

The intestinal juice. The mucosa of the small intestine contains great numbers of fine, finger-like processes — the intestinal villi (Fig. 126). These are responsible for the velvety appearance of the intestinal mucosa. The *intestinal juice* or *succus entericus* is secreted by glands — the *crypts of Lieberkühn* — whose mouths open into the intestinal lumen at the bases of the villi (Fig. 127). The epithelial cells covering the villi are continued into the crypts of Lieberkühn. Many of these cells become converted to *goblet cells* (p. 9) which discharge mucus. The cells which secrete the enzymes of the juice are situated toward the bottom of the crypts.

Composition. The intestinal juice is alkaline in reaction, due to its content of *sodium carbonate* and *bicarbonate*. It contains *enterokinase*, the activator of trypsin (p. 256), and the following enzymes.

1. *Peptidases* (*erepsin*), ferments which effect the final breakdown of the protein molecule into its constituent amino-acids.
2. *Sucrase, maltase* and *lactase*, ferments which act upon the disaccharides, *sucrose* (cane sugar), *maltose* (sugar of malt), *lactose* (milk sugar), respectively.
3. *Lipase.*

Peptidases do not act upon unchanged protein. They act best at a pH of about 8. The intestinal wall itself contains peptidases, and small amounts are present in other tissues of the body, including the blood. The intestinal wall also contains enzymes — *nuclease, nucleotidase* and *nucleosidase* — capable of digesting nucleic acid and its derivatives (p. 295).

Sucrase, maltase and *lactase.* Sucrose is split by sucrase into a molecule each of glucose and fructose; maltose when acted upon by maltase yields two molecules of glucose; and lactose is converted into a molecule each of glucose and galactose, by lactase. The hydrolysis of sucrose is shown in the following equation.

$$C_{12}H_{22}O_{11} + H_2O = C_6H_{12}O_6 + C_6H_{12}O_6$$
$$\text{sucrose} \qquad\qquad \text{glucose} \qquad \text{fructose}$$

Lipase, though in lower concentration in the succus entericus than in pancreatic juice, plays an important role, nevertheless, in the digestion of fat. The importance of its action is shown after abolishing the effect of the pancreatic lipase, as by tying the pancreatic duct. Following this procedure at least 70% of the fat in the food undergoes digestion.

The secretion of intestinal juice. Mechanical types of stimulation are particularly effective in causing a secretion of intestinal juice. The contact with the intestinal mucosa of rough indigestible constituents of the food, and especially distension of the intestinal wall itself by food masses, exert a pronounced excitatory effect upon the intestinal glands.

descend

The secretion is brought about reflexly through the nerve plexuses of the intestinal wall. The extrinsic nerves (vagus or sympathetic) do not appear to have any excitatory effect. If either of these nerves exert any effect at all upon secretion, it is of an inhibitory nature. The question whether or not a hormone plays a role in controlling secretion cannot be answered definitely, though there is some evidence that secretin stimulates the intestinal glands as well as the pancreas.

THE BILE

Composition. Human bile is a clear yellow or orange-colored fluid secreted by the liver cells. Its chief constituents are the *bile pigments,* the *bile salts, lecithin, cholesterol, inorganic salts* and *mucin*. The following table gives the average composition of human bile as it is secreted by the liver.

TABLE 12

Water	974.80	
Solids	25.20	
Mucin and pigments		5.30
Bile salts		9.30
Fatty acids from soaps		1.23
Cholesterol		0.63
Lecithin ⎫ Fat ⎭		0.22
Inorganic salts		8.32

Bile collected from the gall-bladder is much more concentrated than liver bile (see p. 264).

The *bile pigments* are called *bilirubin* and *biliverdin.* They are derived from the hemoglobin liberated from red blood corpuscles, which at all times are undergoing disintegration in the blood stream (p. 32). The conversion of the hemoglobin to bilirubin is effected by the reticulo-endothelial cells of the spleen, liver (Kupffer cells), bone marrow and general connective tissues (p. 50). The pigments consist of the porphyrin part of the hemoglobin molecule; that is, the remnant of the molecule after the globin and iron have been

responsible

removed. Bilirubin is not quite identical, however, with the porphyrin in hemoglobin, for the chemical structure of the porphyrin group is also altered. The iron liberated in the conversion of hemoglobin to bile pigment is stored chiefly in the liver and spleen.

Bilirubin ($C_{33}H_{36}N_4O_6$) is an orange-red pigment; it is the chief pigment in human bile and in the bile of dogs. Biliverdin ($C_{33}H_{36}N_4O_8$) is green and constitutes the greater part

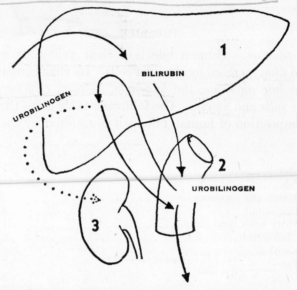

Fig. 128. Diagram illustrating the circulation of bile pigment. 1, liver; 2, intestine; 3, kidney. The dotted line indicates the entrance of urobilinogen into the blood and its excretion by the kidney when the liver is damaged.

of the pigment in the bile of birds and of herbivorous mammals. It is simply an oxidation product of bilirubin.

Upon reaching the intestine, bilirubin undergoes reduction as a result of bacterial action. This reduction product, which gives the yellow-brown color to feces, is called *stercobilinogen* (also called *urobilinogen*). Upon exposure to air a part of the stercobilinogen is oxidized, and is then called *stercobilin* (or *urobilin*). Though the greater part of the stercobilinogen is passed with the feces, a part is absorbed into the portal circulation and returned to the liver, whence it is discharged again in the bile (see Fig. 128). In health, minute amounts of urobilinogen, or none at all, find their way into the general circulation. Any which does escape from the liver into the systemic blood is excreted by the kidney, but the amount is so small that it does not stain the urine; it can be detected only by delicate chemical tests.

The yellow color of the healthy urine is not due, therefore, to this pigment (see p. 210).

The bile salts are *sodium glycocholate* and *sodium taurocholate.* The bile acids glycocholic and taurocholic are produced in the liver by the union of *cholic acid* ($C_{24}H_{40}O_5$) with the amino-acids *glycine* and *taurine* respectively.

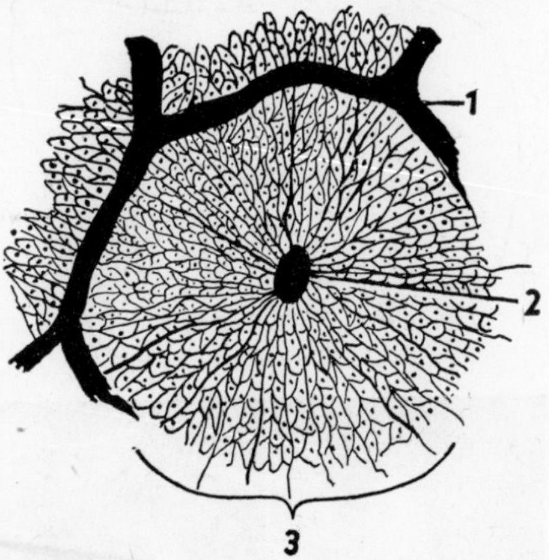

FIG. 129. Diagram of a liver lobule. 1, interlobular vein; 2, central vein; 3, a lobule. The fine lines converging toward the central vein and surrounding the liver cells are the hepatic sinusoids.

The secretion of bile. The cells of the liver are arranged in rows, the so-called liver cords, which radiate like the spokes of a wheel from the centers of the liver lobules (see Fig. 129). On one side of each liver cord is a blood channel (sinusoid), on the other side, a fine vessel (the bile capillary) into which the bile, elaborated by the hepatic cells from the constituents of the blood, is secreted. The bile capillaries join to form larger bile channels which eventually lead into a single vessel — the *hepatic duct.* The liver forms and secretes bile continuously, but, instead of passing directly into the intestine as it is formed, the bile passes into the gall-bladder from which it is discharged from time to time into the duodenum.

The storage of bile and its discharge into the intestine.
The gall-bladder is a small pear-shaped sac which, in the
human subject, has a capacity of about 50 cc. It is situated
on the under surface of the liver (Fig. 130). Leading from
its upper and smaller end is the *cystic duct*. The cystic duct
joins the hepatic duct at an acute angle to form the *common
bile duct*. The latter
joins the pancreatic
duct, the chamber
formed by the fusion
of the two ducts being
known as the *ampulla
of Vater* (p. 255). The
opening of the ampulla
of Vater is guarded by
a ring of muscle called
the *sphincter of Oddi*.
The bile passes from
the hepatic duct into
the common bile duct,
but is prevented from
entering the intestine
by the tonic contrac-
tion of this sphincter.
When the biliary pres-
sure reaches a value of
from 50 to 70 mm. of
water, the bile forces
its way along the cys-
tic duct into the gall-

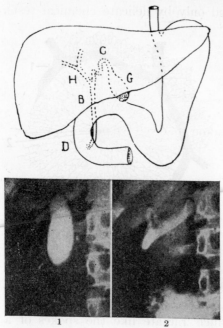

Fig. 130. *Upper cut* shows the relationship
of the gall-bladder and biliary passages to the
liver and duodenum (D). B, common bile duct;
C, cystic duct; G, gall-bladder; H, hepatic
duct. *Below* is an X-ray photograph of the
gall-bladder when distended (1) and after a
meal of fat (2). (After Ivy.)

bladder where it is stored until required. Water and salts
are absorbed from the bile during its stay in the gall-
bladder. The bile of the gall-bladder has, therefore, a much
higher concentration of pigments, bile salts, cholesterol and
lecithin than has bile collected from the hepatic duct. A
ten-fold increase in bile concentration may result from its
stay in the gall-bladder.

The wall of the gall-bladder is composed of a thin layer of smooth muscle lined by mucous membrane. During a meal the gall-bladder contracts, and discharges its contents down the cystic and common bile ducts. The sphincter of Oddi at the same time relaxes, thus permitting free passage of bile into the duodenum. The gall-bladder is supplied with fibers from the vagus and sympathetic nerves, and, undoubtedly, nervous influences play a part in the mechanism of the expulsion of bile. Emptying of the gall-bladder has been observed, for example, following the sight, smell or taste of food. Nevertheless, evacuation of the gall-bladder follows the ingestion of food after all nervous connections of the organ have been severed. The contractions must, therefore, be caused by some material carried in the blood stream. Such a material has been extracted from the mucosa of the duodenum by Dr. A. C. Ivy and his colleagues in Chicago. The hormone, for it must be classed as such, has been named *cholecystokinin*. The injection of a very small amount of this material causes contractions of the gall-bladder in animals or in man. It is quite distinct from secretin, the hormone for pancreatic secretion. Not all types of food are equally effective in causing the production or liberation of the gall-bladder hormone, fatty foods, especially egg-yolk and cream, being by far the most effective. Shortly after a meal of fat the gall-bladder, which may have been quiescent for several hours previously, contracts forcibly and expels its contents into the duodenum. In order to bring about its effect, the fat must first have undergone digestion, apparently. That is to say, the *products* of fat digestion appear to be the essential materials which call the hormonal mechanism into play. Protein and carbohydrate foods are much less effective as stimulating agents than fat.

The functions of the bile. The bile, besides serving as a vehicle for the elimination of pigments and certain other waste products, performs important functions in the intestine. Its main function is concerned with the digestion and absorption of fat. Though the bile does not contain a fat-splitting enzyme, and, therefore, has no direct action upon the digestion of fat, the bile salts, through their power to lower surface tension, aid very greatly in the emulsification of fatty materials in the intestinal contents. The digestion of fat is materially advanced thereby, for the division of the oily materials into small globules increases by several fold the surface exposed to the action of the pancreatic and intestinal lipases. The bile salts have also the property of rendering soluble, in the aqueous fluids of the intestine, the fatty acids liberated during fat digestion. This is the so-called *hydrotropic* action of the bile salts. The dissolved fatty acids, in turn, have the property of lowering surface tension; any soaps which may be formed during digestion, and the cholesterol of the bile, have a similar action. These several factors combine to produce a fine emulsion of fatty material in the small intestine. The bile salts aid fat digestion in another way. They serve as *specific activators* of the pancreatic lipase. That is, quite apart from their emulsifying effect, they enhance very greatly the fat-splitting action of the pancreatic juice. The action of the intestinal lipase is not altered in this specific way by bile.

Bile, important though it is for the efficient digestion of fat, is of still greater importance for *fat absorption*. When bile is excluded from the intestine over 80 per cent of the fat is digested, i.e., split into fatty acids and glycerine. A large proportion of the fatty acids, however, is not absorbed, but appears in the feces. Only recently has the part played by the bile salts in the absorption of fat been elucidated. They unite in the intestine with the fatty acids to form complex compounds which pass readily into the epithelial cells covering the intestinal villi. Here the bile salts are freed again from the union, and are carried in the portal blood to the liver which excretes them again in the bile. This *circulation of the bile salts* has been known for a long time, though its significance was not apparent. The fatty acids liberated from their combination with the bile salts now combine with glycerine which has penetrated into the epithelial cells from the intestinal lumen. The products of fat digestion — fatty acids and glycerine — are thus reunited within the epithelial cells to form neutral fat. The greater part (about 60%) of the synthesized fat passes into the small lymphatics (lacteals) running through the centers of the villi. The course taken by the remaining 40 per cent of the fat is uncertain. It is probably absorbed into the blood of the portal system.

Jaundice (Fr. *jaune* = yellow) or *icterus*. In health, human plasma contains a small quantity of bilirubin. The concentration ranges in different persons and ranges from 0.1 to 0.5 mgm. per 100 cc. The bilirubin of the plasma is that which, having been formed by the reticulo-endothelial cells from hemoglobin of disintegrated erythrocytes, is on its way to the liver for excretion.

When excessive amounts of bilirubin are present in the plasma, the skin, mucous membranes and whites of the eyes are stained yellow. The condition is called *jaundice* or *icterus*. Bilirubin appears also in the urine and sweat, but does not pass into the saliva. An abnormally high concentration of plasma bilirubin may be due to excessive amounts of the pigment being produced, the liver and excretory channels being normal. On the other hand, the quantity of pigment formed in the body may be within normal limits, but the function of the liver is impaired as a result of some toxic or infective process, and does not remove bilirubin readily from the plasma. Again, the bile passages may be obstructed; the bile is then prevented from reaching the intestine. There are therefore three types of jaundice, (1) *hemolytic*, (2) *toxic or infective*, and (3) *obstructive*.

Hemolytic jaundice is seen in conditions which cause increased destruction of red cells, e.g., pernicious anemia, hemolytic anemia and poisoning with certain hemolytic agents. This type of jaundice is not uncommon in the newborn infant; it persists for four or five days after birth. The baby comes into the world with an excess of red cells, which undergo destruction during the first few days, the concentration of bilirubin in the plasma being thus increased to the point at which jaundice appears. The condition is harmless, and indeed may be looked upon as a physiological phenomenon. In the hemolytic types of jaundice the stools are dark, due to the increased pigment excretion; urobilin may appear in the urine.

In the *toxic and infective* types of jaundice the liver cells are injured by some poison or infective process which interferes with their ability to eliminate bile pigment.

Obstructive jaundice is most often the result of blockage of the common bile duct by a gallstone within its lumen, or by a tumor pressing upon it from without. In this type the discoloration of the skin and mucous membranes is usually intense. The feces are pale, being usually described as "clay colored," because pigment is, of course, excluded from the intestinal tract. The urine is usually deeply colored with bilirubin.

Movements of the small intestine. Three types of movement occur in the small intestine, (a) *peristaltic*, (b) *segmenting* and (c) *pendular*.

Peristaltic movement (*peristalsis*). This kind of movement is not restricted to the small intestine, but is characteristic of hollow muscular tubes in general. It has been mentioned as occurring in the esophagus during the third stage of swallowing, and in the pyloric part of the stomach. It is also seen in the large intestine, as well as in the ureter, Fallopian tube and common bile duct. The movement consists of a ring-like contraction of the muscular wall of the tube. The annular contraction, as it travels downwards, causes a certain degree of constriction of the bowel which sweeps before it any material within the lumen (Fig. 131). The movement is readily started by a mechanical, an electrical or a chemical stimulus. The most powerful stimulus is distension of the bowel, i.e., stretching of the muscle fibers.

Filling of the bowel with food material provides just such a stimulus, the contraction occurring immediately behind the stimulated region. Peristaltic movements may follow one another at regular and fairly frequent intervals, the intestinal contents being moved steadily but gently along the canal. At other times a brisk peristaltic contraction appears which travels

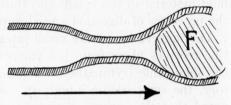

FIG. 131. Diagram illustrating peristalsis. F, food mass. Arrow indicates the direction of the movement.

rapidly along the tube but, after moving the food a considerable distance, may not be repeated for some time. This is called the *peristaltic rush*. Especially strong stimulation, the action of a cathartic or an irritant poison, for example, may set up a peristaltic rush which travels throughout the length of the small bowel. Such a movement may also be initiated reflexly from the esophagus during swallowing, or from the stomach.

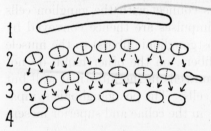

FIG. 132. Diagram showing the effect of the segmenting movements upon the food mass in the intestine. A series of constrictions of the bowel wall suddenly divides the column of food (1) into a number of segments (2). Each of the latter is bisected again the next instant, the adjacent halves fusing as in 3, and being redivided as in 4. The process is repeated over and over again until the food is thoroughly mixed. (After Cannon.)

The segmenting movements are rhythmical constrictions of the intestine which serve to break up and knead the food, to mix it thoroughly with the intestinal juices, and to bring the intestinal contents in contact with fresh absorptive surfaces. These movements also increase the blood and lymph flow in the bowel wall but exert no propulsive action upon the food. They occur at the rate of from 20 to 30 per minute (see Fig. 132).

The pendular movements are simple constrictions of the intestinal wall. They move up and down the bowel for short distances, giving a to and fro movement to the semi-fluid material in the canal, and thus lending further aid to the processes of digestion and absorption.

The innervation of the small intestine. The small intestine receives fibers from the vagus (parasympathetic) and the splanchnic (sympathetic) nerves. The vagus is excitatory, the sympathetic inhibitory (see Pl. 7 A). It will be noted that the actions of these nerves upon the intestine, as compared with the actions upon the heart, are reversed. The bowel wall itself contains two nerve plexuses. One of these lies between the two muscular coats (circular and longitudinal) of the intestine and is called *Auerbach's plexus;* ganglion cells are found among the network of nerve fibers. The other plexus, known as *Meissner's,* lies in the submucosa (Pl. 7 B). The vagal fibers connect with the ganglion cells of Auerbach's plexus; the impulses are thence conveyed by the axons of these cells (postganglionic fibers) to the muscle fibers. The sympathetic fibers, on the other hand, do not form junctions with ganglion cells in the intestinal wall but pass directly to the muscle cells. The postganglionic sympathetic fibers arise from cells in the celiac and superior mesenteric ganglia (p. 464).

Though the bowel movements are influenced by impulses travelling over the vagus and splanchnic nerves, they are not dependent upon them, for the three types of intestinal movement continue after all nerves of extrinsic origin have been sectioned. The peristaltic movements are then carried out through the intrinsic nervous mechanism (plexuses of Auerbach and Meissner). The segmenting and pendular movements are dependent upon the property of rhythmical activity of the muscle fibers themselves, and not upon any nervous mechanism. They continue in a strip of intestinal muscle after its nerve plexuses have been removed or paralyzed by cocaine.

The ileocolic sphincter. The small intestine opens into the upper part of the cecum. The ring of muscle surrounding the opening is called the ileocolic sphincter. It controls the passage of the ileal contents into the cecum and prevents or hinders the reflux of material into the ileum, thus protecting the small bowel from contamination by the putrefactive bacteria which flourish in the large intestine. The sphincter opens and closes during digestion, permitting gushes of ileal contents to enter the cecum. During fasting it remains closed for long periods, but opens within a few minutes after a meal. This indicates a reflex action initiated by the entrance of food into the stomach. The ileocolic sphincter receives motor fibers through the sympathetic; inhibitory fibers have not been demonstrated.

The contents of the ileum are semifluid in consistency and acid in reaction. After its passage through the large intestine the intestinal material becomes more plastic in character as a result of the absorption of water; its acid reaction undergoes little change.

The movements and innervation of the large intestine. Food material reaches the cecum about $4\frac{1}{2}$ hours after a meal. Rhythmical movements resembling the segmenting movements in the small intestine may be seen occasionally in this part of the large intestine, but peristaltic contractions are absent. Regular and frequently recurring peristaltic contractions are absent also from the rest of the large intestine. At certain long intervals, however, a strong peristaltic wave commencing in the upper end of the ascending colon moves swiftly over the transverse colon. This *mass movement*, as it is called, is analogous to the peristaltic rush in the small intestine; it empties the transverse colon, sweeping the material into the descending and pelvic colons. The pelvic colon and lower part of the descending colon serve as a storehouse for the feces until the desire to defecate is aroused.

The cecum, ascending colon and the first third or so of the transverse colon are supplied with motor fibers through the vagus nerves. The remainder of the large intestine, including the rectum and the anal canal, is supplied with motor fibers through the pelvic nerves (parasympathetic from the 2nd, 3rd and 4th sacral segments of the spinal cord). The inhibitory fibers to the entire large intestine are derived from the sympathetic. These two sets of nerves act upon the internal anal sphincter in a reverse fashion; the sympathetic is excitatory, the pelvic nerve inhibitory. As stated previously, the sympathetic is also the motor nerve to the ileocolic sphincter. The external anal sphincter is under voluntary control through the pudendal nerves.

In health, the antagonistic effects of the parasympathetic and sympathetic nerves to the large bowel are nicely balanced. But the balance is sometimes upset. Relaxation and weakness of the walls of the descending and pelvic colons result from overactivity of the sympathetic innervation. The tone of the internal anal sphincter, on the other hand, is exaggerated. The colon is unable to empty itself effectually, and dilatation of its lumen, often to enormous proportions, follows. This condition is called *megacolon* (G. *mega* = large) or *Hirschsprung's disease*. When, on the other hand, the pelvic nerve (parasympathetic) is hyperactive the descending colon becomes firmly contracted; its lumen is obliterated. This — the so-called *spastic colon* — is one cause of chronic constipation (p. 274).

Defecation (evacuation of the bowels) is a reflex act initiated by the passage of feces into the rectum. Normally the rectum is empty, except just before defecation; feces are forced into it from the pelvic colon by a mass movement. The latter movement is often started by the entrance of food into the stomach — *gastrocolic reflex*. This reflex is responsible for the desire to defecate so often experienced a short time after a meal, especially breakfast. The distension of the rectum as it becomes filled with feces acts as a stimulus to afferent nerve endings in the rectal wall. The impulses set up are conveyed to a center in the sacral part of the spinal cord. The efferent nerve fibers pass to the wall of the descending and pelvic colons, rectum and the internal anal sphincter, via the pelvic nerves, and to the external anal sphincter and the striated muscle lying in relation to the rectum, via the pudendal nerves. A higher center for defecation is situated in the medulla oblongata. This is connected to the lower center by tracts of fibers in the spinal cord. The intrarectal pressure necessary to start the defecation reflex is from 40 to 50 mm. Hg.

The movement of defecation consists of a powerful peristaltic contraction of the descending and pelvic colons and rectum, assisted usually by a voluntary contraction of the abdominal muscles, and of the striated muscles lying in relation to the rectum (levatores ani and rectococcygeus muscles). Relaxation of the anal sphincters occurs reciprocally with the contraction of the bowel wall.

Constipation. Persons vary considerably in the frequency with which their bowels are evacuated. In some a bowel movement occurs two or even three times daily, while others may feel no discomfort if an interval of two days or more elapses between movements. The majority of healthy persons have an evacuation daily, usually in the morning after breakfast. Owing to this variability, it is difficult to give a precise definition of constipation. However, when the interval between bowel movements is greater than twenty-four hours and the subject, as a result, suffers distress or discomfort, e.g., headaches, digestive disturbances, etc., or if the feces are abnormally dry and hard, and the evacuation of the bowels difficult, constipation certainly exists.

Constipation is caused most commonly by bad habits. As mentioned on p. 272, the desire to empty the bowel is aroused by the passage of feces into the rectum, and the stimulation of afferent nerve endings in the bowel wall. The act can, however, be voluntarily restrained and, when this is practiced, the rectal wall accommodates its capacity to the bulk of the feces (postural tone, p. 227); the afferent nerve endings are no longer adequately stimulated, and the desire to defecate passes. The retained feces become dry and hard, as a result of the absorption of water. When the habit of postponing defecation in this way is persisted in, the rectum, which normally, except just before evacuation, is empty, contains feces most of the time; it becomes less sensitive to distension, and its muscle, as well as that of the pelvic colon, loses its tone. It is well known that the reflex mechanisms governing the emptying of the bowel are amenable to "training." When the habit of emptying the bowels at a certain hour each day is practised for a while, the desire to do so tends to recur regularly at this time.

Other causes of constipation are (a) *a diet* which leaves too little unabsorbed residue (and so fails to stimulate intestinal activity) or one which contains too little fluid. (b) *A colon which absorbs too readily* and thus causes undue drying of the feces. (c) Hypertonic state of the muscle of the colon — *spastic constipation;* the transverse and descending colons are the seat of a strong tonic contraction which impedes the passage of feces.

The general effects of constipation upon the sense of well-being are too familiar to require description. But their cause is a subject upon which there is much misunderstanding. We hear a great deal of poisons formed in the intestinal tract, and the dire effects which they are supposed to have upon the body. Intestinal intoxication is glibly spoken of, and advertisements in the daily press exhort one to irrigate the colon, in order to remove the noxious materials. There is no doubt whatever that small amounts of powerful poisons are formed in the large intestine as a result of the action of bacteria upon amino-acids which have escaped absorption in the small intestine. Some of these substances — known generally as *amines* — are formed by the removal of a molecule of carbon dioxide from such amino-acids as *alanine, tyrosine, histidine,* etc. Among the more potent of such amines are *ethylamine* (from alanine), *histamine* (from histidine) and *tyramine* (from tyrosine). However, the production of such poisons is a perfectly normal process, and there is nothing more certain than that they cannot be held responsible for the headache, bad breath, furred tongue or any of the other effects of constipation. The body is provided with mechanisms for rendering innocuous the poisons formed in the colon. The first line of defense raised against such substances is in the wall of the bowel itself; here some are destroyed or changed into harmless compounds. The second and most important detoxicating mechanism is in the liver, where the toxic bodies are combined with sulphuric acid or with glycuronic acid. The resulting compounds (*indoxyl sulphuric acid* and *glycuronates*) pass from the liver to the kidney for excretion.

To what then are the symptoms of constipation due? It is now generally conceded that they are of reflex origin. Afferent impulses set up in the distended colon or rectum, though ineffectual in precipitating the defecation reflex, produce reflex effects in other parts of the body, particularly the stomach and blood vessels. The headache is probably due to the effect upon the intracranial blood vessels. The rapid relief from the ill effects of constipation which follows evacuation of the bowels is a common experience, and, in itself, argues strongly against such effects being of toxic origin, for it is inconceivable that poisons could be freed so swiftly from the blood stream. To quote the pertinent comment of Dr. Alvarez, who has devoted much time to a study of the question, "A drunken man does not at once become sober when the whisky bottle is taken from him."

ABSORPTION FROM THE INTESTINAL TRACT

The absorption of food materials is practically confined to the small intestine. Alcohol is absorbed from the stomach, but water, glucose and other substances are absorbed to a negligible extent through the gastric mucosa. Water and, to a certain extent, mineral salts are absorbed from the large intestine; as a result, the intestinal contents undergo a considerable reduction in bulk in their passage through this part of the intestinal tract.

The alimentary tract from a physiological point of view must be considered as lying outside of the body proper. Food material ingested and held within the digestive tube cannot be said truly to have entered the body until it has passed across the intestinal mucosa and been absorbed into the blood. Just as the skin covers the outer surface of the body, so the mucosa of the gastro-intestinal tract constitutes its inner surface. An examination of the interior of the small intestine shows how well this part of the lining of the body has been fashioned for increasing the area exposed for the absorption of food materials. The mucosa is raised into circular folds (*plicae circulares*) which in the upper part of the intestine may be nearly a third of an inch in depth. These and the intestinal villi (p. 259), especially the latter, increase enormously the total absorbing surface (see Fig. 135). It has been estimated that the number of villi in the human small intestine is around 5,000,000 and the absorbing surface not far short of 10 square meters — more than five times the skin surface. The center of each villus is occupied by an arteriole, a venule, and a lymph vessel or *lacteal*. The arteriole leads into a network of capillaries lying just beneath the epithelial covering of the villus. The central vessels are surrounded by areolar tissue together with bundles of smooth muscle fibers. If the intestinal mucosa of a living animal is examined with the low power of the microscope, the villi will be found to be in ceaseless motion, swaying or lashing from side to side, and lengthening and shortening alternately. These movements, by their constant agitation of the intestinal fluids in the immediate neighborhood of the villi, aid very materially the digestive and absorptive processes.

It will be recalled that the intestinal mucosa is impermeable to the large molecules of the three foodstuffs, carbohydrates (starch and the disaccharides cane sugar, maltose and lactose), proteins and fats, but permits the free passage of the smaller molecules, glucose, amino-acids, fatty acids and glycerine liberated by enzyme action. The absorption of these materials is not, however, a simple process of diffusion, in which the intestinal mucosa acts merely as a passive membrane. On the contrary, the epithelial cells covering the villi take an active part in the absorption, as is evidenced by the observation that an increase in oxygen consumption and in carbon dioxide production accompanies the process. Furthermore, the absorption, as shown by the following experiment, is selective. When the three sugars glucose, galactose and fructose, in equal concentrations, are placed in a loop of bowel immersed in saline, glucose passes through the intestinal wall more rapidly than does galactose, and galactose more rapidly than fructose, provided that the intestinal mucosa remains viable and uninjured. After injury or death of the mucosa the three sugars pass through it at equal rates, i.e., simply by diffusion.

After passing through the epithelium of the villi, the glucose and amino-acids are absorbed into the network of blood vessels mentioned above; fat, synthesized in the epithelial cells from fatty acids and glycerine, passes, for the most part, into the lymph channels.

The formation of the feces. The feces are not, simply and solely, unabsorbed residues of the food, but are made up largely of materials *excreted* from the blood. During starvation, for example, the bulk of the feces may not be greatly less than at ordinary times, and a loop of bowel isolated from the rest of the intestine becomes filled after a few days with a pasty mass indistinguishable from ordinary feces. Bacteria make up about 9 per cent of the feces; the other main solid constituents are food residues, which vary considerably in amount with the proportion of indigestible material (chiefly cellulose) in the diet, fats, nitrogenous substances and minerals eliminated from the blood, together

with epithelial cells and leucocytes, shed from the intestinal
mucosa. A very small proportion of digestible food appears
in the feces. In other words, practically all the protein, fat
and carbohydrate which is eaten is absorbed, the food residues of the feces consisting almost entirely of indigestible
substances. Vegetable material, since its framework is composed of cellulose, contributes more to the feces than do
other foods. This indigestible material or "roughage," as
it is commonly termed, serves a useful purpose in that it acts
as a mechanical stimulus, increasing the motility as well as
the secretions of the bowel wall.

CHAPTER VII

METABOLISM AND NUTRITION

Introductory. Metabolism is a general term applied to the various chemical processes, whatever their nature, taking place in living tissues, e.g., the oxidation of food materials with the liberation of energy, the decomposition of compounds into more elementary principles, the chemical transformation of one material into another, and the synthesis of complex compounds from others of simpler constitution, as in the processes of tissue repair and growth, or in the manufacture of internal secretions and enzymes. Reactions involving decompositions are embraced by the term *catabolism;* those of a synthetic nature are referred to as *anabolism.*

Though some of the reactions taking place in the body are accompanied by the absorption of heat (endothermic reactions), in the great majority, e.g., oxidations, heat is evolved (exothermic reactions). The sum total of all the chemical reactions occurring in the body is referred to as *general metabolism*, and is expressed in terms of heat given out by the body in a given time. Those chemical changes, whether of a catabolic or an anabolic nature, which a particular substance, e.g., carbohydrate, fat, protein, purine, calcium, etc., undergoes in the body is referred to as *special metabolism.*

GENERAL METABOLISM

The sun is the source of all energy on the earth. Plant life through its possession of the green coloring matter, *chlorophyl,* is capable of utilizing the energy of sunlight to form carbohydrate material from the carbon dioxide of the atmosphere and water drawn from the soil. The animal body, of course, cannot make direct use of solar energy; it must depend upon the energy stored by the plant or upon that provided by the tissues of other animals. The food — fat, carbohydrate and protein — derived from either of these sources therefore represents stored or potential energy. The carbon of the food, after absorption from the intestinal tract, is oxidized in the tissues. Energy is liberated thereby for muscular activity and for maintaining the vital functions, e.g., the action of the heart, the movements of the gastro-intestinal tract, the excitability of nervous tissues, etc. Thus, the various foodstuffs are to the body as fuel is to an engine; they represent a certain amount of potential energy which the body can convert to other forms of energy — mechanical, electrical, chemical and thermal.

When the body is at rest, that is, when no external work is being performed, the energy liberated from food materials appears ultimately as heat. A heat unit, the large Calorie,[1] is therefore employed as a measure of the energy liberated in the animal body. A Calorie is defined as the quantity of heat required to raise a kilogram of water from 15° to 16° C. Of the energy expended during muscular exercise, as in lifting a weight, walking, etc., about 25 per cent appears as work, the remaining 75 per cent is converted to heat.

The law of the conservation of energy states that, though one form of energy is convertible into any other form, the sum total of the energy in the universe remains constant — energy cannot be created or destroyed. This law holds true for the animal body. That is to say, a given quantity of food when completely oxidized in the tissues yields its entire store of potential energy to the body — the energy intake balances the energy output, as measured by the heat produced and the work performed.

The food may not be completely oxidized in the body; a part may be stored, or, as with protein (see p. 282), a part resists oxidation and is excreted. Nevertheless, an energy

---

[1] The large Calorie used in physiology is written with a capital C to distinguish it from the small calorie used in the physical laboratory.

balance can be struck, if any gain in weight is noted (stored energy) and the quantity of unoxidized residue of protein food in the urine is determined.

Energy is stored in the body as carbohydrate (glycogen) and fat, mainly the latter, whenever the food intake exceeds the energy needs of the body, i.e., when the energy of the food is not all expended in maintaining the vital processes, or in performing muscular work. This is the commonest cause of overweight (obesity). This store of energy, in the form of fat and carbohydrate, is readily available and will be drawn upon should the energy value of the diet at any time fall below the body's energy requirements. During a *prolonged* period of fasting, after the stores of glycogen and fat have been drawn upon and exhausted, the protein of the tissues is utilized to furnish energy.

The bomb calorimeter. The potential energy of a foodstuff is determined by measuring the heat evolved when it is burned in an instrument known as a *bomb calorimeter* (see Fig. 133).

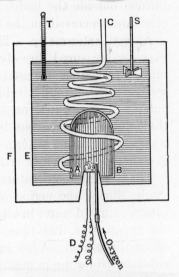

FIG. 133. The bomb calorimeter for determining the energy (calorie) value of foodstuffs (diagrammatic) A, food material placed in the bomb (B) and ignited by means of an electric spark through the wires D. The products of combustion find exit through C. The heat of combustion is absorbed by a known volume of water in E, a brass vessel. F, outer jacket separated from E by heat-insulating material. S, stirrer; T, thermometer. (After Thomsen.)

The heat generated by the animal body may be determined in a manner identical in principle. Now, the quantity of heat liberated by 1 gram of carbohydrate or fat is the same whether the material is burned in the body or in the bomb calorimeter; 4.1 Calories are generated in the oxidation of 1 gram of carbohydrate, 9.3 Calories in the oxidation of 1 gram of fat. Protein, on the other hand, does not undergo complete combustion in the body. The nitrogenous part of the molecule resists oxidation and is excreted in the urine, mainly as urea (p. 291). A gram of protein, therefore, evolves less heat when catabolized than when burned outside the body. In the latter instance, 5.3 Calories are generated, in the former only 4.1.

Animal calorimetry. The heat generated by the body may be measured directly — *direct calorimetry.* The animal is placed in a closed chamber with double insulated walls; coils of copper tubing, through which water is circulated, are situated on the inner walls of the chamber; thus the heat given out by the animal is absorbed. The temperature of the water as it enters and leaves the chamber is recorded by thermometers.

The rise in temperature of the water in degrees centigrade, during the period of observation, multiplied by the total volume of water in kilograms which has passed through the chamber in that time, gives in Calories the heat given off by the animal. A few calorimeters of this type have been constructed for use in man, but their great expense precludes their general use. Indirect calorimetric methods are therefore employed almost entirely in metabolism studies upon the human subject.

Indirect calorimetry. When carbohydrate undergoes combustion in the body the carbon is oxidized to carbon dioxide (CO_2) and the hydrogen to water (H_2O). Thus:

$$C_6H_{12}O_6 + 6O_2 = 6CO_2 + 6H_2O$$
glucose

The body, therefore, reverses the reaction carried out by the green plant which, as already stated, synthesizes carbohydrate from carbon dioxide and water. In the complete oxidation of a given weight of carbohydrate, whether in air or in the tissues of the body, the quantity of oxygen used and of carbon dioxide produced have definite and constant values.

It is also known that for every 1000 cc. of oxygen consumed when carbohydrate is the material oxidized, 5.047 Calories of heat are evolved. That is to say, there is a constant relationship between the quantity of oxygen consumed and the heat evolved. It is evident, therefore, that the heat production of an animal subsisting upon carbohydrate food could be determined, provided that the quantity of oxygen consumed by the animal were known. The relationship between the oxygen consumption and the heat production varies, however, with the type of food undergoing combustion. Carbohydrate material as compared with fat is relatively rich in oxygen. Thus, $C_3H_5(C_{18}H_{33}O_2)_3$ is the formula for *triolein*, a common fat. More oxygen must, therefore, be supplied from a source outside the food itself for the complete oxidation of the carbon and hydrogen in fat than for the oxidation of these elements in an equal quantity of carbohydrate. The consumption of 1000 cc. of oxygen, when fat is oxidized, is accompanied, therefore, by a smaller heat production, namely, 4.686 Calories as compared with the figure (5.047) given above for carbohydrate. The corresponding value for protein is 4.485 Calories.

In order, therefore, to calculate the heat production of the body from the oxygen consumption, one must know the nature of the food mixture (the proportions of carbohydrate, fat and protein) which is being metabolized. This information is obtained from the *respiratory quotient*, which will now be explained.

The respiratory quotient. The volume of carbon dioxide eliminated by the body during a given time, over the volume of oxygen absorbed, is called the respiratory quotient (R.Q.). Thus:

$$\frac{\text{Vol. } CO_2 \text{ eliminated}}{\text{Vol. } O_2 \text{ absorbed}} = \text{R.Q.}$$

From the equation given on page 282 it will be seen that, when the food undergoing combustion is carbohydrate, the volume of carbon dioxide eliminated and of oxygen absorbed

TABLE 13

(After Zuntz and Schumberg, modified by Lusk)

Non-protein respiratory quotient	Calories per liter O₂	Calories derived from	
		Carbohydrate	Fat
		per cent	per cent
0.707	4.686	0	100
0.71	4.690	1.10	98.9
0.72	4.702	4.76	95.2
0.73	4.714	8.40	91.6
0.74	4.727	12.0	88.0
0.75	4.739	15.6	84.4
0.76	4.751	19.2	80.8
0.77	4.764	22.8	77.2
0.78	4.776	26.3	73.7
0.79	4.788	29.9	70.1
0.80	4.801	33.4	66.6
0.81	4.813	36.9	63.1
0.82	4.825	40.3	59.7
0.83	4.838	43.8	56.2
0.84	4.850	47.2	52.8
0.85	4.862	50.7	49.3
0.86	4.875	54.1	45.9
0.87	4.887	57.5	42.5
0.88	4.899	60.8	39.2
0.89	4.911	64.2	35.8
0.90	4.924	67.5	32.5
0.91	4.936	70.8	29.2
0.92	4.948	74.1	25.9
0.93	4.961	77.4	22.6
0.94	4.973	80.7	19.3
0.95	4.985	84.0	16.0
0.96	4.998	87.2	12.8
0.97	5.010	90.4	9.58
0.98	5.022	93.6	6.37
0.99	5.035	96.8	3.18
1.00	5.047	100.0	0

is equal. When, for example, 100 grams of glucose are oxidized, 75 liters of oxygen are absorbed and 75 liters of carbon dioxide produced. The R.Q. is therefore $\frac{75}{75} = 1$. In the complete combustion of fat, which is relatively poor in oxygen, the volume of oxygen used (200 liters per 100 grams) is greater than the volume of carbon dioxide produced (142 liters per 100 grams). The R.Q. is therefore $(\frac{142}{200} =)$ 0.71. The respiratory quotient for protein is 0.80 and for alcohol 0.67.

On an ordinary mixed diet, the R.Q. of the human subject is around 0.85. After fasting for 12 hours it has a value of 0.82. When, as in the fattening of farm animals, fat is being formed from carbohydrate, that is, an oxygen-rich material is being transformed into one poor in oxygen, the R.Q. rises above 1. The heat equivalents of a liter of oxygen at different respiratory quotients are given in table 13.

These respiratory quotients are for mixtures of fat and carbohydrate only (non-protein respiratory quotients). For very precise work, the Calories derived from the metabolism of protein are calculated separately from the quantity of nitrogen excreted in the urine. But, as a matter of fact, only a negligible error is introduced when the figures in the table are used for calculating the heat production, that is, without any attention being paid to the protein metabolism.

The basal metabolic rate (B.M.R.). The heat production of the body 12 hours after the last meal and with the body at complete rest, that is, with the subject lying quietly, is called the *basal metabolism* or the *basal metabolic rate*. It is usually expressed in Calories per square meter of body surface per hour. It may be determined from either the quantity of carbon dioxide eliminated, or from the quantity of oxygen consumed over a known period of time; but the figure for the latter is now most commonly employed (see Fig. 134). The heat value of a liter of oxygen for various metabolic mixtures, as indicated by the respiratory quotients, is given in table 13. As a rule the R.Q. is not actually

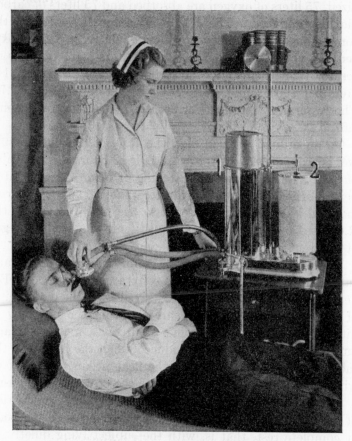

FIG. 134. Showing method of determining the basal metabolic rate by means of the Benedict-Roth apparatus (courtesy of Warren E. Collins, Inc., Boston). Oxygen is inhaled from the spirometer (1) through one of the large-bored rubber tubes. The quantity consumed is recorded on the paper-covered rotating cylinder (2). The subject expires through the other rubber tube. The expired air passes through a canister placed within the spirometer and filled with soda lime which removes the carbon dioxide. The B.M.R. is calculated from the oxygen consumption alone.

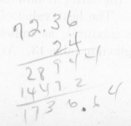

determined, but is taken to be 0.82, for this is its value during fasting, under which conditions, as just stated, the B.M.R. is determined.

Sample calculation of the B.M.R. from the oxygen consumption. If the oxygen consumption over a period of 10 minutes is 2.500 liters, then the total heat production (at an R.Q. of 0.82) is $2.500 \times 4.825 \times \frac{60}{10} = 72.36$ Calories. If the subject has a surface area of say, 1.8 square meters, which is

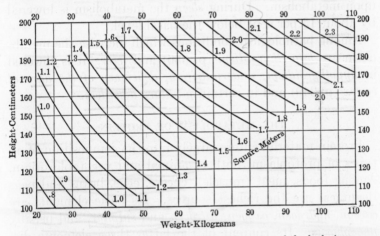

FIG. 135. Du Bois' chart for obtaining the surface area of the body in square meters (as indicated by the slanting lines) from a subject's height and weight. For example, a person 170 centimeters (approximately 5 ft. 8 in.) tall and weighing 70 kilograms (154 lbs.) has a surface area of 1.8 square meters.

the figure for the average male adult, then the hourly heat production per square meter of body surface is:

$$\frac{72.36}{1.8} = 40.2 \text{ Calories.}$$

The surface area of the body bears a relationship to the height and weight and may be obtained for a given person from the chart shown in Fig. 135.

In young healthy adult males the basal metabolic rate is around 40 Calories per square meter of body surface per hour. It is lower in women and higher in children, being around 50 Calories during the first year, and diminishing gradually throughout life. It reaches the adult value at about 20 years; from then it declines more slowly, reaching a value of around 36 Calories in old age.

The physiological conditions which raise the metabolism are *muscular exercise*, a *low environmental temperature* and the *ingestion of food*, especially protein. The term *specific dynamic action* is applied to this stimulating effect of food upon metabolism. During *sleep* the metabolism is lowered by about 15 per cent below the basal level.

Among pathological conditions which increase the metabolism are *hyperthyroidism* (p. 336) and *fever;* it is lowered in *hypothyroidism, undernutrition, deficiency of the adrenal cortex* (p. 349) and in certain *pituitary disorders*.

THE METABOLISM OF PROTEIN

Protein material enters largely into the composition of all types of protoplasm, both of animal and vegetable origin. Among foods, meat (muscle), cheese, eggs, beans and peas (legumes) are the richest sources. Its basic elements are *carbon, hydrogen, oxygen, nitrogen* and *sulphur,* and usually *phosphorus*. Its content of the latter three elements distinguishes it from either fats or carbohydrates, which contain only carbon, hydrogen and oxygen. The body is dependent almost entirely upon protein for its supplies of nitrogen and sulphur, and mainly for its phosphorus.

The amino-acids. The protein molecule is made up of a number of amino-acids linked together. Some twenty different amino-acids have been discovered. The simplest of these is called *glycine* or *glycocol*, which consists of acetic acid in which a hydrogen atom is replaced by an NH_2 group. Thus:

$$CH_3 \qquad\qquad CH_2 - NH_2$$
$$|\qquad\qquad\qquad\quad |$$
$$COOH \qquad\qquad COOH$$

acetic acid   glycine

The majority of the other amino-acids are constructed upon the same general plan. They contain a fatty acid, e.g.,

propionic, valerianic, caproic, succinic, etc., and one or two
NH_2 (amino) groups. An incomplete list of the amino-acids
with their empirical formulae is given in the following table:

TABLE 14

A partial list of the amino acids

Glycine (or glycocoll), $C_2H_5NO_2$, or amino-acetic acid
Alanine, $C_3H_7NO_2$, or α-amino-propionic acid
Leucine, $C_6H_{13}NO_2$, α-amino-isocaproic acid
Aspartic acid, $C_4H_7NO_4$, or amino-succinic acid
Glutamic acid, $C_5H_9NO_4$, or α-amino-glutaric acid
Arginine, $C_6H_{14}N_4O_2$, or δ-guanidin-α-amino-valerianic acid
Lysine, $C_6H_{14}N_2O_2$, or α-ϵ-diamino-caproic acid
Cystine, $C_6H_{12}N_2S_2O_4$, or di-cysteine or di-(β-thio-α-amino-propionic acid)
Phenylalanine, $C_9H_{11}NO_2$, or β-phenyl-α-amino-propionic acid
Tyrosine, $C_9H_{11}NO_3$, or β-parahydroxy-phenyl-α-amino-propionic acid
Tryptophane, $C_{11}H_{12}N_2O_2$, or β-indole-α-amino-propionic acid
Histidine, $C_6H_9N_3O_2$, or α-amino-β-imidazol-propionic acid

There are several types of protein which contain more than
15 *varieties* of amino-acids, but the assortment varies between different types of protein. The *total number* of amino-acids in a protein molecule may be 200 or more. Such
proteins are composed, therefore, of molecules of relatively
enormous size. The molecules of certain other proteins,
such as the protamines, contain much fewer amino-acids
and are correspondingly smaller. There is thus a very wide
variation in the size of the molecules of the different types
of protein. Egg albumin, for example, has a molecular
weight of around 35,000, whereas the molecular weights of
some other proteins are in the neighborhood of 200,000. A
few have a molecular weight of over a million. The shape of
the protein molecule also varies. The molecules of some proteins such as the myosin of muscle and of that forming tendons and ligaments (collagen) are long and fiber-like in
shape, while others, such as those of serum albumin, are
globular. A short classification of proteins is given in table 15.
The growth of body tissue in the young animal, and the repair of protein structure in the adult body are dependent upon
the protein of the diet. But since the tissue protein of a given

TABLE 15

Classification of proteins

Simple proteins

Albumins, e.g., *ovalbumin* of egg-white, *serum albumin*, *lactalbumin* and certain *vegetable albumins*

Globulins, e.g., *serum globulin, fibrinogen, vitellin* of egg-yolk and *legumin* of peas

Glutelins, e.g., *glutenin* of wheat

Gliadins, e.g., *gliadin* of wheat, *hordein* of barley and *zein* of maize

Scleroproteins, e.g., *keratin* of hair, *elastin, collagen* and *gelatin* of connective tissues

Histones, e.g., the *globin* in hemoglobin

Protamines, in spermatozoa, e.g., *salmine* in spermatozoa of salmon

Conjugated proteins, i.e., proteins containing a non-protein group

Nucleoproteins, protein combined with nucleic acid (p. 295)

Chromoproteins, protein containing a pigment group, e.g., *hemoglobin*

Glycoproteins, protein containing a sugar group, e.g., *mucin*

Phosphoproteins, proteins containing a phosphorus group (other than nucleoproteins), e.g., *casein* of milk

Derived proteins, products of the action of acids, heat, or enzymes upon proteins

Metaproteins

Coagulated proteins

Proteoses

Peptones

Peptids, dipeptids, tripeptids and *polypeptids*

animal is different in constitution from the protein of its food, the latter as a rule must be completely broken down into its constituent amino-acids before it can be utilized for building body tissue.

The utilization of protein in the construction of body tissue may be compared to the building of a number of houses of different types from materials obtained from the wrecking of other structures. Each brick and stone in the old buildings is separated, and then sorted and carted to the new sites. Some of this building material will be more suitable for one type of house, some more suitable for other types. Other materials again cannot be used at all, and are therefore discarded as refuse. The new buildings, though constructed from materials taken from the old, will, therefore, be quite different in structure and general plan.

The amino-acids from this analogy are sometimes called the "building stones" of the protein molecule. Under the action of the peptidases of the intestinal juice (p. 260) the protein molecule is completely demolished, in the sense that it is broken up into its constituent amino-acids. The separate amino-acids are absorbed into the blood stream and carried therein to the tissues. Each tissue chooses those which it can make use of, rejecting others.

Those amino-acids which cannot be utilized by the body are broken up; the carbon part of the molecule (i.e., the fatty acid group) is oxidized to carbon dioxide and water, thus furnishing energy to the body; the nitrogen goes to form urea which is excreted in the urine. The removal of the nitrogen group from the amino-acid molecule is called *deamination;* this process occurs in the liver. Certain amino-acids not used for the construction of body protein may, after undergoing deamination, be converted to glucose which is then either oxidized or stored in the liver as glycogen (p. 298). In diabetes the glucose formed from amino-acids is largely excreted in the urine. The diabetic subject, therefore, continues to excrete sugar though he receives no sugar or other carbohydrate; even during fasting he continues to excrete glucose, which is then derived from the protein of his own tissues.

The *urea* in the urine is formed mainly as a result of the deamination of amino-acids composing the protein of the food. Raising the protein content of the diet, therefore, increases the output of urea in the urine and vice versa. But the urea is not entirely derived from the diet; a small part is formed from the nitrogen released by the breakdown of body protein, for the tissues are constantly undergoing disintegration and repair. *Creatinine,* another nitrogenous constituent of the urine, is also derived from tissue protein, but unlike urea it is derived almost entirely from this source. Varying the protein of the diet, therefore, exerts little effect upon the excretion of creatinine. A small quantity of nitrogen, combined in various ways, is also eliminated from the body by passing through the wall of the intestine into the feces.

During starvation or upon a protein poor diet the break-down of body protein of course continues. The body loses nitrogen through the so-called "wear and tear" of tissue protein, but receives none to make good the loss. That is, the output of nitrogen in the urine and feces exceeds that of the food; the body is then said to be in *negative nitrogen balance*. Similarly, the nitrogen output will exceed the intake, and the body will be in negative nitrogen balance, if the food protein is inadequate in amount or of poor quality (i.e., if its assortment of amino-acids is unsuitable for repairing body protein, the non-utilizable amino-acids being excreted in the urine). In the healthy adult, receiving an adequate diet, the nitrogen excreted just balances the nitrogen taken in the food; that is, the nitrogen lost as a result of the break-down of tissue protein is replaced from the food; the remainder of the food nitrogen is excreted. The body is then said to be in *nitrogen equilibrium*.

During growth, after a period of starvation, in pregnancy, in muscular training or in convalescence from some disease which has caused the excessive destruction of body protein, the quantity of nitrogen excreted is *less* than that taken in the food, provided the protein intake is adequate. The body is then in *positive nitrogen balance*. In other words, nitrogen is retained for the construction of body tissue.

The "wear and tear" quota of protein metabolism is reduced by carbohydrate food. For example, the nitrogen excretion is considerably less on a diet containing carbohydrate but no protein, than in starvation. The carbohydrate diminishes the breakdown of tissue protein. This is spoken of as the *sparing effect* of carbohydrate upon protein metabolism.

We have seen that only part of the protein molecule can be oxidized in the body and thus provide energy. Civilized man cannot subsist on protein food alone, because he cannot eat and digest enough to supply the required energy. One gram of protein furnishes 4.1 Calories. A man of aver-

age size has a daily energy expenditure under basal conditions of about 1400 Calories, and between 2500 and 3000
Calories when engaged in light occupation. Now, lean meat
is about 20 per cent protein. Therefore about

$$\frac{1400}{4.1} \times \frac{100}{20} = 1700 \text{ grams}$$

or nearly four pounds of meat would need to be eaten daily,
in order to obtain from protein the energy required by the
body, even at rest. From three to four times this amount
of meat would be required to furnish the energy for heavy
work. On the other hand, a carnivorous animal such as the
dog, which has an energy expenditure of some 600 Calories,
can consume two or three pounds of meat in a few minutes
and can, therefore, derive its total caloric requirement from
such food. The Eskimos are also accustomed to the consumption of relatively enormous quantities of meat and fat.

The relative nutritive values of different proteins. Proteins are not all of equal value in nutrition, for the reason
that the various types differ widely in their amino-acid constitution. Those which possess an amino-acid assortment
most closely resembling that in body proteins possess the
highest nutritive value. Generally speaking, these are of
animal origin, e.g., the proteins of milk, eggs and meat.
Some proteins, such as *gelatin, zein* (in maize) are incomplete,
that is, they lack certain amino-acids which are essential for
growth, and for the maintenance of nitrogen equilibrium in
the adult. Others, such as *gliadin* (in wheat), *hordein* (in
barley) and *legumin* (in peas), will serve to repair body protein in the adult but will not support growth, since they
lack certain essential amino-acids or contain them in insufficient amounts. Animals which receive one or other of
these as their sole protein fail to grow. Wheat, peas and
barley, however, contain other proteins which make good
the amino-acid deficiencies of those which are incomplete
(see table 16). *Lactalbumin* of milk, and *ovalbumin* of egg-

white, the *proteins of meat* and *glutenin* (of wheat) contain
all the essential amino-acids.

TABLE 16

Character of proteins in some common foods

Food	Chief proteins present	Amino-acid constitution
Milk and cheese	Casein	Complete but low in cystine
	Lactalbumin	Complete
Corn (maize) ...	Zein	Lacks lysine and tryptophane and is low in cystine
Eggs...........	Ovalbumin	Complete
	Ovovitelline	Complete
Meat	Albumin	Complete
	Myosin	Complete
Peas	Legumin	Incomplete, low in cystine
Wheat	Gliadin	Incomplete, lacks lysine
	Glutenin	Complete
Gelatin	Gelatin	Incomplete, lacking tryptophane and tyrosine; very low in cystine

In part from M. S. Rose, Foundations of Nutrition.

An essential amino-acid may be defined as one which
must be present in the diet in order that the growth of young
animals shall proceed normally, and that the health of both
young and old animals shall be maintained. In a sense,
probably all the amino-acids are essential in one way or
another for nutrition, but some can be synthesized in the
body, e.g., *glycine*, or formed from others furnished in the
diet.

PURINE METABOLISM

Uric acid ($C_5H_4N_4O_3$), a nitrogenous compound present
in normal urine and blood, is a purine derivative. Purines
are constituents of nucleic acid and this, in turn, is found
in the body combined with protein, the compound being
called *nucleoprotein*. Nucleoprotein is present in the nuclei
of cells generally, and such tissues as those of thymus, liver,

kidney, pancreas and other glandular structures are particularly rich in this material.

Nucleic acid is constituted of four compounds called *nucleotides*. A nucleotide contains a molecule each of phosphoric acid, sugar (a pentose) and a purine (*adenine* or *guanine*) or a pyrimidine group. The nucleoprotein of food is broken down by intestinal enzymes into protein and nucleic acid. The latter is split into its constituent nucleotides by an enzyme in the intestinal juice, called *nuclease*. The nucleotides are absorbed and, through the actions of specific tissue enzymes, are broken into their components. Phosphoric acid is first removed, leaving a pentose-purine (or pyrimidine) compound called *nucleoside*. The sugar is then split off. The fate of the purine derivatives, adenine and guanine, only need concern us here. These, as a result of deamination (splitting off of NH_3) and oxidation by tissue enzymes, give rise to uric acid.

Uric acid is of especial interest because in gout, a painful arthritic condition, its excretion is reduced and its concentration in the blood increased. Uric acid, in the form of crystals of sodium urate, is deposited in the tissues surrounding the affected joint. Meats such as liver, sweetbreads, kidney, etc., which are rich in nuclear material and consequently in nucleic acid, tend, therefore, to aggravate the symptoms of gout.

The origin of uric acid is briefly summarized in the following scheme.

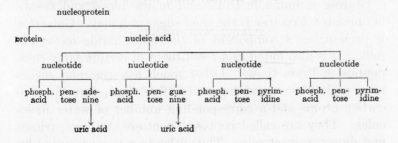

CARBOHYDRATE METABOLISM

Classification of the carbohydrates. Carbohydrates (sugars, starches, etc.) are composed of carbon, hydrogen and oxygen. The last two elements are present in the same proportions as in water. Thus, the three sugars *glucose* (or *dextrose*), *fructose* (or *levulose*), and *galactose* contain six molecules of water and six atoms of carbon, as shown by their formula, $C_6H_{12}O_6$. These sugars are, therefore, called *hexoses*. Though they have a common empirical formula, i.e., the same number of each type of atom, the positions of the atoms in the molecule differ. The structural formulas of glucose, fructose and galactose are given below for comparison.

Glucose   Fructose   Galactose

Glucose is found in fruits and in the blood and tissues of animals. Fructose is the chief sugar of honey. Galactose is present, as a component of the disaccharide *lactose*, in milk. It is also found as a constituent of certain fatty compounds in brain tissue. Other much less common sugars have molecules containing seven, five, four, three or two carbon atoms and a corresponding number of water molecules. They are called heptoses, pentoses, tetroses, trioses and dioses, respectively. Thus a heptose is represented by the formula $C_7H_{14}O_7$, a pentose by $C_5H_{10}O_5$, a tetrose by $C_4H_8O_4$ and so on. Octoses, nonoses and decoses, though not known in nature, have been prepared in the laboratory.

Sugars belonging to the class just outlined are called *monosaccharides*, and may be represented by the general formula $C_m(H_2O)_m$, in which m has the value 2, 3, 4, 5, 6, 7 and so forth.

Disaccharides are sugars composed of two monosaccharide molecules less a molecule of water. *Sucrose* (cane and maple sugars), *maltose* (sugar of malt) and *lactose* (sugar of milk) belong to this group. Though a disaccharide may be made up of other monosaccharides, these three, which are important food elements and therefore of physiological interest, consist of hexoses either of the same or of different kinds. Their formula is $C_{12}H_{22}O_{11}$. They are split (hydrolyzed) into their constituent monosaccharides by the actions of specific enzymes in the intestine. Thus —

$$C_{12}H_{22}O_{11} + H_2O = 2C_6H_{12}O_6$$

Sucrose is hydrolyzed into a molecule each of glucose and fructose, maltose into two molecules of glucose, and lactose into glucose and galactose.

Polysaccharides are made up of a large number of monosaccharide molecules, which may be either pentoses or hexoses, less water. The polysaccharides of physiological importance, namely, the *vegetable starches*, *glycogen* ("animal starch"), *cellulose* and *dextrins* are constituted of glucose molecules, and are therefore given the general formula of $(C_6H_{10}O_5)_x$. Upon hydrolysis they yield glucose.

The history of carbohydrate in the body. Glycogen was discovered by the great French physiologist, Claude Bernard, in 1857. It is found in traces in most tissues of the body and in fairly large amounts in liver and muscle. Muscle may contain from 0.10 to 1.0 per cent of glycogen and, since approximately one-half the total weight of our bodies is muscle, it will be appreciated that the total quantity of muscle glycogen is very considerable. The liver often contains as much as ten or fifteen per cent of its wet weight of glycogen and, though it makes up only about three per cent of the body weight, its total glycogen content is comparable with that of the muscular tissues.

Glucose is found in all body tissues; blood contains approximately 0.1 per cent, but there is considerable variation in the amount in health as well as in disease. It is the most important single carbohydrate with which we have to deal in physiology. As such it can be used as food, passing unchanged from the small intestine into the blood, while complex carbohydrates, such as the disaccharides and polysaccharides (starches and glycogen), must first be hydrolyzed into glucose or other hexoses before they can be absorbed.

Glucose (as well as fructose and galactose) passes from the intestine into the blood of the portal vein, and is deposited in the liver as glycogen. The conversion of glucose to glycogen is a specific function of the liver cells, and is termed *glycogenesis* (literally, glycogen formation). The glucose in the blood is maintained at a fairly constant level by the reconversion of glycogen to glucose, which is then discharged into the general circulation. This process is termed *glycogenolysis* (literally, glycogen breakdown).

Muscle glycogen is derived from the glucose of the blood. During muscular contraction energy is furnished mainly by carbohydrate production; the glycogen breaks down; *hexose diphosphate* is formed which, in turn, yields lactic acid (p. 407). Lactic acid — as well as the three hexoses, glucose, fructose and galactose — is a glycogen former. A part of the lactic acid produced diffuses into the blood and is deposited as glycogen in the liver, as well as in the heart muscle and certain other tissues. Glucose is also formed from the amino-acids of food protein; in starvation or upon a protein-free diet it is formed from body protein. This process is carried out in the liver, and is termed *gluconeogenesis* (literally, the new formation of sugar).

The carbohydrate cycle just outlined may be represented in the following scheme.

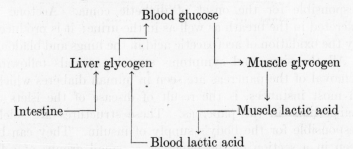

Oxidation of carbohydrate. While it appears probable that glucose is the only sugar oxidized directly in the tissue cells, there may be some utilization of fructose in this manner. The pathway of oxidation of glucose is still debatable.

Insulin and carbohydrate metabolism. Insulin, the anti-diabetic hormone, is produced in the pancreas; when this gland is completely removed from animals a condition known as pancreatic diabetes rapidly develops. This is characterized by a high blood sugar (0.2–0.5 per cent, as compared with the normal of 0.1 per cent), and excretion of sugar in the urine. The extent of the increase of blood sugar (*hyperglycemia*), and of the loss of sugar in the urine (*glucosuria*) is proportional to the carbohydrate content of the diet, but even on a diet composed entirely of protein, or during fasting, the depancreatized animal excretes a considerable amount of sugar. The sugar reserves of the body, i.e., liver glycogen, are rapidly lost. Sugar is then made from tissue protein, the animal losing weight as a result. The fat depôts are also called upon, but it cannot be stated definitely whether the fat is converted to sugar or is always burned directly. At any rate, the increased rate of breakdown of fat results in the accumulation of ketone bodies in the blood (*ketosis*) and urine (*ketonuria*).

The ketone bodies are β-hydroxybutyric and acetoacetic acids and acetone. The two acids may be regarded as intermediate products of the breakdown of fatty acids. Aceto-acetic acid possesses toxic properties, and is held largely responsible for the onset of diabetic coma. Acetone is excreted in the breath as well as in the urine; it is produced by the oxidation of acetoacetic acid in the lungs and bladder.

All the signs and symptoms seen in animals following removal of the pancreas are seen in human diabetes which, in most instances, is the result of disease of the islets of Langerhans in the pancreas. These structures are solely responsible for the body's supply of insulin. They can be seen in a section of the pancreas as small groups of cells lying here and there between the pancreatic alveoli. In diabetes there is also an accumulation of neutral fat in the blood. This phenomenon is known as *lipemia*.

The disturbances of carbohydrate metabolism character-istic of the diabetic state may be explained on the basis of (1) failure of utilization of carbohydrate or (2) abnormal rate of production of sugar from non-carbohydrate sources. Perhaps both processes play a part.

The discovery of insulin has not solved the problem of the etiology of clinical diabetes, but has provided a valuable physiological tool and an effective therapeutic agent. In-sulin administered subcutaneously or intravenously elimi-nates all the signs of diabetes in experimental animals or in human patients. Its action is to promote the storage of glycogen in muscles and liver, to depress the wasteful new production of sugar in the liver, and to increase the oxidation of carbohydrate. The hyperglycemia and glucosuria dis-appear. Ketosis is eliminated. The rapid loss of body tissues is checked.

Insulin has now been prepared in crystalline form; it is a protein containing eight or more amino-acids. The highly purified insulin is absorbed quickly, when administered sub-cutaneously, and efforts have been made to lengthen the period of absorption, i.e., to prolong its action. The most satisfactory preparation thus far developed for this purpose is protamine zinc insulin, which is made by adding protamine and zinc to insulin. Protamine is a simple protein obtained from fish sperm (see table 15).

While a deficiency of insulin causes diabetes, overproduction is responsible for a clinical condition called *hyperinsulinism*. The outstanding features of this disease are a low blood sugar (*hypoglycemia*), and the symptoms incident thereto. A similar condition may be produced in animals by an overdose of insulin. The signs of hypoglycemia are neuromuscular hyperexcitability and hunger. The excitability increases, leading to involuntary twitching of muscles, and later to generalized convulsions. Glucose is the best antidote for an excess of insulin. Other carbohydrates are effective in proportion to their ability to form glucose.

Other hormones and carbohydrate metabolism. The relation of other endocrines to carbohydrate metabolism is dealt with in chapter VIII. The effect of adrenaline is described on p. 345, of the anterior lobe of the pituitary on p. 356 and of thyroxine and cortin on pp. 350 and 337, respectively.

The nervous system and carbohydrate metabolism. In 1855 Claude Bernard showed that injury to the brain which involved the pons and the cerebellum as well as the floor of the fourth ventricle produced hyperglycemia and glucosuria. It appears probable that these lesions set up nerve impulses which caused the breakdown of liver glycogen. This may be due to direct stimulation of autonomic fibers in the liver or may be an indirect result of adrenaline liberation. It will be appreciated that interference with the nerve supply of any of the glands whose secretions affect carbohydrates may exert a profound influence on the metabolism of these substances.

FAT METABOLISM

The neutral fats. The common fats of vegetable and animal tissues are compounds of the higher fatty acids, *palmitic* ($C_{16}H_{32}O_2$), *stearic* ($C_{18}H_{36}O_2$) and *oleic* ($C_{18}H_{34}O_2$), with the triatomic alcohol *glycerol* ($C_3H_5(OH)_3$). Each molecule of glycerol (glycerine) is combined with three molecules of one or other of these fatty acids. The resulting compound (or ester) is called a *neutral fat* or *triglyceride*. Depending upon the particular fatty acids in the triglyceride molecule, the three chief fats are named *tripalmitin, tristearin* and *triolein*, respectively.

The fatty tissues of animals consist of connective tissue in which is deposited a mixture of neutral fats, triolein being in the greatest proportion. Tripalmitin is present in smaller and tristearin in least amount.

The triglycerides are hydrolyzed by the intestinal enzymes (lipases) into their constituents — fatty acids and glycerine. In the presence of alkali, fat is decomposed, the fatty acid then reacting to form soap. Thus,

$$C_3H_5(C_{18}H_{35}O_2)_3 + 3NaOH = 3CH_3(CH_2)_{16}COONa + C_3H_5(OH)_3$$

| tristearin | sodium hydroxide | sodium stearate (a soap) | glycerol |

Fat-like substances — sterols and phospholipids or phosphatides. The *sterols* are secondary alcohols which are present in animal and vegetable tissues in combination with fatty acids. This group of compounds (*sterol esters*) has a fatty or wax-like consistency.

Cholesterol is widely distributed throughout animal tissues, both as such and as *cholesterol esters*. It was first isolated from gallstones and is an important constituent of bile, hence its name (G. *chole* = bile), and of blood. It is closely related chemically to cholic acid, vitamin D and the sex hormones. Cholesterol and its esters are especially abundant in the sheaths of nerves, brain tissue and skin.

Ergosterol is found in plant tissues; it acquires antirachitic properties upon irradiation with ultraviolet light.

The *phospholipids* or *phosphatides* are essential constituents of animal and vegetable cells. Brain, muscle, liver, bile, milk and eggs contain these substances in especially large amounts. To this class of substance *lecithin, cephalin* and *sphingomyelin* belong. Upon hydrolysis they yield fatty acids, phosphoric acid and a nitrogenous base. The nitrogenous element in lecithin is *choline*.

Animal fat is formed from the fat of the food as well as from carbohydrate. It represents a store of energy which the body can draw upon as need arises (e.g., during a prolonged period of fasting). The fat of the food is, of course, not deposited in the tissues unchanged. The fatty acids derived from the ingested fat are recombined with glycerol in such proportions as to produce a fat characteristic of that of the animal's own body (i.e., with the proper mixture of the three types of neutral fat).

It will be recalled that the caloric value of fat (9.3) is more than double that of either carbohydrate or protein, which makes it the ideal energy-storing material. Furthermore, fatty tissue is almost pure fat, whereas carbohydrate and protein materials are laid down in the tissues with a large quantity of water.

The phospholipids are believed to play an important part in fat absorption and fat metabolism. Fatty acids, it is thought, must first be transformed to phospholipids before they can be transported across cell membranes.

The liver and fat metabolism. This organ occupies such a central position in any consideration of fat metabolism that particular attention must be directed to it. The liver is the principal if not the only site of production of the ketone bodies (see p. 299). Under a great variety of pathological conditions neutral fats accumulate in the liver. In diabetes, in anemias and after various types of poisoning, large deposits of fats are found in this organ. This finding suggests that normally fat is being transported steadily from the depôts to the liver but that under the above-mentioned conditions either an excess is brought to the liver or the cells of this tissue are unable to deal with a normal amount.

Oxidation of fats. The fact that the long chain fatty acids are oxidized very readily in the body makes the detection of intermediate products a difficult matter. The observations of Knoop in the intact animal suggest that the so-called β-oxidation takes place, i.e., that there is successive removal of groups of two carbon atoms. The fact that the ketone bodies, i.e., those with four carbon atoms, are formed only from fatty acids with an even number of carbon atoms obviously supports the theory of β-oxidation. The results of *in vitro* experiments, however, suggest that rupture of fatty acid chains takes place at various points in the chain. It is thus apparent that our knowledge of fat oxidation is very incomplete.

The digestion and absorption of fat are dealt with in chapter VI.

THE REGULATION OF BODY TEMPERATURE

The temperature of the human body is determined by placing a thermometer in the mouth, axilla (armpit) or rectum. In health the mouth temperature is around 98.6° F. The temperature in the axilla is about a degree lower than this, and the rectal temperature about a degree higher. The body temperature does not remain at a constant level throughout the twenty-four hours, but is from 1° to 1.5° lower in the early morning than in the late afternoon. The cause of this diurnal fluctuation in body temperature is unknown.

The body temperature represents the balance struck between the heat generated by the active tissues, mainly the muscles and liver, and that lost from the body to the environment. It is remarkable how constant the body temperature is under varying conditions. Little change in body temperature occurs though the air temperature rises to 100° F. or falls to zero, nor does the extra heat produced during light work occasion a rise in temperature. Strenuous muscular exercise may, however, cause a temporary rise in temperature of from 1° to 4° F.

Animals such as mammals and birds (warm-blooded animals) which can maintain a constant body temperature against variations in the temperature of their environment are called *homoiothermic*. Those species, e.g., fish, frogs and reptiles (cold-blooded animals), which are unable to regulate their body temperature are called *poikilothermic*. Their body temperature is that of the environment (see Fig. 136).

Heat balance. It is obvious that the quantity of heat produced in the body (see p. 280) must just balance the quantity lost to the environment. If the body produced more heat than it gave off, the retained heat would cause a rise in temperature; if it lost more than it generated, the temperature would fall. The daily heat production, that is, the metabolism, of the adult human body is around 3000 Calories. This quantity of heat is dissipated in the following ways.

Physical factors in temperature control. 1. *Radiation, convection and conduction.* Through these three physical processes the body,

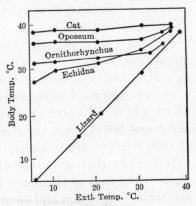

Fig. 136. Variation in body temperature of different types of animals by exposure for two hours in an environment rising from 5° to 35° C. (After Martin.)

like any other warm object, loses heat to the cooler air surrounding it, and to any cooler objects in contact with it or in its immediate neighborhood. The heat lost in this way can be increased or diminished through variations in the quantity of blood flowing through the skin. On a hot day, for example, the vessels of the skin dilate; more blood is, therefore, brought from the deeper parts of the body to the surface, and heat loss accordingly increased. In cool weather the vessels of the skin constrict, a greater proportion of the total blood volume is distributed to the internal structures; heat loss is thereby reduced. In very cold weather, though the skin vessels are constricted, vessels of the nose, ears, fingers, toes, etc., are dilated in order that these outlying parts shall be supplied with warm blood, and thus prevented from freezing. Another important factor is the variation in blood volume which results from changes in environmental temperature. The blood is increased in volume by heat, and is thus capable of absorbing and conveying more heat to the surface of the body for elimination through radiation, convection and conduction. Cold causes the reverse effect, namely, a reduction in blood volume and, in consequence, a diminished heat loss.

2. *Evaporation of water from the lungs and skin.* The latent heat of evaporation of water is about 0.6 Calorie, that is, this quantity of heat is absorbed in the vaporization of 1 cc. of water. Under ordinary atmospheric conditions about 300 cc. of water are vaporized from the lungs daily, and about 500 cc. from the skin. This represents a heat loss of $(800 \times 0.6 =) 480$ Calories.

It is clear that when the environmental temperature is higher than that of the body, heat cannot be dissipated by radiation, convection and conduction; the body would gain rather than lose heat were it entirely dependent upon these processes. At such temperatures, evaporation of water from the skin and lungs plays the leading role in the regulation of body temperature. The sweat glands are stimulated, and visible sweating appears when a rise of from 0.5 to 1° F. in body temperature occurs. The rise in body temperature may result from an increase in the temperature of the environment or from increased heat production, as in muscular exercise.

The effect upon the sweat glands is brought about through a center in the brain from which they receive impulses through the sympathetic nerves. A rise in temperature of the blood supplying the center is the most potent factor in causing the secretion of sweat. This is shown by the fact that heating the carotid artery causes sweat secretion from the toe pads of the cat, though the paws themselves are kept cool. Sweating may also be induced reflexly, i.e., from the stimulation of afferent nerves in the peripheral tissues, skin, muscles, etc.

In dogs and cats functional sweat glands are absent from the body surface, being confined to the skin of the pads of the paws. In these animals rapid breathing (panting) and, in consequence, increased vaporization of water from the lungs, is relied upon to increase heat loss at high temperatures.

3. Of the total heat lost from the body, over 95 per cent is eliminated through (1) and (2) discussed above. The remaining 5 per cent is lost in the urine and feces, and in raising the inspired air to body temperature.

The quantities of heat lost daily in each of the several ways just described are given (in round numbers) in the following table.

		Calories
(a)	Radiation, convection and conduction	2100
(b)	Evaporation from the skin	500
(c)	Vaporization of water from the lungs	300
(d)	Warming inspired air	80
(e)	Urine and feces (i.e., heat of these excreta over that of the food)	50
	Total daily heat loss	3030

Variations in the quantity of heat lost through these physical factors are capable, under ordinary circumstances, of maintaining the body temperature at the normal level, but at very high environmental temperatures or when, as in strenuous muscular effort, heat production is very greatly increased, the mechanisms of temperature control may be inadequate; the body temperature then rises.

The chemical factors in temperature control. At low environmental temperatures the physical mechanisms are incapable alone of reducing heat loss sufficiently to prevent a fall in body temperature. Chemical regulation then comes into play, i.e., heat production increases. The body's fires, so to speak, are fanned. The point in the temperature scale where physical factors are aided by chemical means in the control of body temperature is called the *critical temperature*. It varies of course with the nature and thickness of the clothing, but for the naked human body it is around 30 C. (84 F.).   Cold therefore acts as a powerful stimulus to metabolism.   The greater heat production in response to cold is brought about mainly by increased tone and, in some instances, by involuntary contractions of the skeletal muscles (shivering), and of the smooth muscle of the skin (goose-

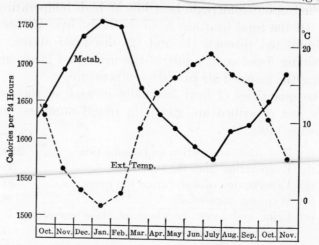

Fig. 137.   Showing the effect of external temperature upon metabolism.
(From Martin after Gessler from observations upon himself.)

flesh).   A person when cold usually indulges, also, in some form of muscular activity — walking, swinging his arms, or stamping his feet — which very materially increases his heat production (see Fig. 137).

In cold climates protein food, owing to its specific stimulating effect upon metabolism (*specific dynamic action*, p. 288), gives valuable assistance to the chemical mechanism of temperature control.   On the other hand, a high protein diet is unsuitable in hot weather, since the greater heat production which it induces throws an additional burden upon the mechanisms responsible for heat dissipation.

Heat-controlling centers.   The main center for the control of body temperature is situated in the fore part of the hypothalamus — that region at the base of the brain near the origin of the pituitary stalk. Section through the brain behind this area renders an animal poikilothermic, i.e., incapable of maintaining the height of its temperature independently of the temperature of its environment. This operation also paralyzes the skeletal muscles; the power to increase heat production is therefore lost. Stimulation of the center causes a rise in temperature. The center exerts its influence upon body temperature through the autonomic nervous system causing vasoconstriction or vasodilatation, sweating, contraction of smooth muscle in the skin, and the liberation of adrenaline from the adrenal medulla which, as mentioned on p. **345**, stimulates heat production.

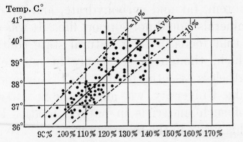

Fig. 138.   Chart from Du Bois showing the effect upon metabolism of an increase in body temperature (fever).

Fever or pyrexia. A rise in body temperature above the normal level, unless of a temporary nature as in strenuous exercise, or as a result of exposure to a high air temperature, is called fever. The highest body temperature compatible with life is between 107° and 108° F. The rise in temperature is due primarily to an *impairment of the mechanisms for heat elimination,* e.g., increased blood volume, vasodilatation and sweat secretion, and not to increased heat production. At the commencement of a fever, for example, the skin is pale and dry; the metabolism is not increased. Heat elimination is reduced; heat is therefore retained in the body and the temperature rises. Having reached a certain height, the temperature remains fairly steady, for now heat elimi·

nation keeps pace with heat production; a balance is struck, but at a higher level than in health. Though, as just mentioned, increased heat production is not responsible for the onset of the fever, the higher temperature induced through heat retention causes, in turn, greater heat production, for the heat generated in the body is the result of chemical reactions, mainly oxidative in nature and, like chemical reactions in general, they are accelerated by a rise in temperature (see Fig. 138). A rise of 1° F. in body temperature increases the metabolism by 7 per cent.

THE VITAMINS

It was discovered some years ago that diets composed of purified protein, fat and carbohydrate, and containing the essential minerals would not support life. It was concluded, therefore, that foods in their natural state contained substances which, though present only in minute amounts, were nevertheless essential to life. Sir F. Gowland Hopkins, of Cambridge University, was among the first to suspect the presence of such materials in natural foods. In 1906 he expressed his views in the following words. "No animal can live upon a mixture of pure protein, fat and carbohydrate; and even when the necessary inorganic material is carefully supplied, the animal still cannot flourish." The chemical nature of these materials was unknown, so they were called simply *accessory food factors*. Later these vital elements were thought to belong to a group of nitrogenous substances known as amines. They were therefore named *vitamines*. It was soon found, however, that this conclusion was false, and it was suggested that the terminal "e" be dropped. The generic term *vitamin* was then generally adopted. There are a number of different vitamins. Each is designated by a letter of the alphabet. The vitamins A, D, E and K are soluble in fats and fat solvents (the fat-soluble vitamins); vitamin B_1, the B_2 complex and vitamin C are soluble in water (the water-soluble vitamins).

A summary of the vitamins is given below.

Vitamin A (antixerophthalmic)

Vitamin B complex { B₁ or thiamin (antineuritic)

chief factors of the B₂ complex { riboflavin
nicotinic acid
pyridoxin (B₆)
pantothenic acid }

Vitamin C (antiscorbutic)
Vitamin D (antirachitic)
Vitamin E (antisterility)
Vitamin K (antihemorrhagic)

Vitamin A ($C_{20}H_{30}O$), the antixerophthalmic vitamin. The chief sources of vitamin A are fish liver oils (e.g., cod and halibut), dairy products and certain vegetable foods. The following is a list of materials especially rich in this vitamin.

Fish liver oils
Butter and cream
Egg yolk
Carrots, yellow maize (corn), spinach, peas, beans and other yellow and green vegetables

It is not strictly correct to say that plants contain vitamin A. They contain rather a yellow pigment called *carotene* ($C_{40}H_{56}$) which, after being taken into the animal body, is converted by the liver into vitamin A according to the following equation:

$$C_{40}H_{56} + 2H_2O = 2C_{20}H_{30}O$$

Carotene, being a precursor of the vitamin, is called *provitamin A*. The green and yellow parts of plants contain more of the provitamin than do the paler portions. The content of vitamin A in milk and butter varies with the carotene content of the fodder of the cow. After ingestion the carotene is transformed in part to vitamin A and secreted as such in the milk. A part of the carotene is also secreted unchanged. Vitamin A itself is colorless, so that a pale milk may be just as rich a source of the vitamin as one more deeply colored. The vitamin A of fish liver oils is also derived ultimately from plant life. Small invertebrates of the sea, known as copepods, feed upon marine plants, and serve in turn as food for small fish. The latter convert the carotene, originally formed by the plant, into the vitamin. Larger fish devour the smaller fish and store the vitamin so obtained in their livers.

Vitamin A deficiency. When the diet is deficient in vitamin A (and in the provitamin), the epithelium lining the respiratory and alimentary tracts, as well as the ducts of certain glands, becomes abnormal. It undergoes transformation to the stratified squamous type. Such mucous surfaces are especially susceptible to infection. Inhibition of lachrymal secretion, followed by drying of the cornea (*xerophthalmia*), is an outstanding effect of vitamin A deficiency. In some instances softening of the cornea (*keratomalacia*), which may progress to ulceration and consequent blindness, results. Vitamin A is necessary for

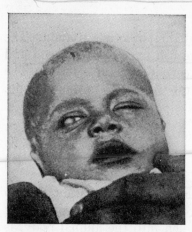

Fig. 139. Xerophthalmia in a child caused by vitamin A deficiency. (After Bloch.)

the regeneration of the visual purple of the retina which, in health, readily takes place after the eyes have been exposed to light (p. 474). *Night blindness* (*hemeralopia*) is, therefore, a common accompaniment of vitamin A deficiency. A sufferer from this disorder sees well in bright light, but is quite or almost blind in dim light. Vitamin A deficiency may lead also to degenerative changes in the long fiber tracts of the spinal cord, and in certain of the peripheral nerves.

The diets of persons on this continent are rarely deficient in vitamin A to the point where serious abnormalities supervene; but in India, China and other Eastern countries the diet is frequently deficient in this and other vitamins. Also in the lumber camps of the north country, especially during the winter months, and in Newfoundland villages, night blindness and other signs of vitamin A deficiency occasionally make their appearance. Infants reared upon a badly planned

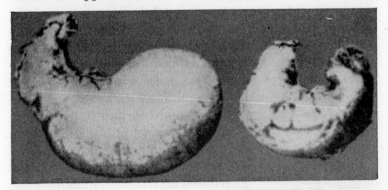

artificial diet may also suffer from deficiency of vitamin A (Fig. 139).

The vitamin B complex. Beriberi is a disease of rice-eating countries. Its chief features are paralysis of the limbs (due to degenerative changes in the peripheral nerves — *polyneuritis*), dilatation of the heart and edema. It was shown by Eikjman, a physician working in the Dutch West Indies, to be due to a dietary deficiency. He

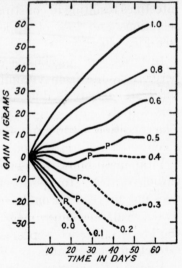

FIG. 140. *Upper figure* (after Harris): *left*, distended stomach in vitamin B₁ deficiency due to loss of tone of gastric muscle; *right*, normal stomach. *Lower figure*: curves showing effect of graded quantities of vitamin B₁ upon growth of nine groups of rats; P, point where polyneuritis developed; broken lines are drawn from the points where some individuals of the group died. Figures from 0.0 to 1.0 indicate grams of whole wheat (B₁) received by the respective groups. (After Chase.)

demonstrated that the essential factor missing from the diet was contained in the coverings of the rice kernel. Persons who live almost exclusively upon a diet of *polished* rice, i.e., rice from which the pericarp (bran) and germ have been removed in the milling process, develop the disease, but are readily cured by giving them unpolished rice or an extract prepared from the rice "polishings." This factor in the polishings of rice which protected against beriberi was designated *vitamin B* or the *antineuritic vitamin*. From researches of recent years it has been shown that so-called vitamin B is actually a complex substance consisting of several vitamins, only one of which is protective against beriberi. This latter, the antineuritic principle, has been synthesized and is now known as vitamin B_1 or *thiamin*.

Other effects of vitamin B_1 deficiency are (a) *gastro-intestinal disorders* (e.g., reduced motility of the stomach and intestines resulting in constipation, inhibition of the digestive secretions and loss of appetite), and (b) *arrested growth* (see Fig. 140).

In birds, e.g., pigeons, a condition analogous to human beriberi results from vitamin B_1 deficiency. Its chief features are, paralysis due to involvement of the peripheral nerves (polyneuritis) retraction of the head and convulsions. The condition is cured in a remarkably short time by feeding a concentrated preparation of vitamin B_1 (see Fig. 141).

Vitamin B_1 appears to be essential for the metabolism of carbohydrates. In its absence, carbohydrate metabolism does not proceed normally. Lactic acid accumulates in the blood, heart and brain. The accumulation of lactic acid in the brain substance appears to be responsible for the head retraction seen in birds.

Vitamin B_2 complex is almost always found in association with vitamin B_1. Those vitamins which have been discovered to be associated with B_1 and originally grouped with the latter under the designation "the B_1 complex" are now referred to as the B_2 *complex*. The latter consists of several vitamins. The most important in respect to human nutrition are *riboflavin*, *nicotinic acid (niacin)*, *pyridoxin* and *pantothenic acid*.

Riboflavin is one of a group of yellow fluorescent pigments found in animal tissues. Liver, kidney and milk are especially rich sources of this factor of the B_2 complex. When it is lacking from the diet reddening of the eyes, due to the growth of fine blood vessels into the cornea, results. A sensation of burning and itching of the eyeballs is experienced. There is intolerance to bright light which may be so severe that the eyes cannot be opened.

Fig. 141. *Upper photograph*, pigeon suffering from polyneuritis; *lower*, the same bird an hour after treatment with vitamin B_1. (After Funk, redrawn.)

Nicotinic acid (niacin). A disease occurring among the poor of the Southern United States and less commonly in some European countries has recently been recognized as being due, mainly at least, to a deficiency of this vitamin. The chief features of this disease, which is known as *pellagra*, are reddening and drying of the skin together with, in the severer cases, nervous and gastro-intestinal disturbances. It occurs in those who subsist mainly upon maize.

Pyridoxin. Rats on a diet deficient in pyridoxin develop a cutaneous disorder consisting of reddening and scaliness of the skin and loss of hair. There is some indication that this factor is concerned with the synthesis of hemoglobin and for the manufacture of erythrocytes. The regeneration of blood following hemorrhage is hastened by feeding pyridoxin.

Pantothenic acid. The function of this vitamin in human nutrition has not been shown clearly, but its action appears to be bound up with that of riboflavin.

Vitamin C, the antiscorbutic vitamin. Vitamin C is present in greatest amounts in citrus fruits (e.g., lemons, limes, oranges and grapefruit). It is also contained in most other fruits and green vegetables. Tomatoes and red and green peppers are exceptionally rich sources; potatoes, turnips, meat and milk contain moderate amounts. Vitamin C has been identified chemically as *ascorbic acid* ($C_6H_8O_6$). It possesses high reducing powers, and has been synthesized in the laboratory.

Vitamin C serves the important function of maintaining a healthy state of the walls of the capillaries. When it is lacking from the diet, the cement substance interposed between the endothelial cells, and holding them together, becomes deficient. The vessels as a consequence develop leaks which permit the escape of blood into the surrounding tissues.

Scurvy (scorbutus) is caused by vitamin C deficiency. The chief manifestation of this disease is bleeding from the mucous membranes, beneath the skin and into joints. The skin, as a result of numerous capillary hemorrhages (*petechiae*), may show extensive mottling. The gums are swollen and inflamed, and bleed easily. The subjects become anemic, weak and emaciated. Unless fresh food containing the vitamin is supplied, death results. Scurvy, though unusual in the general population except in times of famine, was a common disease in sailors, soldiers, explorers and others who, of necessity, subsisted upon diets lacking in fresh fruits, vegetables, meat and milk. Scurvy is readily produced in guinea-pigs by placing them upon a diet of hay and oats, i.e., one lacking in green stuffs. The disease is sometimes seen in persons living on the outskirts of civilization, such as lumbermen, especially during the winter months when fresh food is difficult to procure, and provision for a supply of vitamin C in concentrated form has not been made. The disease may also appear in infants who are artificially fed; infantile scurvy (*Barlow's disease*) should, however, never occur, since the administration of tomato or orange juice is a certain preventive.

Vitamin D ($C_{28}H_{44}O$), the antirachitic vitamin. This vitamin is formed by the action of ultraviolet light upon certain

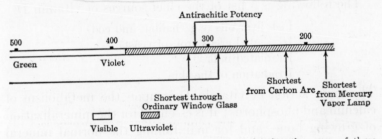

Fig. 142. Scheme of wave lengths of spectrum, showing the range of those possessing antirachitic power. Figures in millimicrons (mμ). (Redrawn and modified from Blunt and Cowan.)

waxy compounds known as sterols. Among such compounds are *ergosterol*, found in yeast, and *cholesterol*, present in the skin and other animal tissues. The ultraviolet rays cause a rearrangement of the atoms in the sterol molecule, thereby endowing it with the properties characteristic of vitamin D. Vitamin D is formed naturally by the action of sunlight upon a sterol in the skin closely associated with cholesterol, and is prepared commercially by irradiating yeast (rich in ergosterol) by means of the mercury vapor lamp or the carbon arc. Such artificial preparations of vitamin D are referred to as *viosterol*, or simply as *irradiated* or *activated ergosterol*. The wave lengths in the ultraviolet part of the spectrum which are effective in the formation of this vitamin have a range of from 250 to 313 mμ [1] (see Fig. 142). Vitamin D has been synthesized in the laboratory. It is a yel-

[1] mμ = millimicron, the one-millionth part of a millimeter.

low crystalline substance which has been named *calciferol*. The richest natural sources of the vitamin are fish liver oils, especially those from the cod and halibut. These large fish obtain the vitamin from smaller species upon which they feed, e.g., herring, whiting, etc. The small fish in turn acquire the vitamin from invertebrate marine forms, such as copepods and molluscs, which probably synthesize it. Some authorities believe that the cod and certain other fish are also capable of synthesizing vitamin D.

The following is a list of the chief sources of vitamin D.

> Fish liver oils (e.g., halibut and cod)
> Irradiated ergosterol (of yeast)
> Irradiated milk
> Irradiation of the skin

The main action of vitamin D is upon the metabolism of calcium and phosphorus; it is essential for the mineralization of growing bone, and for maintaining the normal mineral composition of the adult skeleton. It also plays an important role in dental health; defective tooth structure, leading to decay of the teeth (*dental caries*), results when the diet is deficient in the antirachitic vitamin. When the vitamin in the form of viosterol is administered in excessively large doses, a marked rise in the calcium of the serum (hypercalcemia) results, calcium being drawn from the skeleton to the blood. The calcium of the urine is increased. Vitamin D acts, in this respect, like the hormone of the parathyroid glands. Toxic symptoms resembling those caused by overdosage with parathyroid extract also follow the administration of large amounts of viosterol. The manner in which the vitamin, in physiological dosage, exerts its effect upon calcium metabolism is not altogether clear. According to some it increases the absorption of calcium from the intestinal tract; its chief action, however, appears to be upon the skeleton, influencing, in some manner not understood, the deposition of calcium and phosphorus in the developing bone.

Rickets (rachitis) results from vitamin D deficiency. It is a disease of young children, chiefly, between the ages of 6 months and 3 years. Its essential feature is defective development of the bones. The deposition of phosphorus and calcium is interfered with; the bones are therefore soft and yielding. Deformities of the limb bones and spine and defective ossification of the skull bones result. The head is somewhat larger than normal with a prominent brow; soft areas may be felt in the skull. The abdomen is large and round, which has given rise to the term "pot belly" (see Fig. 143). The disease occurs most often in bottle-fed infants, especially in those who are growing rapidly and receiving a diet containing a large proportion of carbohydrate. Rickets is readily cured or prevented by the administration of vitamin D, either in the form of cod liver or halibut liver oil, viosterol or irradiated milk, or by exposing the child to

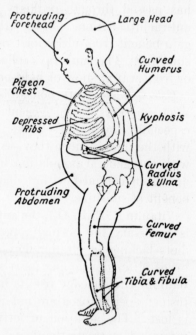

Fig. 143. Diagram showing the chief features of infantile rickets. (After Harris.)

ultraviolet radiations (sunlight, the mercury vapor lamp or carbon arc). The value of sunshine in the treatment of rickets was pointed out in 1880 by Palm, an English physician, but it is less than 25 years since the curative effects of ultraviolet irradiation and of cod liver oil have come to be generally recognized.

Rickets is seen most commonly in the large cities of northern latitudes, since infants in these localities are less exposed to sunshine than are those in southern climates. The disease is almost unknown in the tropics. The smoke and dust of cities also act as a screen through which the shorter wave lengths of the sun's rays cannot penetrate. It should be remembered, furthermore, that window glass is opaque to radiations shorter than 320 mμ. Sunshine that has passed through ordinary glass therefore possesses no antirachitic action. On the other hand, a person in order to gain benefit from ultraviolet radiation need not be in direct sunshine. The sun's rays reflected from the sky (skyshine), or from water, snow or light-colored objects are effective.

Osteomalacia (soft bones) is a disease — essentially the same as rickets — which occurs in adults in eastern countries, especially India and China. Women are mainly affected with the disease since they, as well as receiving in common with the general population little vitamin D in their diet, are often confined within doors and thus deprived of the benefit of sunshine.

Vitamin E ($C_{29}H_{50}O_2$), **the antisterility vitamin.** Vitamin E is necessary for normal reproduction. Female rats upon diets lacking in vitamin E become pregnant, but the embryos, after developing for a short time, die. In male rats vitamin E deficiency results in degenerative changes in the testes; spermatozoa are not produced and the sex instinct is lost. The addition of lettuce or other food containing vitamin E corrects the defects of either the male or female reproductive functions.

Vitamin E is fat-soluble and has been obtained in crystalline form. Its chief sources are green vegetable foods, e.g., lettuce, peas, alfalfa and the germ of various cereals. Wheat germ oil has a very high vitamin E content.

Vitamin K (**the anti-hemorrhagic vitamin**). This vitamin is found in largest amounts in alfalfa, spinach, cauliflower, cabbage and other green foods and less abundantly in cereals, carrots and yeast. Chicks and other farm birds develop a fatal hemorrhagic disease when this vitamin is lacking from the diet. The hemorrhages are due to a low concentration of prothrombin in the blood. This, as mentioned on page 59, is an essential factor in the coagulation of the blood. Hemorrhages in the human subject are rarely if ever

TABLE 17

Summarizing the principal facts concerning the vitamins

Name	Chief functions	Effects caused by deficiency	Chief sources
Vitamin A antixerophthalmic	Maintains the integrity of epithelial tissues. Essential for the regeneration of visual purple.	Xerophthalmia. Keratomalacia. Conversion of columnar epithelium to squamous type. Night blindness.	Carrots. Lettuce. Alfalfa. Yellow corn. Butter, cream and milk. Egg yolk.
Vitamin B₁ (thiamin) antineuritic	Promotes appetite. Essential for growth. Maintains the tone of the gastro-intestinal tract.	Beriberi. Polyneuritis. Loss of appetite. Loss of tone of the gastro-intestinal tract. Failure of growth.	Yeast. Germ of wheat and other cereals.
B₂ complex Riboflavin	—	Vascularization of cornea, eye defects.	Liver, kidney, milk.
Nicotinic acid	—	Pellagra	Liver, yeast, wheat germ.
Pyridoxin	—		Vegetable fats, wheat germ, kidney, meats.
Pantothenic acid	—	—	Liver, kidney, egg-yolk, yeast, wheat germ.
Vitamin C antiscorbutic	Maintains the integrity of the capillary walls.	Scurvy.	Citrus fruits. Tomatoes. Turnips.
Vitamin D antirachitic	Regulates calcium and phosphorus metabolism. Essential for the normal development of bones and teeth.	Rickets. Osteomalacia. Dental caries.	Cod liver and halibut liver oils. Exposure of the skin to ultraviolet irradiation.
Vitamin E antisterility	Essential for reproduction.	Death of young in uterus. Sterility of male, degenerative changes in testes, failure of spermatogenesis.	Lettuce. Watercress. Wheat germ.
Vitamin K	Necessary for the production of prothrombin by the liver.	Hemorrhagic tendency	Alfalfa and other green foods.

due to the lack of vitamin K in the diet, but the vitamin is not absorbed from the intestine in the absence of bile. Therefore, in obstructive jaundice in which bile does not enter the intestine, a tendency to bleed is a common feature. It is now the custom to give vitamin K by injection or by mouth accompanied by bile or bile salts before operating upon a patient with obstructive jaundice. The prothrombin concentration of the blood is raised thereby and the defect in the clotting mechanism corrected.

THE PRINCIPLES OF DIETETICS

The importance of a well-balanced diet for the normal growth and development of the young, and for the health of both young and old, is recognized today as never before. There seems little doubt that the finer physique and better health of the present generation is largely the result of the more varied and ample character of modern diets (see Fig. 144). Deficiency diseases which have been so prevalent in the past, especially among the poor, are now comparatively rare. Rickets and scurvy, for example, have almost vanished from civilized communities and, were the knowledge which has been gained from modern research sedulously applied, the eradication of these and other diseases due to defective diets — such as beriberi and pellagra — would soon be an accomplished fact. In planning a diet the following factors must be taken into account:

1. The caloric (energy) requirement of the subject.
2. The proportions of the three main types of food — carbohydrate, protein and fat.
3. The vitamin requirement.
4. The mineral constituents.

Determination of the caloric requirement. A man of average size and following a light occupation has an average energy output of from 2500 to 3000 Calories daily. In order that the body's tissues shall not be called upon to furnish any of the required energy, the caloric value of the diet must not be less than the energy expenditure; otherwise the body would lose weight. Nor should the caloric value of the diet be greater than the energy expended. The excess energy would then be simply stored as fat (see p. 263). Excess of energy intake over energy output is the usual cause of obesity. In order, therefore, to calculate the caloric require-

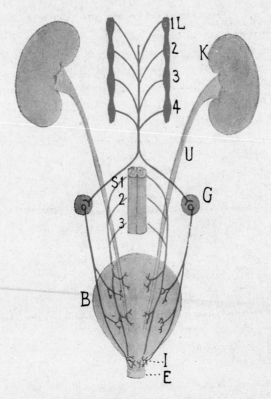

PLATE 6

Diagram of the innervation of the urinary bladder. B, bladder; E, external sphincter; G, hypogastric ganglion; I, internal sphincter; K, kidney; U, ureter. L. 1, 2, 3, 4 refer to the ganglia of the lumbar sympathetic chain. S. 1, 2, 3, indicate the first, second and third sacral segments of the spinal cord.

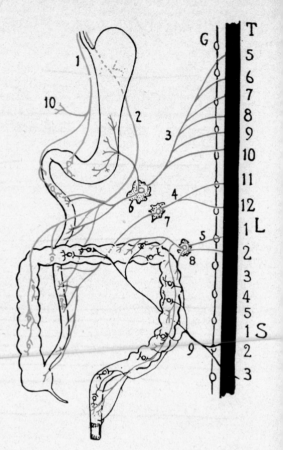

PLATE 7A

Diagram of the nerve supply of the gastro-intestinal tract. 1, 2, vagus nerves. All vagal fibers, preganglionic and postganglionic, in *red*, sympathetic in *blue*, pelvic nerve *black*. 3, 4 and 5, splanchnic nerves (sympathetic); 6, 7 and 8, prevertebral sympathetic ganglia; 9, pelvic nerve; 10, to liver; G, gangliated cord of sympathetic; T, 5–12, thoracic segments of spinal cord; L, 1–5, lumbar segments; S, 1–3, sacral segments.

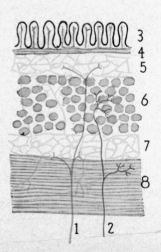

PLATE 7B

Nerve plexuses of the intestinal wall. Preganglionic fibers of vagus (1) in *red;* postganglionic fibers of sympathetic (2) in *blue;* plexuses (5 and 7) in *yellow.* 3, intestinal villi; 4, muscularis mucosae; 5, submucous (Meissner's) plexus; 6, circular muscular coat, fibers shown in cross section; 7, myenteric (Auerbach's) plexus; 7, longitudinal muscular coat.

Fig. 144. *Upper photograph*, class of elementary school children at Southwark, England, in 1894. *Lower photograph*, corresponding class thirty years later. The improvement of this group over that in the upper photograph is attributed largely to the more adequate diet received by the children in the lower group. (After Harris.)

ment in any given case, one must first know the energy expenditure during the resting state, that is, the basal metabolism (p. 285). To this is added the energy expenditure of the particular occupation in which the person is engaged.

The energy expended daily by different persons, or by the same person at different times, varies widely, depending upon the extent of the exercise undertaken. The energy allowances for work of several grades are given in the following table.

	Daily energy expenditure (above basal) Calories
Sedentary life	500– 600
Light work, e.g., professional and business men	600–1200
Moderate work, e.g., mechanics	1200–1500
Heavy work, e.g., laborers, lumbermen, athletes, etc.	1500–4000 and upwards

The metabolism during sleep is lower than the basal metabolism by from 15 to 20 per cent. The lower metabolism of the eight hours of sleep must, therefore, be taken into account in determining the caloric requirements. The calculations just outlined are exemplified in the following table.

Basal metabolism (16 hours)	1200 Calories [1]
Metabolism during sleep (8 hours)	500 "
Allowance for light work	800 "
Total	2500 Calories

The basal metabolism of a healthy subject can be derived from his height and weight (see chart, Fig. 135). The energy values of the various articles of diet are obtained from

[1] This is about 40 Calories per hour for a man having a surface area of 1.8 square meters.

standard tables, and the quantities apportioned accordingly. For example, beef (all edible) has an energy value of about 1300 Calories per pound; butter yields 3600 Calories per pound, milk 325, eggs 765, cheese 2200, sugar 1860 and white bread 1200. Children, owing to their greater activity and the requirements of growth, should receive a more ample diet in proportion to their size than that of the average adult. A boy of 16 years, for example, especially if he is growing rapidly and taking part in athletics, requires as much food as a full-grown man engaged in light work.

The proportions of carbohydrate, fat and protein. A little over 50 per cent of the total caloric requirement should be furnished by carbohydrate food, about 35 per cent by fat and 12 per cent by protein. The protein in the diet of the average adult should be from 70 to 90 grams daily, or around 1 gram per kilogram of body weight. Children, especially in the early years of life, require a higher protein intake (2 to 3.5 grams per kilogram) than do adults, and a larger proportion (60 to 90 per cent) of the total protein should be of the highest biological value, such as is furnished by milk, eggs and meat. In adults receiving 80 to 90 grams of protein daily, at least 50 per cent should be first class. If the protein is mainly of low biological value, e.g., vegetable proteins, the total allowance must be larger.

Fat is an indispensable element of the diet. Fats not only contain fat-soluble vitamins, but also certain unsaturated fatty acids (linoleic and linolenic acids) which cannot be synthesized in the body, yet are essential for normal nutrition.

The mineral requirement. *Sodium, potassium, magnesium* and *phosphorus* are present in adequate amounts in a diet which is ample in other respects and, as a rule, no special attention need be paid to them. Sodium chloride, for example, besides that which is present naturally in many foodstuffs is added in cooking, and as table salt in quantities determined by individual taste. Protein foods constitute the chief source of the phosphorus of the diet and, when the allowance of protein is adequate, the phosphorus intake takes care of itself. Potassium and magnesium are derived from cereals and vegetables, and are also present in sufficient amounts in an ordinary diet.

The minerals in which the diet is most likely to be deficient are *calcium, iron* and *iodine*. The intake of calcium, which enters so largely into the composition of bone, is especially likely to be inadequate in the diets of children. According to Professor Sherman, children require at least a gram of calcium per day. The adult requirement is about 0.8 gram daily. As a result of the deposition of mineral in the bones of the fetus, the demand for calcium increases during pregnancy when the allowance should be from 1.5 to 2 grams daily. Milk is especially rich in calcium, containing about a gram per quart. Cereals and certain vegetables, such as beans, peas and turnips, are also good sources of this mineral, but the calcium of milk, as compared with that of vegetables, is more readily absorbed. Only a small part of the calcium in cereals and vegetables is utilized by the body. Meat contains minimal amounts. Milk is therefore, especially for children, the best source of calcium.

Iron is an indispensable constituent of the diet, since it is necessary for the synthesis of hemoglobin. The daily requirement is from 15 to 20 mgm. The chief sources of food iron are meats (especially liver), eggs, and such vegetables and cereals as spinach, beans and peas, whole wheat and oatmeal. Milk is very poor in iron. *Copper* is also essential for the synthesis of hemoglobin (p. 33), but the quantity required is so very small that any ordinary diet contains adequate amounts.

Iodine is an essential constituent of the thyroid hormone; goiter (p. 332) results when the diet is deficient in this element. Sea-foods are the chief natural sources of iodine, though many brands of table salt contain small quantities (1 part in 100,000) which have been added by the manufacturer. The daily requirement of iodine is placed at about 15 micrograms.[1]

[1] A microgram or gamma (γ) = $\frac{1}{1000}$ milligram.

THE ENDOCRINE GLANDS

Introduction. Glands, such as those of the mouth, stomach and intestines, which deliver their secretions into the alimentary tract, or those, such as the lachrymal, mammary and sweat glands, which discharge upon the surface of the body, are called *glands of external secretion* or *exocrine* glands. The glands which we are about to consider do not possess ducts or any openings to the exterior; their secretions pass into the blood stream, and are thus conveyed to the various tissues of the body upon which they exert their action. These glands are, therefore, called *endocrine glands or organs, ductless glands* or *glands of internal secretion*.

The secretions of the endocrine glands are for the most part excitatory in their actions; they *stimulate* the growth and development, or the functional activity of certain tissues; internal secretions acting in this manner are, therefore, called *hormones* (G. *hormaō* = I excite). The term hormone is not, however, restricted to the secretions of the ductless glands. Any substance formed by a tissue of the body and carried in the blood stream to act as an excitant to some other tissue or organ may be called a hormone. Thus, carbon dioxide, which acts upon the respiratory and vasomotor centers, and secretin (p. 258) which causes the secretion of pancreatic juice, come into this category. *Chalone* is a corresponding term which is sometimes used to designate an internal secretion having an *inhibitory* action.

Our knowledge of the ductless glands has been advanced enormously during the past twenty years, and especially within the last ten. The methods used in the investigation of endocrine function are three in number. *First*, an extract

of the gland tissue may be prepared, which is then injected
into animals and a study made of its effects. *Second,* a
given gland may be excised, and the subsequent life history
of the animal followed, careful notice being taken of its development and growth, or of any unusual feature. *Third,*
studies may be made upon subjects in whom one or other
gland is known to be deficient or overactive. The first and
second methods are often employed together. For example,
after extirpation of the gland, the animal is treated with an
extract prepared from the same type of gland, observations
being made of the power of the preparation to correct the
defects resulting from the operation. This is called the
substitution or *replacement* method.

Potent extracts of a number of ductless glands have now
been prepared. These preparations, with the exception of
thyroid extract, are relatively or quite inactive when given
by mouth; their full effect is exerted only when given by
injection.

Most of the ductless glands are present in all orders of
vertebrates, and an extract obtained from the gland of one
order exerts, as a rule, its specific effect when administered
to a member of another order. Thus the hormone of the
sheep's thyroid influences the growth and development of
frog larvae (tadpoles).

THE THYROID GLAND

The thyroid gland is composed of two *lobes* which lie one
on either side of the larynx (see Fig. 145). Under the microscope the glandular tissue is seen to be composed of a mass
of alveoli lined by a single layer of cuboidal epithelial cells.
The alveolar cavities are filled with a homogeneous gelatinous
material called *colloid;* this is secreted by the lining cells
and contains the thyroid hormone.

The thyroid is supplied with nerves, but whether these
have any secretory function is questionable. It is certain,
at any rate, that a hormone liberated by the pituitary gland

(thyrotropic hormone, p. 354) is of much greater importance than are nerve fibers in the control of thyroid activity.

Excision of the thyroid (thyroidectomy) in young mammals, e.g., pigs, goats, calves, rabbits, etc., results in retardation of skeletal growth, and failure of sexual development

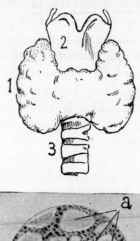

(Fig. 146). Tissue oxidations are depressed, the basal metabolic rate falling after the operation to 60 or even 50 per cent of the normal. The skin becomes thick and leathery in texture, the hair sparse, dry, lusterless and brittle. The long bones continue to grow in thickness, but longitudinal growth is very slow. The administration of thyroid extract after thyroidectomy prevents the onset of these effects or, if they have appeared, abolishes them or at least arrests their progress.

The effects following thyroidectomy in lower orders are even more striking. Thyroidectomized tadpoles, for example, do not develop into frogs. Metamorphosis is at once resumed, however, upon the addition of thyroid extract to the water in which the thyroidless animals live (Fig. 147). Furthermore, the administration of thyroid extract to normal tadpoles causes them to metamorphose in about a third of the usual time. The effect of thyroid extract upon the axolotl — an aquatic form allied to the frog — is still more extraordinary. In the adult form this animal is purely aquatic in its habits, possessing gills, a finned tail and four short limbs, suggesting some fabulous gigantic

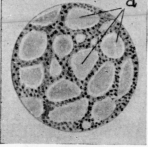

Fig. 145. *Upper drawing*, 1, thyroid gland; 2, thyroid cartilage; 3, trachea. *Lower*, microscopical appearance of the gland; a, alveoli containing colloid.

FIG. 146. Photograph showing a thyroidectomized cretin lamb about fourteen months old and a normal sheep of the same age. The thyroids had been removed from the cretin about twelve months previously. (After Sutherland Simpson.)

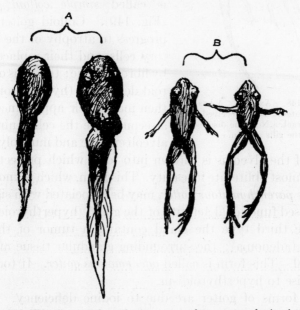

FIG. 147. The effect of thyroidectomy upon the metamorphosis of tadpoles. A, thyroidectomized, B, normal frogs of the same hatching. (After Allen, redrawn.)

tadpole whose metamorphosis, after proceeding so far, has become arrested (Fig. 148). Thyroid feeding causes this creature to lose its gills and fin, to develop air-breathing organs, and forsake the aquatic life of its kind.

Goiter is a term applied to chronic enlargement of the thyroid. When the enlargement is not associated with any general effects referable to disturbed function of the thyroid, it is called *simple goiter*. Goiter may, however, be accompanied by underfunctioning or by overfunctioning of the thyroid — *hypothyroidism* and *hyperthyroidism*, respectively.

FIG. 148. Axolotls. A has not been treated. B has received thyroid extract. Note the disappearance of the gills and fin.

The histological appearance of the goitrous thyroid varies. In one type the alveoli are enlarged, irregular in size and shape, and filled with colloid material. This is called *simple colloid goiter* (Fig. 149). Colloid goiter may progress to atrophy of the secretory cells, and their replacement by fibrous tissue; the signs of thyroid deficiency (hypothyroidism) then make their appearance. In a second type the cells lining the alveoli enlarge and multiply; the wall of the alveolus is thrown into folds which project into, and almost obliterate its cavity. This form, which is known as *diffuse parenchymatous goiter*, may be associated with signs of increased functional activity of the gland (hyperthyroidism). In the third type the gland contains a tumor of thyroid tissue (adenoma); the surrounding glandular tissue may be normal. This form is called *adenomatous goiter*. It too may give rise to hyperthyroidism.

All forms of goiter are due to iodine deficiency. It is, therefore, in regions where the iodine of the soil is low, such as those far removed from the sea (which contains large stores of iodine), that goiter is prevalent. The inhabitants of mountain villages, e.g., in the Alps, Pyrenees and Himalayas, have been among the chief sufferers. Through the ages iodine has been leached from the soils of these regions and, as a consequence, the water and food have a very low iodine content. Since the importance of iodine for normal thyroid function has been recognized, small amounts of iodine are taken by the population of goitrous districts; as

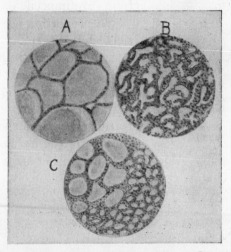

Fig. 149. Goiter. Microscopical appearance of the thyroid in colloid (A), parenchymatous (B) and adenomatous (C) goiter. In C a portion of normal gland tissue is seen on the left.

a result of this preventive measure goiter is much less prevalent today than in the past. Iodine, as we shall see presently (p. 337), is an essential constituent of the thyroid hormone.

Hypothyroidism (*thyroid deficiency*). In infants and young children thyroid deficiency produces effects essentially similar to those seen in animals following thyroidectomy. The defects of physical, sexual and mental development form a characteristic picture to which the term *cretinism* is applied; the child is called a *cretin*. These child victims of thyroid deficiency are dwarfed to a marked degree and, unless the condition is corrected at an early age by the administration of thyroid extract or thyroxin (p. 337), their height when they reach adult age may be no greater than that of a nor-

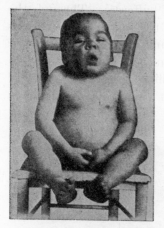

FIG. 150. A cretin.
(After Falta.)

mal child of 7 or 8 years. The sexual organs do not develop, nor do the secondary characters of sex appear. The basal metabolic rate is lowered. Mental growth is, as a rule, very seriously retarded; many cretins are imbecile or idiotic, and a large proportion are deaf mutes (Figs. 150 to 152). The facial features are coarse; the bridge of the nose is depressed; the tongue in many instances is enlarged and, as if too large for the mouth, protrudes between the lips. The skin of the entire body appears thick and puffy, due to the deposition of a gelatinous

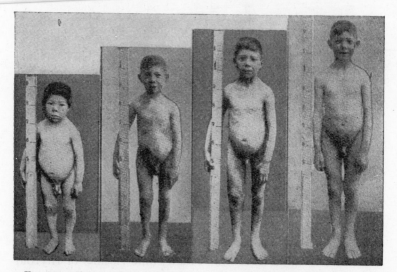

FIG. 151. Showing the effect of thyroid extract in correcting cretinism. First photograph taken at age of 4½ years before treatment was commenced, others taken at one, two and three years subsequently. (From Joll after Hertoghe.)

fluid in the subcutaneous tissues. The hair is dry, brittle and sparse.

Cretinism is very commonly associated with goiter, and is therefore most prevalent in goitrous districts. As already mentioned, goitrous enlargement may lead to atrophy of the secretory cells.

Myxedema. This condition is the result of thyroid deficiency commencing in adult life. Its general features, namely, the low metabolic rate, the thickness and puffiness of

Fig. 152. A group of cretins in an institution. (After Falta.)

the skin (myxedema) from which the condition originally got its name, the scantiness and dryness of the hair, are the same as those just described for cretinism. But inasmuch as full development, skeletal, sexual and mental, has been attained before the onset of the disease, many of the characteristic features of cretinism are absent. Myxedematous subjects, though they are apathetic and lethargic and think slowly, are not mentally defective.

The myxedematous subject is very quickly restored to normal by thyroxin or thyroid extract. The cretin may also be stimulated to normal growth and development by thyroid treatment, provided this is started at an early age (p. 334). The longer that treatment is postponed, the less benefit will be derived from treatment and, if the condition has existed for years, little benefit will result (see Figs. 151 and 153).

Hyperthyroidism, thyrotoxicosis (*overactivity of the thyroid*). Hyperthyroidism occurs in two forms. In the first form, called *exophthalmic goiter*, the whole gland is enlarged and shows histological evidence of increased activity; the

FIG. 153.   Myxedema.   *Left*, before treatment with thyroid extract.
Right, after treatment.   (From Joll.)

microscopical picture is that of parenchymatous goiter. The chief features of this condition are (a) enlargement of the thyroid, (b) elevation of the basal metabolic rate, (c) disturbances of carbohydrate metabolism, e.g., reduction in the glycogen stores, hyperglycemia and glucosuria, (d) nervousness and tremor, (e) rapid action of the heart and (f) protrusion of the eyeballs (*exophthalmos*, see Fig. 154).

In the other form of hyperthyroidism the gland contains a tumor of thyroid tissue (adenoma); the gland surrounding the tumor may show little abnormality. In this condition, called *toxic adenoma*, exophthalmos is absent; the other features described above for exophthalmic goiter are present.

The thyroid hormone. It was shown nearly fifty years ago that the thyroid was a gland of internal secretion. An English physician, George Murray, in 1891 prepared a glycerine extract of sheep's thyroids. This preparation, when administered by injection to a subject of myxedema, restored him to normal within a very short time. It was discovered later that thyroid tissue, dried and powdered and given by mouth was equally effective. At this time, nothing was known regarding the chemical nature of the hormone, but it was soon found that thyroid extracts contained iodine combined with protein. This iodine-protein compound was called *thyreoglobulin*. The active principle of the extract was later obtained in crystalline form. It was shown to contain a large proportion (60 per cent) of iodine; it was named *thyroxine*. Thyroxine — the thyroid hormone

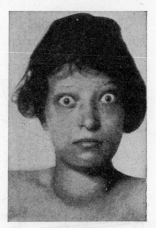

Fig. 154. Exophthalmic goiter. (After Crotti.)

— has since been synthesized. It is derived from the amino-acid tyrosine, and has the following formula.

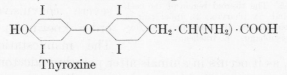

Thyroxine

Thyroxine, whether prepared from thyroid tissue or synthesized, has an action identical with that of the dried gland, but is much more potent. A fraction of a milligram, given daily, is sufficient to maintain the basal metabolic rate of a subject of myxedema at the normal level.

The thyroid hormone appears to act as a catalyst (p. 223) hastening very greatly oxidation in the tissues. When given to a normal animal, the metabolic rate is raised and the other signs of hyperthyroidism (except exophthalmos) make their appearance. The effects are not observed, however, until the lapse of several hours after the hormone has been administered, and are not fully developed until the lapse of from 8 to 10 days. But, even though a single dose is given, the effects persist for 5 or 6 weeks.

THE PARATHYROID GLANDS

The parathyroid glands are two pairs of small oval structures (about a quarter of an inch long) lying in close relation

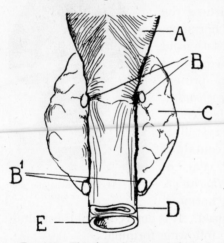

to the thyroid. The upper pair are situated, one on each side of the midline, behind the upper poles of the thyroid lobes; the lower pair lie behind, or a little below, the inferior poles of the thyroid (Fig. 155). Removal of the parathyroids (*parathyroidectomy*) causes increased excitability of the neuromuscular tissues, which culminates in a severe convulsive disorder known as *tetany*.

FIG. 155. The thyroid region of the neck from behind. A, pharynx; B, upper pair of parathyroid glands; B¹, lower pair; C, thyroid; D, esophagus; E, trachea.

The manifestations of tetany, as it occurs in animals after parathyroidectomy, are as follows: (a) twitchings and spasmodic contractions of the muscles, which usually increase in violence until the whole body is thrown into convulsions, (b) rapid breathing, (c) acceleration of the heart, (d) rise in temperature, (e) death usually occurs from exhaustion or from asphyxia resulting from spasm of the muscles which close the opening of the larynx (*laryngeal spasm*).

Parathyroid deficiency resulting in tetany is sometimes seen in the human subject following removal of the thyroid for goiter, the parathyroids being inadvertently or unavoidably removed with the thyroid. The phenomena of parathyroid deficiency in man are usually much less pronounced than those which follow parathyroidectomy in animals. Twitchings, nervousness and an occasional spasm of the facial or limb muscles, are often the only manifestations. In other instances, tetany is in a latent form and is revealed only by means of special tests (p. 341).

The function of the parathyroid glands. Normal blood contains from 5 to 6 mgm. of calcium per 100 cc.; this is all

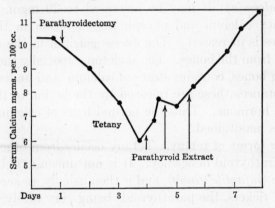

Fig. 156. The effect of parathyroid extract on the calcium of the blood in parathyroid tetany. A single dose of extract was given when the serum calcium had fallen to 6 mg. per cent and the symptoms of tetany had reached their height. (After Macleod and Taylor.)

contained in the plasma, so that the concentration of calcium in the plasma (or in the serum, for none is removed in the clot) is from 9 to 11 mgm. per 100 cc. Parathyroidectomy causes a pronounced fall in the serum calcium (*hypocalcemia*). When the serum calcium level falls to about 6 mgm. per cent, tetany appears and increases in severity with further reduction in the serum calcium concentration. Injections of calcium relieve the condition within a few minutes; there is no doubt, then, that calcium deficiency and the development of the tetanic state are directly related. These observations led to the conclusion that the parathyroids are concerned in some way with the control of calcium metabolism. This view of parathyroid function was amply confirmed in 1925, by the important discovery made by Professor Collip of Montreal. He found that an extract prepared from the parathyroid glands of cattle, when administered by subcutaneous injection to parathyroidectomized animals, raises the serum calcium to normal and abolishes all the manifestations of tetany (Fig. 156).

When normal animals are given repeated doses of parathyroid extract, the serum calcium is raised above normal (*hypercalcemia*); it may be increased to 20 mgm. or more per cent; calcium and phosphorus excretion in the urine and feces is increased. The excess calcium in the serum is derived from the bones. The skeleton, especially the ends of the long bones, contains stores of calcium, and under normal circumstances these are released by the action of the parathyroid hormone. Thus the normal level of calcium in the serum is maintained.

Other forms of tetany. Tetany occurs from other causes than parathyroid deficiency. It is not uncommon in young children (*infantile tetany*), and is then usually an accompaniment of rickets, the parathyroids being very rarely at fault. The serum calcium, however, is low and, as in parathyroid tetany, it is the hypocalcemia which is directly responsible for the tetanic seizures. Tetany is also seen in *osteomalacia* (p. 320) — an adult form of rickets occurring in China and India; in *sprue* — a rare condition associated with defective absorption of calcium from the intestine; and in certain other conditions, e.g., *alkalosis*, which may result from persistent vomiting (loss of HCl), forced breathing (excessive elimination of CO_2) or the administration of large doses of an alkali, such as sodium bicarbonate.

In the tetany of children, the hands and feet assume characteristic attitudes (see Fig. 157). This phenomenon is referred to as *carpo-pedal spasm*. Spasm of the laryngeal muscles with attacks of asphyxia are common; the child becomes blue (cyanosis), but, presently, the obstruction to breathing is overcome, the air being then drawn into the chest with a high-pitched "crowing" sound. In other instances generalized convulsions occur.

In either infants or adults, the serum calcium is sometimes reduced below the normal level, but not quite low enough to bring on a tetanic attack, under ordinary circumstances. This is called *latent tetany*. A typical tetanic seizure may result, however, from some upset in the general health. Latent tetany may be detected by the following tests. (a) Tapping over the facial nerve in front of the ear causes twitchings of the muscles of the face, if latent tetany exists. This is called *Chvostek's sign*. (b) *Erb's sign*. The muscles show increased excitability to stimulation by a galvanic current. (c) *Trousseau's sign*. Tying a tourniquet around the arm above the elbow, so as temporarily to occlude the blood supply, causes the hand to assume the characteristic attitude.

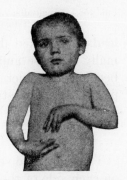

Fig. 157. Child with tetany showing the characteristic attitude of the hands. (After Falta.)

Hyperparathyroidism (*excess of the parathyroid hormone*). In *animals* overdosage with parathyroid extract causes (besides the hypercalcemia and the increased excretion of calcium and phosphorus, already mentioned) very grave effects, e.g., depression and muscular weakness, hemorrhages into the stomach and intestines. Death occurs within a few days. If given in smaller doses over a long period, softening of the bones, as a result of the removal of calcium, results. *In man*, there is little doubt that excessive amounts of the extract would produce similar effects.

A rare disease, known as *osteitis fibrosa cystica*, is caused by overactivity of the parathyroid glands themselves. A tumor of one or other of the four glands is usually present; this secretes excessive amounts of the parathyroid hormone into the blood stream, producing effects closely similar to those resulting from overdosage with extract, namely, hypercalcemia, increased excretion of calcium and phosphorus in the urine, and softening of the bones, which in some cases

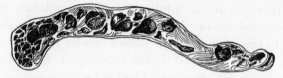

FIG. 158. Longitudinal section of bone showing structural changes in osteitis fibrosa cystica. (Drawn from a photograph after Hunter.)

leads to marked deformity. The bony tissue, which normally is dense and contains a high percentage of mineral, becomes de-mineralized and more fibrous in character. In places the bone structure is replaced by cavities (cysts) of various sizes and shapes (see Fig. 158).

THE ADRENAL GLANDS (OR SUPRARENAL CAPSULES)

These are two somewhat pyramidal structures lying, one on each side of the body, in contact with the upper pole of the kidney. Each gland measures from 1 to 2 inches in length. The adrenal gland is actually two glands in one, for each consists of two functionally distinct parts — a central portion called the *medulla*, and a surrounding zone of tissue called the *cortex*. In certain fish (the *elasmobranchs*) the two parts are quite separate (Fig. 159). The tissue corresponding to the mammalian adrenal medulla is present as several small groups lying in close relation to the ganglia of the sympathetic chain. The two parts of the adrenal gland have quite different origins, and there is no evidence that their functions are in any way related. The medulla develops from a group of cells, split off from the neural crest of the early embryo, to which the ganglion cells of the sympathetic nervous system also trace their ancestry. It is important to remember this fact in

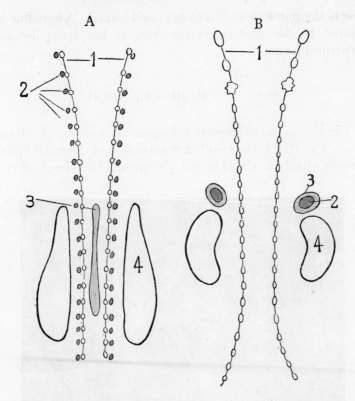

FIG. 159. Adrenal tissue in Elasmobranch fish (A), in mammals (B). 1, sympathetic chain of ganglia; 2, medullary tissue; 3, cortical tissue; 4, kidney.

order to understand the functions of this part of the gland. The cortex, on the other hand, arises from a mass of cells in close relation to those from which the sex glands (testes and ovaries) are developed.

The functions of the adrenal medulla. Nearly 50 years ago two physiologists in Edinburgh (Professor Schafer and Dr. Oliver) showed that an extract of the adrenal medulla caused a pronounced rise in blood pressure when injected subcutaneously or intravenously. The active principle of the extract was later isolated in pure crystalline form and finally synthesized. It was named *epinephrine*, but *adrena-*

line is the name more commonly used today. Adrenaline is related to the amino-acid tyrosine; it has the following structural formula:

$$HO \hspace{-0.3em}\left\langle\!\!\!\!\!\overset{\text{OH}}{}\!\!\!\!\!\right\rangle\!\!CH(OH)\cdot CH_2\cdot NHCH_3$$

The rise in blood pressure following an injection of adrenaline (Fig. 160) is the result of constriction of the small blood vessels, chiefly of the skin and abdomen. The vessels of the

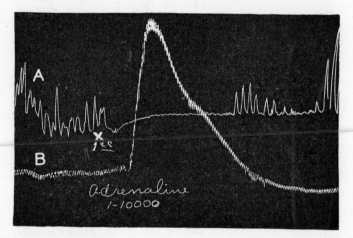

FIG. 160. Showing effect of adrenaline upon intestinal contractions (A) and blood pressure (B). 1 cc. of 1 in 10,000 adrenaline solution injected at X. (Modified from Jackson.)

heart (coronaries) and of the skeletal muscles are dilated by adrenaline. The heart is slowed; this action is the result of the rise in blood pressure (Marey's law, p. 143) for if the vagus nerves are first cut the heart is accelerated by adrenaline. The quantity of adrenaline required to produce the latter effect is minute. The denervated heart, i.e., the heart completely isolated from nervous control by interruption of the vagus and sympathetic pathways, is accelerated by as little as 1 part of adrenaline in 1,400,000,000 parts of blood;

it therefore provides the most sensitive test object for detecting the presence of adrenaline in blood or other fluid.

Other effects produced by the extract of the adrenal medulla are inhibition of the movements of the intestine, and contraction of the pyloric, iliocolic and internal anal sphincters. It relaxes the smooth muscle of the bronchioles, thus causing dilatation of these parts of the bronchial tree. It is, therefore, of great value in relieving spasm of the bronchioles in attacks of asthma. Adrenaline inhibits the wall of the urinary bladder, but causes contraction of the ureter, and of

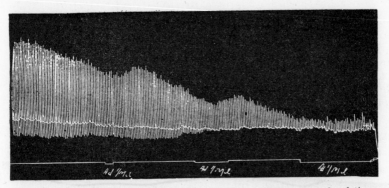

Fig. 161. Showing the effect of adrenaline in postponing muscular fatigue. Note the increase in the height of the contractions following each injection of adrenaline. (After Corkill and Tiegs.)

the sphincter of the bladder. In most animals the uterus contracts under the influence of adrenaline. It dilates the pupil of the eye and contracts the smooth muscle of the skin through which the hairs or feathers are elevated. It exerts a favorable effect upon the contraction of skeletal muscle; an isolated muscle subjected to repeated stimulation fatigues less readily if treated with adrenaline (Fig. 161).

Adrenaline also raises the metabolic rate; this is spoken of as its *calorigenic* action. It increases the sugar content of the blood by causing an increased breakdown of glycogen to sugar in the liver. The decomposition of muscle glycogen is also accelerated, lactic acid being produced which, escaping into the circulation, raises the level of the lactic acid in the blood. The lactic acid is carried to the liver and there reconverted to glycogen. These effects in their relation to the carbohydrate cycle are shown in the following scheme:

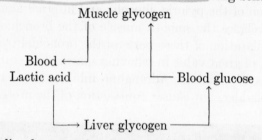

Muscle glycogen

Blood ← Lactic acid ——→ Blood glucose

Liver glycogen

Adrenaline hastens the clotting of blood; but this effect is brought about only if the adrenaline is injected into the body. It exerts no effect upon the clotting process when added to blood after it has been shed, i.e., when added to blood in a test tube.

Most of the effects listed above as following adrenaline administration can be produced by stimulation of sympathetic nerve fibers. Indeed, the actions of adrenaline may be summed up by saying that it imitates the effects of sympathetic excitation. This remarkable *sympathomimetic* action is perhaps not so surprising when we recall that the adrenal medulla and sympathetic nerve cells have a common origin (p. 342).

The emergency theory of adrenal function. By a great number of ingenious experiments, Professor Cannon and his several associates at Harvard University have demonstrated in a striking manner that the hormone of the adrenal medulla serves an *emergency function.* It reinforces the action of the sympathetic nervous system to raise the defense mechanisms of the body against the dangers and rigors of the environment. These workers experimented with cats in which the heart had been denervated by cutting the vagus nerves and excising the stellate ganglion of the sympathetic chain. It was found that fright (caused by a barking dog), exposure to cold, asphyxia, the administration of an anesthetic, pain, or muscular contraction caused acceleration of the heart. Since the cardiac acceleration could not have been caused by nervous influences, and did not occur after removal of the adrenals, it must have been due to the action of adrenaline discharged from the animal's own adrenal glands.

Under quiet, resting conditions the blood contains only a negligible amount of adrenaline, about one part in one or two billion; but during states of excitement or any of the conditions just mentioned about .004 mgm. per kilogram of body weight may be discharged from the glands per minute. It is believed, therefore, that the adrenal medulla functions only under circumstances which demand some special effort on the part of the body, as when an animal is defending itself or running down its prey, fleeing from danger or exposed to cold. It will be recalled that the reactions of an animal under such circumstances, e.g., the bristling of fur or the ruffling of feathers (caused by the contraction of the smooth muscle in the skin), the dilatation of the pupil, the acceleration of the heart and, in certain cold-blooded species, the contraction of the melanophores (pigment cells) of the skin, are characteristic of sympathetic stimulation or of adrenaline administration. Other physiological adjustments which increase the efficiency of the body to the maximum in times of stress, such as the mobilization of sugar from the liver (fuel for muscular work), the rise in blood pressure and the diversion of blood from the skin and splanchnic region to the vessels of the brain, heart and contracting muscles, the dilatation of the bronchioles, and the postponement of muscular fatigue, are brought about through the sympathetic nervous system, as well as by the hormone of the adrenal medulla. The increased coagulability of the blood caused by adrenaline would also seem to be a part of the general defense reaction, for should a wound be sustained, bleeding will be more quickly stanched.

The *secretion of the adrenal medulla* is under the control

of the sympathetic nervous system. Stimulation of the splanchnic nerve causes the liberation of adrenaline, and prolonged stimulation causes exhaustion of the adrenaline stores. It is a very interesting and significant fact, in view of the functional relationship between the adrenal medulla and the sympathetic nervous system, that the fibers to the adrenal, unlike any other sympathetic fibers, do not form connections with ganglion cells but pass directly to the cells of the medulla. The adrenal cell thus takes the place of the sympathetic ganglion cell. A center controlling adrenal secretion is situated in the medulla oblongata. A higher center is present in the hypothalamus.

When the blood pressure raising (pressor) effect of adrenal extracts was first discovered, it was naturally suggested that the adrenal glands were responsible for maintaining the normal arterial blood pressure. The fallacy of such an idea is proved by the observation that destruction of the medullary tissue of both adrenals is not followed by a fall in blood pressure. Animals subjected to this operation show no abnormality. The adrenal medulla then, unlike the adrenal cortex, is not indispensable. Nor is there any evidence that socalled *high blood pressure* (*essential arterial hypertension*) is due to the secretion of excessive amounts of adrenaline.

Sympathin. It has been shown by Professor Cannon and his colleagues that the sympathetic nerves bring about their effects through the medium of a chemical substance liberated from their terminals. This substance resembles adrenaline in action and is called *sympathin*. It is released from the nerve endings by the nerve impulses and then acts upon the peripheral organ, e.g., smooth muscle of the skin, heart muscle, etc. Sympathin, however, is not identical with adrenaline. Adrenaline, as we have seen, causes both inhibitory and excitatory effects, according to the particular organ upon which its action is exerted. But there are two kinds of sympathin: one — sympathin I — is inhibitory; it is liberated from the nerve endings in such structures as the intestine, coronary vessels, etc.; the other — sympathin E — is excitatory and is liberated by sympathetic nerves going to the heart, the walls of the cutaneous and splanchnic blood vessels, the smooth muscle of the skin, etc.

The functions of the adrenal cortex. Animals die in from 10 to 15 days after complete removal of the adrenal glands. We have seen that excision of the adrenal medulla alone is not fatal; the cortex, therefore, is the part of the gland which is essential to life. If $\frac{1}{6}$ or so of the total amount of cortical tissue is left, the animal survives; this part of the gland must, therefore, produce a highly potent hormone.

During the time that the animal survives after double adrenalectomy, the following effects are observed: (1) loss of appetite, vomiting, fall in body weight, muscular weakness and, just before death, profound prostration; (2) subnormal body temperature and reduced basal metabolic rate; (3) concentration of the blood, due to a loss of plasma water; (4) reduction in the sodium chloride of the blood and a rise in the potassium, calcium, phosphate and non-protein nitrogen; (5) hypoglycemia; (6) signs of renal failure. The hormone of the adrenal cortex controls the metabolism of water and salts. In the absence of the adrenal cortex sodium and water are excreted in excessive amounts, whereas potassium escapes into the body fluids from the tissue cells, where normally it is in relatively high concentration. Excretion of this mineral by the kidneys is also impaired; its concentration therefore rises in the blood.

The adrenal cortex also exerts an influence upon carbohydrate metabolism which is due apparently to a hormone other than that controlling the metabolism of water and salt.

Destructive disease of the adrenal cortex, usually of a tuberculous nature, occurs in man. The manifestations of this condition, which is known as *Addison's disease*, are similar to, though less acute than, those just described as resulting from adrenalectomy in animals. The disease, if untreated, is gradually progressive, death occurring within two or three years. A bronze or dirty gray discoloration of the skin, which is not seen, as a rule, in animals after adrenalectomy, is a prominent feature in Addison's disease. Anemia and gastro-intestinal disturbances are also outstanding features of adrenal deficiency in the human subject. The pigmentation is due to an increase in the normal pigment (*melanin*) of the skin.

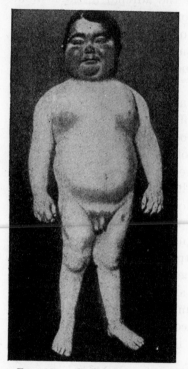

A hormone of the adrenal cortex has been obtained by extraction which, when administered subcutaneously, prevents the effects of adrenal deficiency in experimental animals or in Addison's disease. This hormone is called *cortin*.

The adrenal cortex performs other functions besides those just described. Several observations suggest that it influences the development of the sex functions. Enlargement of the adrenal cortex, for example, or tumors of cortical tissue sometimes occur, accompanied by sexual abnormalities. In children with such growths, precocious development of the sexual organs and of the secondary sex characters (see p. 365) is seen; these subjects often also show unusual muscular development for their age (Fig. 162). Women who are the victims of cortical enlargement or tumor become obese, and masculine in appearance; hair grows

Fig. 162. Child aged 4½ years suffering from adrenal tumor. Note the florid "beefy" face and the precocious development of the genital structures. (After Guthrie.)

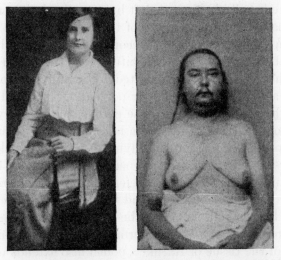

Fig. 163. Virilism due to tumor of adrenal cortex. *On left*, at age of 28 years before the onset of the disease; *on right*, at age of 35 years. (After Lescher.)

upon the face and chest, and their disposition tends toward "mannishness." This condition is referred to as *virilism* (Fig. 163).

THE PITUITARY BODY OR GLAND (HYPOPHYSIS CEREBRI)

Development and structure. The pituitary gland is connected by a narrow stalk, called the *infundibulum*, to the base of the brain just behind the optic chiasma. In man it is oval in form and measures a little over half an inch in its longest diameter. It is lodged within a small recess in the base of the skull, known as the *sella turcica* (L. = Turkish saddle). The pituitary consists of an anterior and posterior portion. These have separate origins and are different in structure and function. The anterior part arises from the embryonic mouth cavity as a hollow pouch (*Rathke's pouch*); the posterior part is formed by a downgrowth of nervous tissue from the base of the developing brain. Rathke's pouch grows upwards and, meeting the downgrowth from the brain, fuses with it. The cavity of Rathke's pouch be-

comes reduced to a narrow cleft by pressure against the posterior part; the anterior wall of the pouch, i.e., the portion
lying in front of the cleft, becomes thickened and is now
called the *pars anterior* of the pituitary.   The posterior wall
of Rathke's pouch is represented by a thin shell of tissue
closely applied to the posterior portion of the gland, and is
called the *pars intermedia.*   The part of the pituitary developed from the base of the brain is called the *pars nervosa.*

The portion of the pituitary lying in front of the cleft, i.e.,
the pars anterior, is readily separated from the rest of the
gland and is more commonly referred to as the *anterior lobe*,
whereas the portion lying behind the natural line of cleavage
offered by the cleft is called the *posterior lobe.*   The latter
therefore includes the pars intermedia and the pars nervosa.
A part of the tissue of Rathke's pouch also extends upwards
as far as the base of the brain, where it covers a mass of nerve
cells in this situation known as the *tuber cinereum.*   This
part of the pituitary, usually included as part of the anterior
lobe, is called the *pars tuberalis.*   As development proceeds,
the connection of the pituitary with the mouth cavity disappears, but that with the base of the brain persists and,
as mentioned above, is called the pituitary stalk or infundibulum.

The several parts of the pituitary are summarized in the
following table (see also Fig. 164).

Origin
{
From the mouth
cavity
{ Pars anterior
Pars tuberalis
Pars intermedia } Anterior lobe

From the base
of brain
{ Pars nervosa
Pituitary stalk
(infundibulum) } Posterior lobe
}

The anterior lobe consists of cords of cells separated by
relatively wide blood channels (sinuses).   The cells are of
three main types, (a) those which are stained poorly by ordinary dyes — *chromophobe* cells, (b) those which stain with

acid dyes — *acidophil* cells and (c) those which stain with basic dyes — *basophil* cells.

The posterior lobe of the pituitary receives numerous fibers from nerve cells situated in the region of the brain near the origin of the infundibulum. Some of these fibers can be traced into the anterior lobe. The structure of the pars nervosa is quite different from that of the anterior lobe. It contains nerve fibers, spindle-shaped cells called pituicytes, neuroglial cells and hyaline bodies. These latter are cells

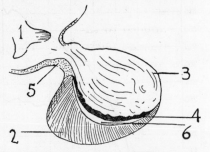

FIG. 164. Diagram of pituitary. 1, third ventricle of the brain; 2, pars anterior; 3, pars nervosa; 4, pars intermedia (black); 5, pars tuberalis; 6, cleft.

filled with a clear homogeneous material; their function is doubtful, though they are believed by some to furnish the active principle of the posterior lobe secretion.

The functions of the anterior lobe. The functions of the anterior lobe of the pituitary are many. The growth of the skeleton, the development of the sex glands and the activity of the thyroid, adrenal and parathyroid glands are dependent upon this part of the pituitary. Within the last ten years the anterior lobe has been the object of intensive investigation. A number of separate active principles or hormones, each of which exerts its specific effect when injected into animals, have been obtained by the extraction of anterior lobe tissue. It has been aptly termed the master gland of the endocrine system (see Fig. 184, p. 375).

Arrest of skeletal growth follows removal of the pituitary (*hypophysectomy*) from young animals, and the sex glands do not develop; the thyroid and cortex of the adrenal atrophy. The daily transplantation of anterior lobe tissue into the hypophysectomized animals is followed by the resumption of growth, development of the atrophic testes or ovaries, and restoration to normal of the adrenal cortex and thyroid gland. The effects of hypophysectomy can be corrected also by anterior lobe extracts, and extracts have been prepared which will abolish one or other defect caused by hypophysectomy, but leave the others almost or quite uncorrected. That is to say, extracts more or less pure in one or other of the pituitary hormones are now available. These extracts are also capable of causing their respective effects in normal animals. Thus, young rats treated daily with a purified growth extract attain a size nearly double that of untreated animals of the same litter (Fig. 165).

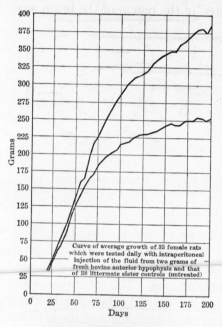

Curve of average growth of 33 female rats which were tested daily with intraperitoneal injection of the fluid from two grams of fresh bovine anterior hypophysis and that of 38 littermate sister controls (untreated)

The characteristic effect of the *growth hormone* has also been demonstrated on puppies (Fig. 166). The anterior pituitary principle which acts upon the thyroid is called the *thyrotropic hormone*. An animal receiving an extract containing this hormone shows marked hypertrophy and increased

FIG. 165. *Above,* curves showing the effect upon the growth of rats of daily injections of an extract of the anterior lobe of the pituitary. *Upper curve,* treated animals; *lower curve,* untreated litter mate sisters. (After Evans.) *Below,* photograph of a normal (*left*) and hypophysectomized rat of the same litter. (Van Dyke.)

Fig. 166. The effect of an extract of the anterior lobe of the pituitary upon the growth of the dachshund. Normal dog *on left;* dog of same litter *on right,* injected. (After Van Dyke.)

activity of the thyroid gland and, in consequence, a rise in the basal metabolic rate (Fig. 167). The pituitary principle which acts upon the adrenal cortex is known as the *adrenotropic hormone.* The anterior pituitary elaborates two hormones which act upon the gonads or sex glands; they are called the *gonadotropic hormones,* and will be considered in the section on the sex hormones. A hormone which stim-

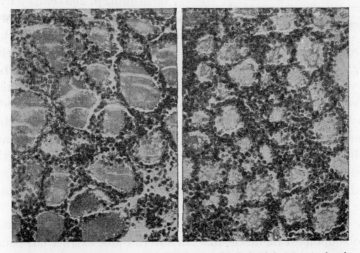

Fig. 167. The thyrotropic hormone. Section of thyroid from normal guinea-pig on the *left,* that of litter mate treated with 8 mg. of anterior lobe substance on *right.* (After Van Dyke.)

ulates the mammary glands to secrete milk is also liberated by the anterior lobe; this is known as *prolactin*, and will be described with the gonadotropic hormones (p. 366). There is evidence, moreover, that parathyroid activity is controlled by the anterior pituitary, but a hormone having this *parathyrotropic* action has not yet been obtained by extraction.

The anterior pituitary also exerts a pronounced effect upon carbohydrate metabolism, liberating a hormone which raises the sugar of the blood, thus antagonizing the action of insulin. This so-called *diabetogenic action* of the anterior lobe of the pituitary can be demonstrated by the following experiments: (a) Hypophysectomy, by removing the source of the sugar-raising principle, results in a fall in the blood sugar. (b) Removal of the pancreas alone (removal of the source of insulin, p. 299) causes hyperglycemia and the other signs of diabetes, but if the pituitary is removed as well,

FIG. 168. Showing effect of hypophysectomy upon the size of the adrenal. Adrenal from hypophysectomized animal on the *right*, from normal animal on the *left*. Note that the effect is exerted chiefly upon the cortex. (After P. Smith.)

little or no rise in blood sugar occurs; there may, indeed, be hypoglycemia when the animal is fasting. The transplantation of anterior lobe tissue into such a pancreatectomized-hypophysectomized animal causes the appearance of the usual effects of pancreatectomy. A pituitary extract with an effect upon carbohydrate metabolism, but free from growth effects, has not been prepared, so it is impossible to say whether the diabetogenic effect is due to a separate principle or is simply one of the effects of the growth hormone.

Recent work has demonstrated an effect of the anterior lobe upon fat metabolism. An anterior lobe extract has been prepared which, when injected into an animal upon a diet of fat, causes the accumulation of ketone bodies — *acetoacetic* and *β-hydroxybutyric* acids — in the blood and their appearance in the urine. Associated with this *ketogenic action* of the pituitary are a reduction in body fat and an increase in the fat of the liver. So far, an extract with a ketogenic effect, but free from all other pituitary effects has not been prepared. Whether it is due to a separate and distinct hormone is therefore unknown.

The physiology of the posterior lobe. An extract of the posterior lobe of the pituitary has been used in medicine for a number of years. It is sold under various trade names,

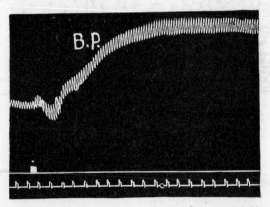

FIG. 169. Showing the effect of pituitrin upon the arterial blood pressure. B.P , carotid blood pressure; white square indicates the injection of 0.5 cc. pituitrin. (After Herring.)

e.g., *pituitrin, infundin,* etc. It produces the following effects when injected subcutaneously.

a. A rise in arterial blood pressure as a result of general vasoconstriction (Fig. 169). This action differs from that of adrenaline, for, all vessels — cutaneous, muscular, coronary, etc. — are constricted alike.

b. Contraction of the smooth muscle of the intestine, uterus, gall-bladder, urinary bladder and ureter. The contraction of the uterus is referred to as the *oxytocic effect.* The potency of a given posterior pituitary extract is assayed by testing its oxytocic effect upon the excised uterus of a virgin guinea-pig. It is for the oxytocic effect that the extract is most commonly employed in medicine, being given to cause uterine contractions in the later stages of labor.

c. Reduced production of urine — *antidiuretic effect.*

d. *Hyperglycemia, glucosuria and reduction of liver glycogen.*

e. *"Expansion"* of the melanophores in the skin of various cold-blooded vertebrates. The skin of the frog is abundantly supplied with melanophores. These are irregularly

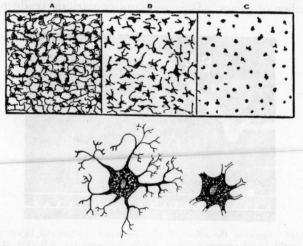

Fig. 170. Melanophores of frog's skin. A, fully expanded; B, partially contracted; C, fully contracted, i.e., collection of pigment at centers of the cells. (Redrawn from Hogben.) *Below,* enlarged views of a melanophore, expanded on the *left,* contracted on the *right.*

shaped cells possessing several branching processes and granules of a dark pigment (Fig. 170). The processes of adjacent cells interlace with one another to form a rich network. The pigment at one time may be concentrated near the center of the body of the cell; the next moment the granules may migrate and fill the processes. In the former event the skin is pale, in the latter it is dark. The movements of the pigment granules, and the consequent darkening or lightening of the skin depend upon the illumination of the environment; thus, by changing its color to match its surroundings, the animal is rendered less conspicuous to its enemies. An injection of pituitrin causes the granules to move into the branching processes, the animal then becoming a deep brown or green (Fig. 171). Hypophysectomy, on the contrary, by removing the supply of posterior lobe principle, results in permanent pallor of the skin. Blinding the animal, as by sealing its eyes with wax, abolishes the skin responses so long as the eyes are closed. The skin color remains unaltered in light or shade. The effects are evidently initiated by light reflexes, and are brought about in the following way. The pituitary secretes the melanophore-expanding principle continuously, so long as no light, or light of low intensity, falls upon the retina; the skin is then dark. Retinal illumination, on the other hand, sets up nerve impulses which suppress

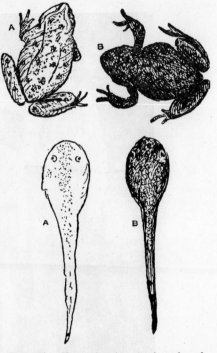

FIG. 171. *Upper drawing*, A, the color of a normal frog. B, the same frog after the injection of an extract of the posterior lobe of the pituitary. (Redrawn from Hogben.) *Below*, the effect of hypophysectomy upon the color of tadpoles. A, hypophysectomized; B, normal.

temporarily the pituitary secretion; the skin therefore becomes pale. Many species of fish and certain lizards and toads possess a similar mechanism for altering the depth of color of their skins in conformity with the illumination of their immediate environment. The pigment granules in some forms are red (*erythrophores*), in others yellow (*xanthophores*).

The several effects of posterior lobe extract are due, not to one, but to at least three and possibly four, distinct principles. A short time ago two substances in the form of white powders were separated from the relatively crude posterior lobe extract (pituitrin). These are known as *pitressin* and

—Courtesy Toronto Daily Star.

Fig. 172. Giantism.

pitocin. The former is vasoconstrictor (pressor), intestine-stimulating and antidiuretic in action; the latter contains the uterine-stimulating (oxytocic) principle. Both raise the sugar of the blood. The melanophore-expanding effect is caused only by pitressin, though it appears that this effect is due to a separate principle which is merely associated as a

contaminent with pitressin; there is convincing evidence
that it is a separate hormone elaborated by the *pars intermedia*. Indeed pitressin and pitocin are far from being
pure substances, and it is possible that the antidiuretic effect
of the former is also due to a distinct hormone.

Disorders of the pituitary in man. *Giantism and acromegaly — hyperpituitarism*. The great stature of those persons whom one sees in circuses or occasionally reads about
in the daily papers, is caused by overactivity of the anterior
lobe of the pituitary. Some of these *giants* are between 8 and

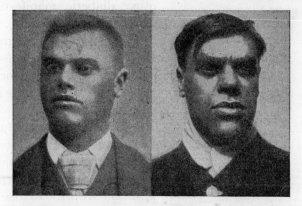

FIG. 173.   Acromegaly.   *Left*, at age of 25 years, before the onset of the
malady; *right*, 13 years later.   (After Cushing.)

9 feet tall (Fig. 172). Of course, general overgrowth of the
skeleton can occur only if the hyperpituitarism commences
during the natural period of growth. Hypersecretion of the
growth hormone of the pituitary after adolescence does not
cause an increase in stature. Nevertheless, the stimulating
effect of the hormone upon growth is seen in the bones of the
face, hands and feet. This condition, resulting from hyperpituitarism in adult life, is called *acromegaly* (G. *acron* = extremity, *megas* (megal-) = large); the appearance of a person
suffering from it is characteristic. The nose and lower jaw,
especially the latter, are abnormally prominent, and the
forehead unusually massive where it ordinarily forms a

slight eminence above the eye sockets. The skin of the face is thick and coarse. There may be overgrowth of hair upon the chest; in women hair may appear upon the face. There are often signs of overproduction of other hormones of the

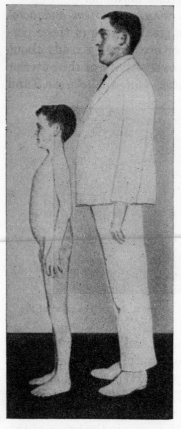

anterior lobe of the pituitary, e.g., hyperthyroidism (thyrotropic hormone), signs of overstimulation of the sex functions (gonadotropic hormones), or hyperglycemia, glucosuria and other diabetic manifestations (diabetogenic principle). The disease is gradually progressive (see Fig. 173). In most instances a pituitary tumor composed of acidophil cells is found after death.

Dwarfs — hypopituitarism. Deficiency of the anterior lobe secretion produces dwarfism. There are two main types of pituitary dwarf. In one type the diminutive body is of normal proportions, or rather, shows the proportions of the normal child, the head being large, relatively, to the rest of the body (see Fig. 174). These subjects may or may not show failure of sexual development. This variety of dwarf is usually intelligent, and not unattractive in appearance; it is referred to as the *Lorain type.* The midget of the circus belongs to this group.

Fig. 174. Lorain type of pituitary dwarf, age 21 years. Man on the right 5 ft. 7 in. (After Lisser.)

In the second type of pituitary dwarf the chief features, other than the stunting itself, are obesity and arrested

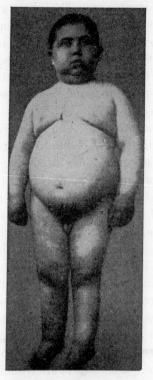

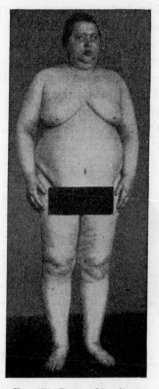

Fig. 175. Fröhlich's type of dwarfism (juvenile type of dystrophia adiposogenitalis). (After Cushing.)

Fig. 176. Dystrophia adiposogenitalis in a woman. (After Zondek.)

sexual development. Children affected by this pituitary disorder are often subnormal mentally, usually lethargic or somnolent, and have large appetites, especially for sweets. The fat boy of Pickwick Papers was undoubtedly an example of this disorder. The condition is called *dystrophia adiposogenitalis* or *Fröhlich's type* of dwarfism. It is thought to be due to destructive disease involving the posterior lobe or the base of the brain in the region of the origin of the pituitary stalk (hypothalamic region), together with deficiency of the growth hormone of the anterior lobe (see Fig. 175).

Essentially the same disorder occurs in adolescents or

adults but, of course, dwarfing is absent. The obesity is often extreme; the sex functions are suppressed. When it occurs in the male the fat has a feminine distribution, i.e., over the hips, thighs and chest; the skin is smooth and soft, the hair is scarce or absent from the face and body, but fine and plentiful on the head; in disposition, such persons tend toward effeminacy (see Figs. 176 and 177).

Pituitary cachexia or *Simmons disease*. This is a rare but very grave disease of the pituitary. It is due to atrophy of the anterior lobe occurring in early or middle adult life. The manifestations of the condition are those of a premature senility. For example, a person, giving every appearance of healthy youth, may within five years or so show all those features which one ordinarily associates with old age. The skin becomes dry, sallow and wrinkled, the hair gray and sparse, the body emaciated and the sexual organs atrophic. The bones are frail and appear to diminish gradually in size. Hypoglycemia (due to deficiency of diabetogenic principle) often occurs. Mental changes ultimately supervene.

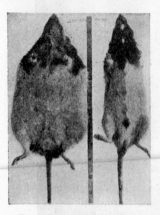

FIG. 177. Adiposity in a female rat following partial destruction of the pituitary by the injection into it of chromic acid; hypothalamus also probably injured. Litter mate normal female rat on the *right*. (After P. Smith.)

Diabetes insipidus. This is the name given to a disorder characterized by excessive thirst and the passage of large quantities of very dilute urine. It is due to disease of the posterior lobe of the pituitary, or of the base of the brain in the region of the infundibulum (hypothalamus) which, as we have seen, sends nerve fibers to the pars nervosa. Suppression of the secretion of the antidiuretic principle of the posterior lobe is evidently the cause of the excessive urine production (*polyuria*). Administration of posterior lobe extract temporarily relieves the condition. For a period of several hours after a single dose has been given by hypodermic injection or sprayed into the nostrils, the urine is reduced in volume and much less dilute.

The sex glands of the female are called the *ovaries*, those of the male, the *testes* (see Chapter XII). The gonads are also referred to as the *primary organs of sex*. The uterus, Fallopian tubes and vagina of the female, and the epididymis, seminal vesicles, prostate and penis of the male, are called the *accessory organs of sex*. Those changes which make their appearance at the time of sexual maturity (puberty) and which in many species distinguish at a glance the male from the female, are known as the *secondary sex characters*. In the human subject these include the growth of hair upon the pubis and in the axillae of both sexes, the bass voice and beard of men, and the development of the breasts of women. The large comb, wattles, spurs and tail feathers of the rooster, and the antlers of the stag, are other examples of secondary sex characters.

Excision of the sex glands, whether of the male or female, is called *castration*. Excision of the female gonads is also termed *ovariectomy*, or *spaying*. The effects of castration upon the male have been known from ancient times. When this operation is performed upon the male chicken (cockerel), the secondary sex characters do not appear; sex instinct is suppressed. The body weight of the castrated birds, which are known as *capons*, is greater, however, than that of uncastrated males of the same age. Castration of young stags prevents the development of the antlers. In boys who have been castrated before the age of puberty (a practice even of the present day, in certain countries), the larynx does not develop, and the voice remains high-pitched, the accessory organs of sex do not mature, and the secondary sex characters fail to appear. The operation exerts an effect upon fat deposition, the subjects tending toward obesity. The proportions of the skeleton are also altered, the bones of the lower limbs tending to be increased in length relatively to the trunk. That the gonads are endocrine organs is shown by the fact that the effects of castration in animals can be prevented by grafting tissue of the excised gland into some other part of the body. Any influence which the transplanted tissue can then exert upon other tissues must, obviously, be through the blood stream.

The sexual phenomena of the mature female. The organs of sex in both the male and the female animal mature at a definite age which varies in different species. At this time, which is called *puberty*, the reproductive functions commence. Sex desire is aroused and mating occurs. The *reproductive period* extends throughout the greater part of the animal's life; it ends with atrophic changes in the sex organs and the gradual suppression of sexual activity. In the human species puberty occurs at from 13 to 15 years of age, being usually a little earlier in girls than in boys. The secondary sex characters already described now make their appearance.

In the majority of animal species, the female will receive the male only at a certain period or periods of the year. These so-called *mating seasons* are characterized by certain sexual phenomena which are generally referred to by animal breeders as "heat" and by physiologists as *oestrus*. Oestrus, and the sex phases immediately preceding and following it, are together referred to as the *oestrous cycle*. The phase preceding oestrus is called *pro-oestrus;* that following it *postoestrus*. The changes during pro-oestrus consist of swelling and increased vascularity of the vulva and vagina. The uterus becomes enlarged and its glands hypertrophy. In some animals, at this time, bleeding occurs from the uterus and appears externally. The changes of pro-oestrus are preparatory in nature, the female organs being brought into a condition suitable for the reception of the male and the fertilization of the ovum. The Graafian follicles in the

ovary (p. 528) are undergoing maturation. Oestrus itself
is the period during which ovulation occurs and the female
will mate. The changes occurring during postoestrus are
anticipatory to the implantation of the fertilized ovum in
the uterus. The uterine mucosa hypertrophies and its
glands show increased secretory activity. During postoestrus the corpus luteum is developing. The uterine
changes in postoestrus resemble those taking place during
pregnancy which, indeed, are an extension or continuation
of the former.

In a number of animals the postoestrous preparation
of the uterus for the implantation of the fertilized ovum,
i.e., for pregnancy, is a very prominent feature of the

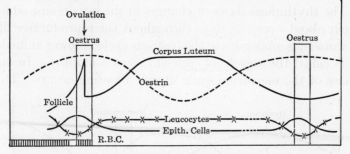

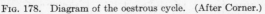

Fig. 178. Diagram of the oestrous cycle. (After Corner.)

oestrous cycle. Postoestrus in such species is therefore
called *pseudopregnancy*. If fertilization of the ovum by a
sperm cell occurs, the uterine changes of postoestrus merge
into those of pregnancy. If fertilization does not result, the
uterus returns to its resting state and all sexual activity
subsides, until the commencement (pro-oestrus) of the next
oestrous cycle.

Some animals, such as the dog, are called *monoestrous*,
since a single oestrous cycle occurs in each mating season.
The term *anoestrus* is applied to the quiescent periods intervening between the mating seasons. In other species, such
as the cow, mouse and rat, a series of oestrous cycles occurs
during each mating season; such animals are termed *poly-
oestrous*. The interval elapsing between any two oestrous

cycles is then termed *dioestrus* and the period between mating seasons, as in the case of monoestrous animals, is called anoestrus.

The phases of the oestrous cycle in a monoestrous animal are shown in the following scheme and in Fig. 178.

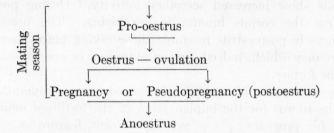

The rhythmical series of changes in the sex organs, which occur about every 28 days throughout the reproductive life of women, is analogous to the oestrous cycle of lower animals. It is called the *menstrual cycle* (L. *mens* = month). In one phase of the menstrual cycle uterine bleeding occurs. This

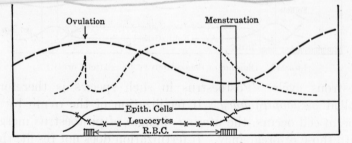

Fig. 179.   Diagram of the menstrual cycle.   (After Corner.)

phase is referred to as *menstruation* or the *menstrual period;* it has a duration of from 3 to 5 days.   Ovulation occurs about midway between the menstrual periods, that is, on the 14th or 15th day following the commencement of the bleeding (see Fig. 179).

Though, as just mentioned, the menstrual cycle corresponds to the oestrous cycle, the two differ in this respect, that bleeding, which is a prominent feature of the former, is absent or inconspicuous in the latter. It is not possible to say to what phase of the oestrous cycle (whether to pro-oestrus or postoestrus) menstruation itself corresponds. Since bleeding in certain species occurs in pro-oestrus, it has been assumed by some that such bleeding is analogous to menstruation; others have thought that menstruation corresponds to the end of postoestrus, i.e., to the breakdown of the uterine mucosa built up during postoestrus. There are objections to both these views.

The first menstrual cycle commences at puberty. Toward the end of the reproductive period, the cycles become irregular and finally cease at from 45 to 50 years of age; the suppression of the menstrual cycle at this time is called the *menopause*. It is accompanied by atrophic changes in the ovaries and the accessory organs of reproduction. Psychic phenomena, depression or irritability are common during this period. Instability of the vasomotor system, causing sudden flushing of the face, and a sensation of warmth — *hot flushes* — are of frequent occurrence.

Ovarian hormones. The phenomena of the oestrous and menstrual cycles, described in the preceding section, are dependent upon hormones produced in the ovary. The Graafian follicles of the ovary increase in size during pro-oestrus (or, in the human subject, in the phase of the menstrual cycle immediately following menstruation) and become filled with fluid; the ova enlarge and approach maturity. A hormone called *oestrin* or *theelin* is produced at this time by the cells lining the follicles. A mature follicle, or several follicles rupture during oestrus (or in women midway between the menstrual periods) and discharge the ovum (ovulation). The cells lining the ruptured follicle are then transformed into bodies containing a yellow fatty material called *lutein* (Fig. 180). These luteal cells replace the small blood clot which filled the follicle after its rupture. The yellow mass so formed is called the *corpus luteum* (yellow body); it is virtually a small temporary ductless gland, for it produces an internal secretion — the *hormone of the corpus luteum* or *progestin*.

Oestrin or *theelin* is responsible for the changes in the accessory organs of reproduction during pro-oestrus and oestrus, for the psychic phenomena of oestrus and for the development of the secondary sex characters of the mature female. It is therefore sometimes called the female sex hormone, and corresponds to the male hormone elaborated by the testes (p. 371). As already mentioned, removal of the ovaries of a young female animal prevents it from becoming sexually mature. The accessory organs fail to develop, oestrus does not occur, the secondary sex characters do not appear and the sex instinct is never manifested. Injections of oestrin into such an animal correct all these effects of castration.

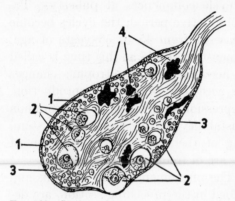

Fig. 180. Section of ovary; 1, immature, 2, mature Graafian follicles; 3, germinal epithelium; 4, corp. lutea.

On the other hand, young immature animals treated with oestrin show precocious sexual development.

Theelin was obtained, some few years ago, in crystalline form from female urine. It has the formula $C_{18}H_{22}O_2$. Another slightly different form, $C_{18}H_{24}O_3$, called *theelol*, was found later to be excreted in the urine.

The *hormone of the corpus luteum — progestin —* prepares the uterus for the reception of the fertilized ovum. It is responsible for the uterine changes characteristic of post-oestrus or pseudopregnancy, and for the development of the placenta — the organ which enables the embryo to receive nourishment from the mother during pregnancy (p. 544). For example, if a pregnant rabbit is castrated early in pregnancy or if the corpora lutea are excised, the embryo dies and is expelled from the uterus (*abortion*). The hormone of the corpus luteum can be prepared from hog's ovaries. This preparation, when injected into castrated animals, permits pregnancy to continue to full term. Normally, if fertilization of the ovum occurs the corpus luteum continues to increase in size until the later months of pregnancy, its hormone exerting a constant influence upon the growth and functional integrity of the placenta. On the other hand, if the ovum remains unfertilized the life of the corpus luteum is short. After exerting its hormonal influence for a time and causing the uterine changes characteristic of pseudopregnancy, it undergoes degeneration. In the human subject, changes in the uterine mucosa occur after ovulation analogous to those of pseudopregnancy but, again, failure of the ovum to become fertilized is followed by degeneration of the corpus luteum. The uterine mucosa then reverts to its resting state; it is at this time that menstruation occurs (see Figs. 178 and 179).

The male hormone — testosterone. In 1929 McGee obtained the male hormone in crude form by the extraction of bull's testes with acetone. This preparation was shown to cause the growth of the comb and wattles of the castrated cockerel (capon) and to bring about the normal development of the accessory organs (penis, seminal vesicles and prostate) of castrated male rats (Fig. 181). In immature rats treated with the extract, the accessory sex organs develop and sexual maturity is reached prematurely. The extract also stimulates the comb growth in hens and inhibits ovulation.

More recently, the hormone has been obtained in crystalline form from testicular tissue. This purified material is called *testosterone*, and has the empirical formula $C_{19}H_{30}O_2$. The hormone has also been obtained in crystalline form from male urine. Chemically, this material differs slightly from testosterone and has been designated *androsterone;* its activity is also much less ($\frac{1}{7}$ to $\frac{1}{10}$) than that of testosterone. The male hormone does not appear in the urine of boys until after the 10th year, but oddly enough it is present in the urine of normal women. The male hormone belongs, with the ovarian hormones, to the class of substances known as sterols (p. 302). Both testosterone and androsterone have been synthesized in the laboratory from cholesterol. This suggests the possibility that the male hormone is formed in the body from this substance, which is a constituent of nearly all animal tissues.

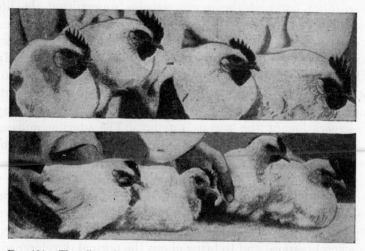

FIG. 181. The effect of testis hormone (from urine) upon comb growth. *Upper* photograph, capons which received daily injections over a period of 15 days. *Lower* photograph, untreated control group. (Funk, Harrow and Lejwa.)

Cells in the interstitial tissue of the testes — the so-called *cells of Leydig* — are generally believed to manufacture the male hormone. That these cells and not the spermatogenic cells (p. 532) are responsible seems evident from the fact that castration effects do not follow irradiation of the testes with X-rays which destroys the spermatogenic cells but leaves the cells of Leydig unaffected.

The relation of the anterior lobe of the pituitary to the sexual functions — gonadotropic hormones. The anterior lobe of the pituitary of either male or female contains two hormones which act upon the gonads. In the female one of these *gonadotropic hormones* stimulates the growth and maturation of the Graafian follicles in the ovary. Thus indirectly this hormone causes oestrin production. It was at one time called prolan A, but this term has fallen into disuse, and the hormone is now generally referred to as the *follicle stimulating hormone* (*F.S.H.*) of the anterior pituitary. The other gonadotropic hormone of the pituitary acts upon the second phase of the ovarian cycle, i.e., it stimulates the growth of the corpus luteum. This hormone, which was originally designated pro-lan B, is now generally referred to as the *luteinizing hormone* (*L.H.*). It, therefore, through its stimulating effect upon progestin formation, causes, indirectly, the changes in the uterine mucosa characteristic of pseudopregnancy and of the corresponding phase of the menstrual

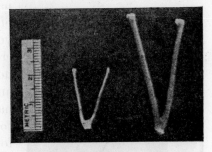

Fig. 182. Effect of hypophysectomy upon the uterus. *On right,* uterus of normal rat; *on left,* that of an hypophysectomized rat. (After Van Dyke.)

cycle, or, if pregnancy ensues, of the development of the placenta (cf. p. 543). Both gonadotropic hormones, whether derived from female or male pituitaries, produce analogous effects upon the testes. The follicle stimulating hormone acts upon the elements of the testes corresponding to the lining cells of the Graafian follicles, namely, the spermatogenic cells. The luteinizing hormone acts upon the cells of Leydig.

Removal of the pituitary is followed by atrophy of the gonads and, secondarily, of the accessory sex organs (Figs. 182 and 183). Transplantation of tissue of the anterior lobe or injections of anterior lobe extracts prevent these otherwise inevitable results of hypophysectomy. The anterior lobe of the pituitary is therefore ultimately responsible for the sexual development of the male or female animal. The phenomena of puberty, namely, the development and maturation of the gonads and, through the intermediary of the hormones liberated by the latter, the growth of the accessory organs of sex and the development of the secondary sex characters, are dependent upon the gonadotropic hormones.

The anterior lobe of the pituitary also liberates a hormone which stimulates milk secretion in the mother, after the birth of the young. This hormone is called the *lactogenic principle* or *prolactin*. It is obtained from the pituitary by acid extraction. If the pituitary is removed late in pregnancy, only a small quantity of milk is secreted after the young are born, and the secretion soon dries up. This hormone evidently also exerts an influence upon the maternal instinct, for hypophysectomized animals do not care for their young like normal mothers. Furthermore, injections of prolactin arouse the maternal instinct in young virgin rats; they commence to build a nest from straw, wool or other soft material which they can gather. The actions of the various hormones of the pituitary are summarized in Fig. 184.

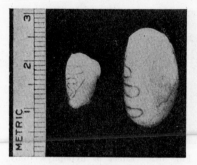

Fig. 183. Testis of hypophysectomized rat *on left;* that of normal animal on *right.* (After Van Dyke.)

The hormones of the placenta. The placenta contains two hormones. One of these is oestrin, the other, called by Collip the *anterior pituitarylike (A.P.L.) principle*, acts upon the ovary, stimulating the growth of the corpus luteum. It also stimulates, though to a slight extent, the maturation of the Graafian follicles. The oestrin found in the placenta is apparently manufactured by this organ, and does not simply represent a store of the hormone produced by the ovary. This conclusion is justified by the observation that in pregnancy large quantities of oestrin continue to appear in

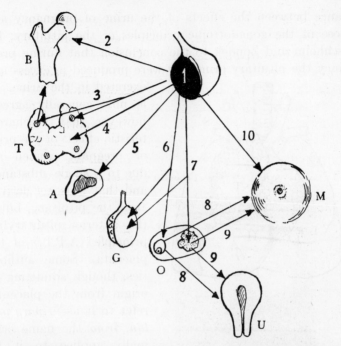

Fig. 184. Diagram illustrating the effects exerted by the anterior lobe of the pituitary. 1, anterior lobe; 2, growth hormone; 3, parathyrotropic hormone; 4, thyrotropic hormone; 5, adenotropic hormone; 6 and 7, gonadotropic hormones; 8, oestrin; 9, progestin; 10, prolactin. B, bone; T, thyroid; A, adrenal; G, testis; O, ovary, showing a Graafian follicle and a corpus luteum; U, uterus; M, mammary gland.

the urine, though the ovaries have been removed. A.P.L. also appears in the urine of pregnant women. This fact is the basis for the well known test for pregnancy. Two German workers, Aschheim and Zondek, found that the injection of a small quantity of urine of a pregnant woman into a young (sexually immature) mouse caused within 100 hours the following effects:

a. The onset of oestrus
b. Small hemorrhages into some of the Graafian follicles
c. The formation of corpora lutea

The Aschheim-Zondek test for pregnancy is almost infallible; its error is only about 1 per cent. The close resemblance between the effects of the urine of pregnancy and those of the gonadotropic principles of the pituitary, led Aschheim and Zondek to the conclusion that during pregnancy the pituitary principles were produced in excess and excreted in the urine. It is now generally agreed, however, that the characteristic effects of the urine of pregnant women are due to a single substance, and that it is *not* derived from the pituitary, but is the anterior pituitarylike principle (A.P.L.) of the placenta. Some authorities, though admitting its origin from the placenta, refer to it as *urinary prolan*, from the name originally applied to it by Aschheim and Zondek.

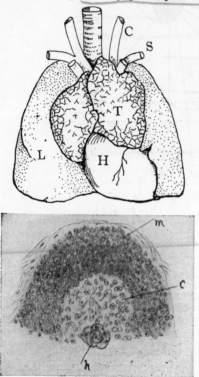

FIG. 185. Showing the relation of the thymus to the thoracic viscera and great vessels. C, common carotid artery; H, heart; L, lung; S, subclavian artery. *Below*, section through a lobule of the thymus. *c*, cortex; *m*, medulla; *h*, Hassall's corpuscle.

THE THYMUS

The thymus lies behind the upper part of the breastbone and extends upwards for a short distance into the neck. Below, it lies in relation to the base of the heart and the great vessels. It is of relatively large size in the infant, but commences to shrink at about the age of puberty and, by adult life, is much reduced in bulk. The thymus is of soft texture and of a pale pink color. On dissection it is seen to consist of two zones (Fig. 185). The outer zone or *cortex* is composed of cells resembling lympho-

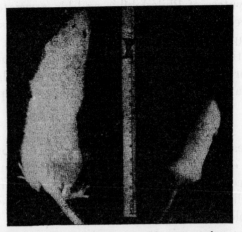

FIG. 186. Effect of thymus extracts. *At right*, untreated control rat 14 days old; *at left*, 15 day old rat of third generation receiving thymus extract. (After Rowntree, Clark and Hanson.)

cytes; the inner zone contains peculiar bodies called *Hassall's corpuscles*, formed of epithelial-like cells arranged concentrically around a mass of granular cells.

Many functions have been attributed to the thymus. Though proof is lacking, it is concerned in all probability with the production of lymphocytes. The structure of the cortical portion of the organ suggests such a function. Several endocrine functions at one time or another have been attributed to it, but most of the theories which have been advanced are based more upon conjecture than upon fact.

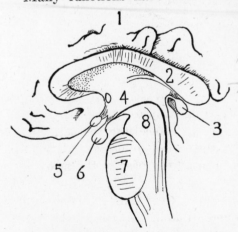

FIG. 187. Diagram to show position of the pineal gland. 1, cerebral hemisphere; 2, corpus callosum; 3, pineal; 4, 3rd ventricle of the brain; 5, optic chiasma; 6, pituitary; 7, pons; 8, midbrain.

Dr. Rowntree of Philadelphia and his associates claim to have secured evidence that the thymus exerts a stimulating influence upon growth and development. When an extract of thymic tissue was injected into succeeding generations of rats, the progeny of the later generations were larger than untreated animals and showed precocious development.

THE PINEAL BODY

The pineal is a small body lying deep in the brain under the shelter of the posterior extremity of the corpus callosum (p. 439; see also Fig. 187). Though its structure suggests the possibility that it serves some endocrine function there is no reliable evidence that such is the case.

CHAPTER IX

THE PHYSIOLOGY OF NERVE AND MUSCLE

The structure of the nerve fiber. The peripheral nerves are constituted of bundles of nerve fibers bound together by connective tissue. The outermost covering or sheath of the nerve is called the *epineurium* (see Fig. 188). Each nerve fiber is the process of a nerve cell whose body is situated in the central nervous system (brain or spinal cord), or in one of the outlying ganglia (e.g., ganglia of the posterior spinal nerve roots). Some nerve fibers transmit messages, e.g., sensations of touch, pain, sound, etc., from the periphery to the central nervous system and give rise to a sensation of one kind or another. They are, therefore, *sensory* in function. Others carry messages to the muscles causing them to contract, and are, therefore, called *motor* nerve fibers. Certain nerves are composed entirely of sensory fibers; some contain only motor fibers; others again contain both types of fiber, and are called *mixed* nerves.

The nerve fiber, then, whether in a peripheral nerve or in the central nervous system itself, is the conducting unit of the nervous system, and may be compared to a single wire in an electric cable or in the central exchange of a telephone system. The message which the fiber transmits is called the *nerve impulse.* Nerves which transmit impulses from the periphery to the nerve centers are called *afferent;* those which transmit impulses in the opposite direction are called *efferent.* Now, of course, all sensory nerve fibers are afferent, but not all afferent fibers are sensory, for some transmit impulses which make no impression upon consciousness — they arouse no sensation. Similarly, all motor fibers are efferent, but not all efferent fibers are motor, since certain fibers of the autonomic nervous system terminating in glands are secretory in function.

Each fiber entering into the composition of the peripheral

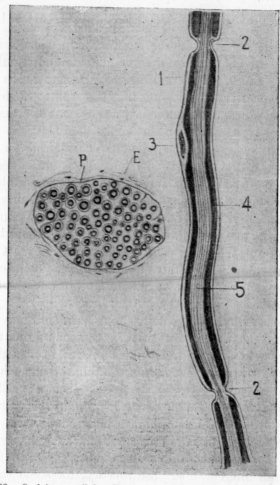

Fig. 188. *On left*, a small bundle of nerve fibers in a peripheral nerve. Note medullated fibers of different sizes. P, perineurium; E, epineurium which separates adjacent bundles of fibers and ensheathes the nerve. *On right*, drawing showing the structure of the nerve fiber. 1, neurilemma; 2, node of Ranvier; 4, myelin sheath; 5, axis cylinder showing neurofibrils.

nerves consists of a delicate filament of protoplasm — the *axis cylinder* — ensheathed by a layer of fatty material called *myelin*.

The *myelin sheath* is enclosed, in turn, by a very thin transparent membrane known as the *neurilemma* or *sheath of Schwann*. The myelin sheath is interrupted at regular intervals; at these points the neurilemma dips sharply toward, and comes almost into contact with, the axis cylinder. These interruptions give the impression of a series of equally spaced constrictions along the nerve fiber; they are called the *nodes of Ranvier*. The axis cylinder contains a number of fine thread-like strands known as *neurofibrils* which run throughout its length (see also p. 416).

Not all types of nerve fiber possess a myelin sheath, but most of those in the ordinary cranial and spinal nerves are so constituted. Such are called *myelinated* or *medullated* fibers. Certain ones, such as the postganglionic fibers of the autonomic nervous system (p. 460), are devoid of a myelin sheath, and are therefore called *amyelinated* or *non-medullated* fibers.

Degeneration of nerve. Since the nerve fiber, as just mentioned, is simply the elongated process of a nerve cell, its nutrition depends upon its remaining a part of the cell. When, therefore, a nerve fiber is sectioned or crushed, degenerative changes begin almost at once in the section distal to (i.e., beyond) the point of injury. These changes, as they occur in a peripheral nerve, were first described by Waller, a physiologist of the last century, and are usually referred to as *Wallerian degeneration*. The first alteration in the fibers of the nerve appears within 24 hours after the injury. The neurofibrils in the axis cylinder become wavy or tortuous, and then break up into sections. Next the myelin sheath swells and droplets of myelin appear. The myelin itself undergoes decomposition into its constituents — fatty acids, etc. Finally, usually within two or three weeks following the injury, the debris resulting from the degenerative process is cleared away, nothing remaining of the nerve fiber but an empty tube — the neurilemma (Fig. 189). The nerve fiber on the proximal side (i.e., on the side toward the nerve cell) of the section also degenerates as far as the first node of Ranvier, and even the body of the cell itself may show degenerative changes (*retrograde degeneration*), consisting of disappearance of the Nissl bodies (p. 416) and shrinkage of the nucleus.

The degenerative changes just described are readily detected by treating the tissue with a suitable stain and examining thin sections of it beneath the microscope. Most of the knowledge which we possess of the origin and course of the various fiber tracts in the brain and cord (Chapter X) has been gained from experiments upon animals in which

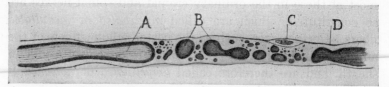

Fig. 189. Degenerating nerve fiber two days after section. A, end of proximal segment of nerve; B, drops of myelin derived from the myelin sheath; C, nucleus of neurilemma; D, neurilemma.

the method of section and degeneration has been employed, or from the examination of nervous tissue of subjects who have died of nervous disease. The location of the degenerative changes following experimental injury to fibers in one or other part of the brain or cord, or resulting from disease, indicates the direction from which the affected fibers originated. For example, if after section of a fiber tract in the cord degeneration occurs above the point of section, the cell bodies of the sectioned fibers must be situated below. Also, by destroying a group of nerve cells in one or other situation and examining tissue taken from different parts of the nervous system for degenerative changes, the course taken by the fibers of the injured cells can be traced. (See also left-hand cut Fig. 217, p. 433.)

Degeneration of the peripheral nerves may result from

causes other than mechanical injury. Peripheral nerve degeneration is seen in poisoning by certain chemicals (e.g., lead), in vitamin deficiency (A and B₁) and in certain nervous diseases (e.g., infantile paralysis). It is most important in such conditions, or following mechanical injury to a nerve trunk, to have some means of detecting the presence of degeneration, and of determining the extent to which the degenerative process has progressed. Such information is afforded by testing the affected nerve or nerves with an electrical current. The current is applied to the skin overlying the motor nerve trunk. When the nerve is completely degenerated it fails to respond (as shown by the absence of a contraction of the muscle) to either the faradic (inter-

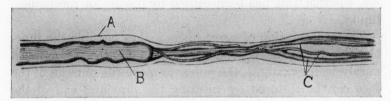

Fig. 190. Regenerating nerve fiber. A, neurilemma; B, proximal segment of nerve fiber showing bulbous end; C, neurofibrils which have sprouted from the end of the original fiber. (After Ranvier, redrawn.)

rupted) or to the galvanic current. When the current is applied directly over the muscle, a sluggish response is obtained with the galvanic current, but none with the faradic. These abnormal responses of the nerve and muscle to electrical stimulation constitute the *reaction of degeneration*.

Nerve regeneration. Provided that the two ends of a divided nerve are not too widely separated, the continuity of the nerve ultimately becomes restored — the nerve is said to have undergone regeneration. The neurofibrils of the proximal section of the nerve fiber (i.e., the part extending from the cell body to the point of section) grow distally and, entering the empty neurilemmal tube of the degenerated fiber, gradually extend throughout its entire length (Fig. 190). The neurofibrils later become embedded in a ground of protoplasm. Thus, a new axis cylinder is formed. The rate of growth of the axis cylinder varies in different types of nerve from 0.25 to 2.5 millimeters per day. A myelin sheath is formed later, and finally the function of the nerve may be completely restored. The sprouting neurofibrils sometimes cross a gap of several millimeters separating the two segments of the nerve — a truly remarkable phenomenon. The force or influence which directs or attracts them into their proper channels is unknown. A neurilemma is absolutely necessary for the regeneration process. The fibers of the central nervous system, and of the optic and auditory nerves, which do not possess neurilemmal sheaths, are incapable of regeneration after interruption of their continuity, whether this has been caused by disease or mechanical injury.

The regeneration of nerve fibers makes possible the junction by operation of one nerve with another. In facial paralysis, for example, the power to move the muscles of the face can be restored by suturing the proximal end of the hypoglossal nerve to the distal end of the degenerated facial nerve. The latter nerve is regenerated by the growth of neurofibrils from the former.

The physiological properties of the nerve fiber. *Excitability* and *conductivity* are the outstanding properties of the nerve fiber. Though living tissues in general possess these properties, they are developed to the highest degree in nerves. When the nerve fiber is stimulated by means of an *electric shock*, *mechanically*, as by a pinch, *thermally*, as by the application of a heated glass rod, or *chemically*, as by touching it with a crystal of common salt, a disturbance is set up at the point of stimulation which is called the *local excitatory state*. If the stimulus is sufficiently strong to raise the latter to a certain critical value, a disturbance spreads at high velocity along the nerve. This propagated disturbance or wave of excitation, set up by stimulating the nerve fiber, is called the *nerve impulse*.

When a constant (galvanic) current, such as that derived from an ordinary dry cell, is used as a stimulus, it is found that excitation of a nerve, muscle or other excitable tissue occurs at the instant that the current is closed, and again when the current is opened. Though, of course, the current continues to flow during the intervening period, it does not excite the tissue, provided that its intensity remains unchanged. The closing or making current (make shock) causes excitation of the nerve or muscle at the *cathode*, i.e., at the point where the current leaves the tissue. The opening or breaking current (break shock) causes stimulation at

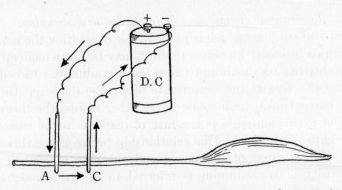

FIG. 191. Illustrating stimulation of a nerve by means of a constant current. D.C, dry cell; A, anode; C, cathode.

the *anode*, i.e., where the current enters the tissue (see Fig. 191). The stimulus caused by making the current is the stronger of the two, so that when the current strength is gradually reduced a point is reached at which a response occurs only with a make shock.

Anelectrotonus and catelectrotonus. When a constant current is sent through a section of nerve by means of a pair of electrodes placed in contact with it, the excitability and conductivity of the nerve in the region of the *anode* is reduced. These properties of the nerve in the region of the *cathode* are increased. The reduced excitability and conductivity at the anode is called *anelectrotonus;* the enhancement of these properties at the cathode is known as *catelectrotonus*.

The qualities of a stimulus. The prime factors in excitation of nervous or muscular tissues are *intensity, rate of change* and *duration* of the stimulus.

1. *Intensity or strength of the stimulus*. An electric shock, which is the most convenient and commonest type of stimulus used in the laboratory, must be of a certain minimal voltage. The electrical stimulus whose voltage is just sufficient to excite is said to be of *threshold* or *liminal* strength. A stimulus weaker than this is called *subthreshold* or *subliminal*.

2. *The rate of change in the intensity of a stimulus*. An electrical stimulus which is just capable of exciting the nerve when its intensity increases rapidly, may be quite ineffective if it reaches its maximum value more gradually. In order to be effective at the slower rate of change the strength of the current must be increased. In other words, the threshold of excitation rises as the rate of increase in the current strength diminishes. This relationship between the threshold of excitation of the nerve and the rate of change in intensity of the stimulus is referred to as *accommodation*. Rate of change is a factor of just as great importance in other types of stimulation. We are all familiar with the fact that changes in the environment, whether of temperature, sound, or movement, are more likely to be effective if they occur suddenly.

3. *Duration — chronaxie*. Since, as mentioned above, a constant current excites only at the make and break, though the current continues to flow in the intervening period, it had been thought that the *duration* of a current played no part in excitation. But it is known now that the current must flow for a certain minimal time, measured in thousandths of seconds, in order to excite. That is to say, if the time elapsing between the make and break of the current is too short the tissue is not excited, no matter how strong

the current may be. Thus, alternating currents of very high frequency but having a strength of several thousand volts, do not stimulate when passed through the body.

The length of time during which a current must flow in order to excite a nerve or muscle varies with the strength of the current, the time being shorter with a strong than with a weak current. The excitability of a given nerve or other tissue may be measured by determining the minimal intensity of a current which, if allowed to flow for an indefinitely

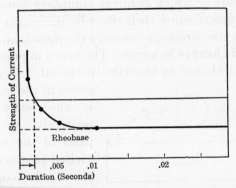

FIG. 192. Time-duration curve. The chronaxie is the time interval marked by the intersection of the vertical interrupted line with the upper horizontal line, the latter representing a strength of current twice the rheobase. Its value in this instance, as indicated by the arrow, is .002 sec.

long period, will excite, i.e., the time factor is not considered. On the other hand, the excitability can be measured by using a current of a *standard strength*, and determining the minimal time during which it must flow in order to excite. The current of a strength just sufficient to excite, but of indefinitely long duration, is called the *rheobase*. A current of double this strength is then employed as the standard, and the minimal duration for excitation measured. This time factor is called the *chronaxie* of the tissue in question. In other words, chronaxie is a measure expressing the *shortest duration for excitation of a current having a strength twice the rheobase* (Fig. 192).

The chronaxies of the different types of excitable tissue, and of nerves and muscles of the different species, as well as of the same species, show wide variation. Rapidly acting tissues, such as voluntary muscle, have shorter chronaxies than the more slowly acting, such as smooth muscle. The tissues of warm-blooded animals have, in general, shorter chronaxies than those of cold-blooded species. The chronaxies of thick nerve fibers, which conduct at high velocity, are shorter than those of fibers of smaller diameter and slow conduction. A nerve and the muscle which it supplies have chronaxies of nearly the same value, and certain drugs — such as curare — which paralyze voluntary muscle, are believed by some to cause their effect by increasing the disparity between the chronaxie values of the muscle and its nerve.

Electrical changes in nerve. The nerve impulse is accompanied by a change in electrical potential. Any part of a nerve in the excited state is electrically negative, relatively, to all other parts of the nerve. The excited part is as the negative pole (copper) of a battery; any inactive part corresponds to the positive pole (zinc). If, therefore, a pair of electrodes are in contact, one with an excited part of the nerve, the other with a resting part, and the two electrodes connected

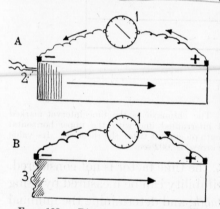

FIG. 193. Diagram illustrating action current (A) and current of injury (B). 1, galvanometer; 2, stimulus; 3, injured part of tissue (see text).

through a sensitive electrical recording apparatus, a current flows and causes a movement of the indicator of the instrument. The direction taken by the current is from the unexcited part of the nerve (+) to the excited part (−), through the instrument, and from excited to unexcited part through the nerve. Thus, the electrical circuit is completed (see Fig. 193 A). A similar electrical phenomenon occurs in muscle and other excitable tissue — *any active tissue being relatively negative to inactive tissue.*

The current thus set up in excited tissue is called the *action current.* Injured nerve or other tissue is also relatively negative to healthy tissue; the current set up when the injured and uninjured sections of the tissue are connected by a conductor is called the *current of injury* or *demarcation current* (see Fig. 193 B).

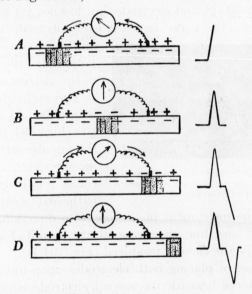

Fig. 194. Showing the production and recording of a diphasic action current (see text).

The excited state, as we have seen, travels rapidly over the nerve fiber. By placing electrodes upon a length of nerve, and connecting them with a sensitive electrical apparatus, such as the string galvanometer, or with an amplifier and cathode ray oscillograph it is possible to detect the passage of nerve impulses, whether these are set up by artificial stimulation or occur naturally. By means of special photographic apparatus a permanent record of the action currents can be obtained (see Fig. 194), and their velocity and magnitude determined. For example, if the electrodes are placed upon two uninjured parts of a nerve, and one end of the nerve stimulated, the impulse when it reaches the first electrode causes this to be relatively negative to the second electrode. The indicator of the electrical recording apparatus swings away from the zero position. This causes a stroke to be inscribed above the base line in the photographic record (Fig. 194 A). When the impulse passes from beneath the first electrode, but has not yet reached the second (i.e., the nerve beneath each electrode is inactive

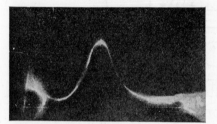

and so of equal electrical potential), the indicator of the instrument returns to zero and a downstroke is inscribed in the record (see Fig. 194 B). When the impulse arrives at the second electrode this becomes relatively negative to the first; a current flows

FIG. 195. Action potential wave recorded by means of the cathode ray oscillograph. After Erlanger and Gasser.)

through the instrument in the opposite direction, a curve below the base line appearing in the record (Fig. 194 C). Thus a *diphasic curve* is produced (Fig. 194 D).

If instead of placing both electrodes upon uninjured tissue, the nerve beneath the second electrode is crushed, as is the usual practice in recording the action currents, the current resulting from the difference in potential between the injured and uninjured portions (current of injury) undergoes a sharp reduction in strength when the impulse reaches the first electrode. That is, the action current opposes the current of injury. This variation in strength (negative variation) of the injury current appears as a single wave in the record. A second wave, directed oppositely to the first, does not appear, since the impulse cannot reach the electrode placed upon the crushed section of nerve. Such a record is called *monophasic* (see Fig. 195).

The most convenient and reliable means which we possess for investigating the properties of the nerve impulse is provided by the analysis of the electrical changes recorded from the nerve. The strength of the action current, as indicated by the amplitude of the recorded curves, their frequency and velocity, can be readily determined; such values are taken as corresponding to those of the nerve impulses themselves.

THE NATURE OF THE NERVE IMPULSE

The "all or none" principle (or law). The "all or none" principle, as it applies to the contraction of heart muscle, has been already defined (p. 112). This principle applies also to the nerve impulse and to the contraction of the individual fibers of skeletal muscle. For example, a stimulus just strong enough to excite the nerve fiber causes the transmission of an impulse which, as gauged by the action current, is of the same magnitude, and has the same velocity as one set up by a stimulus of much greater strength. In other words, a stimulus which is capable of causing a response at all causes the *maximum* response.

The nerve impulse may, therefore, be compared to a spark travelling in a fuse of gunpowder for, of course, it is immaterial in so far as the size of the spark and the rate of its transmission are concerned, whether the fuse has been ignited by a small or by a large flame (which is comparable to the stimulus applied to the nerve). For the sake of illustration other comparisons may be drawn between the nerve fiber and a fuse of gunpowder. The nerve impulse and the spark are self-propagated; both derive the energy for their transmission from the material through which they pass. They, therefore, do not undergo any diminution with distance, differing in this respect from a sound wave or a wave set up in water, which undergoes a reduction in amplitude and velocity as the distance from its point of origin lengthens.

If a section of the nerve fiber is treated with a narcotic,

e.g., ether or alcohol, conduction in the narcotized region is depressed, the velocity and magnitude of the impulse are reduced in passing through it. But the impulse, upon entering the unnarcotized section of nerve, regains its original value — further proof for the statement that the conduction of the impulse is dependent upon energy derived from the nerve fiber itself. A wave in air or water, once having undergone a reduction in force as a result of some resistance in its path, is not restored to its original value after having emerged

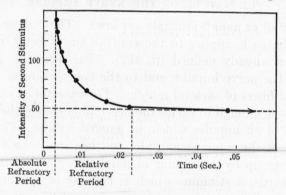

Fig. 196. Curve of the recovery in the sciatic nerve of the frog. Two stimuli were applied to the nerve, the second stimulus being separated from the first by various time intervals and of just sufficient strength to excite. Intensity of stimulus is plotted along the ordinate, time along the abscissa. The interrupted horizontal line indicates the threshold strength of current required to excite the resting nerve. During the absolute refractory period (about 0.003 sec. in this instance) a stimulus, however strong, will not excite. The excitability returns gradually during the next 0.02 sec. (relative refractory period). (After Adrian.)

from the medium offering the resistance. The spark in gunpowder behaves, however, like the nerve impulse. If a section of the fuse is dampened the spark is less intense and travels more slowly through this section, but at once flares up again upon reaching the dry section of powder beyond.

The absolute and relative refractory periods of nerve. The nerve fiber, after the passage of an impulse, is for a short time unable to conduct. The transmission of the impulse has exhausted for the moment the nerve fiber's store of energy; this must be replenished before a second impulse can be conducted. This brief interval following the passage of the impulse and during which the fiber will not conduct, is called the *absolute refractory period* (see Fig. 196). The nerve fiber in this state may be likened to the gunpowder fuse after the spark has passed, leaving only a trail of ash; a fresh train of powder must be laid before a second spark can travel the same path. The duration of the absolute refractory period of frog's nerve is from 0.002 to 0.003 second, and of mammalian nerve about 0.001 second. It is followed by a longer period during which the energy of the fiber is being gradually restored. This is called the *relative refractory period;* it has a duration of from 0.01 to 0.02 second. During this time, the conductivity of the fiber is below normal, a stronger stimulus than usual being required to set up an impulse which, as judged by the action current, is of smaller magnitude. The conductivity increases progressively, reaching that of resting nerve at the termination of the relative refractory period.

The velocity of the nerve impulses. In mammalian myelinated nerves the impulse travels at a velocity of from 90 to 100 meters per second, i.e., at about the speed of a revolver bullet. The impulses in unmyelinated mammalian nerves and in all nerves of cold-blooded animals, whether myelinated or unmyelinated, travel at much slower rates. Nerve fibers of large diameters transmit impulses at a higher velocity than those of small diameter. In the small non-medullated fibers of some cold-blooded animals the rate of conduction of the nerve impulse is less than 0.2 meter per second.

The frequency of nerve impulses. The length of the absolute refractory period determines the maximum frequency at which the nerve fiber is capable of transmitting impulses. In mammalian nerve, for example, the absolute refractory period has a duration of $\frac{1}{1000}$ second. In other words, a period of $\frac{1}{1000}$ second must elapse after the passage of an impulse before the fiber can again conduct. The maximum frequency is, therefore, around 1000 per second.

Action currents of this frequency have actually been demonstrated by means of the cathode ray oscillograph. A single fiber in the nerve trunk was separated from its neighbors by careful dissection and laid across a pair of electrodes connected to the recording apparatus.

The relation of the frequency of the impulses to the magnitude of the response. It has been mentioned above that the individual nerve impulse cannot, so far as is known, be varied in magnitude or in any other character by altering the strength of the stimulus. It may naturally be asked then, "Why does a stronger stimulus produce a greater effect?" A strong stimulus, for example, causes a more intense sensation than a weaker one when applied to a sensory nerve ending, or a more powerful contraction when applied to a motor nerve. The greater sensation caused by the stronger stimulus is due entirely to the higher frequency of the impulses. Increasing the strength of the stimulus causes a rise in the frequency of the impulses discharged along each nerve fiber; when applied to a nerve trunk, the stronger stimulus also excites more nerve fibers than the weak one. These two factors, namely, the frequency of the impulses in each nerve fiber and the number of fibers involved, that is, the number of impulses reaching consciousness in a unit of time, determine the intensity of the sensation. Similarly, the magnitude of the muscular response when a motor nerve is stimulated, is related to the frequency of the impulses discharged along the individual nerve fibers, as well as upon the number of fibers excited. Each nerve fiber of a mammalian motor nerve terminates by dividing into some hundred branches, each of which supplies a muscle fiber. Now, as we shall see (p. 398), when a muscle is stimulated by a single electric shock it gives a single contraction or *twitch*, but if stimulated by a series of such shocks in rapid succession the resulting twitches become fused into a sustained contraction or *tetanus*, which exerts a force considerably greater than that of the single twitch.

In a voluntary movement of the human arm, for example, the impulses pass from the central nervous system to the muscles at varying frequencies — from 5 to 50 or more per second. At the lower frequencies the individual contractions are incompletely fused and the movements are weak. Complete fusion of contractions occurs at the higher frequencies, a powerful movement resulting.

In some types of contraction, such as the tonic contraction of the muscles which maintain the body's posture, the impulses are transmitted at moderately high frequencies, but only a proportion of the nerve fibers going to the muscle are active at one time, i.e., the impulses are discharged from the central nervous system asynchronously along the several fibers composing the motor nerve. As a consequence, the fibers of the muscle are never all contracted at once; they contract in rotation. Since the muscle fibers respond in relays, some resting while others contract and vice versa, this type of contraction, though generally less powerful than that which results in movement, is able to be maintained for relatively long periods without causing fatigue.

The nature or quality of sensation aroused by stimulating a sensory nerve ending varies with the particular nerve ending excited. For example, stimulation of certain nerve endings in the skin causes a painful sensation, of others a sensation of touch, of others again, a sensation of heat or of cold. The optic nerve transmits impulses which arouse visual sensations. The acoustic and olfactory nerves and the nerves of taste when stimulated give rise to their own peculiar sensations. To what is this specificity of the sensory nerves due? There are two possibilities. (a) The fibers constituting the several types of nerve may differ in some fundamental way from one another, so that the impulses set up may have some distinguishing characteristic. In other words, each type of fiber may convey to consciousness a message peculiar to that type of fiber. (b) The fibers themselves may be unspecific and the impulses which they transmit may be all alike, the different kinds of sensations, pain, touch, visual, auditory, etc., being then dependent upon the particular region of the brain where the impulses are received. That is, the different regions of the brain interpret, each in its own way, the messages which they receive, though these are all identical in their general characters.

The latter conception appears to be the true one. All the evidence indicates that the impulses, along whatever type of nerve they are transmitted, though they may differ in minor details, are essentially the same in character. For example, the action currents recorded from the optic nerve, from a motor nerve or from a cutaneous sensory nerve, show no characteristic differences which might reasonably be considered as a basis for the several qualities of sensation. The center in the brain in which the impulses arrive is the determining factor. Impulses reaching one part of the cerebral cortex cause a visual sensation but, if these same impulses could be directed to the auditory center of the brain they would, according to this view, give rise to a sensation of sound.

Chemical changes in nerve. Until a few years ago attempts had failed to demonstrate any increase in oxygen consumption or of carbon dioxide production by nerve during its activity. Nor could any rise in temperature of the nerve be demonstrated during the passage of the impulse. It was, therefore, thought that the conduction of the nerve impulse was a purely physical process. By the application within recent years of more refined methods of investigation it has been shown quite conclusively, however, that conduction in nerve is essentially chemical in nature. A resting nerve produces a small quantity of heat (70×10^{-6} calories per gram of nerve per second) which is increased by over 50 per cent during activity. The resting nerve also consumes oxygen and produces carbon dioxide, the gaseous exchanges undergoing a definite increase when the nerve is stimulated.

Carbohydrate is not, apparently, the fuel from which the energy for the conduction of the impulse is derived. During stimulation no reduction in the glycogen content of the nerve occurs, the disappearance of sugar is not accelerated and lactic acid is not produced. Nerve conduction differs, therefore, in this respect from muscular contraction (p. 408). But, as in muscular contraction, the immediate source of the energy for nerve conduction is furnished by the explosive breakdown of phosphocreatine. The phosphocreatine undergoes resynthesis after the passage of the impulse, i.e., during the refractory period, the conductivity of the nerve being thus restored. The source of the energy for the recovery process is unknown. That the recovery process is essentially different from that occurring in muscle is evident from the fact that it occurs in the absence of oxygen. A nerve placed in nitrogen will therefore continue to respond to stimulation for a relatively long time — three hours or so.

THE PHYSIOLOGY OF MUSCULAR CONTRACTION

Our knowledge of the physiology of muscular contraction has been gained largely from studies of the isolated muscle of the frog. The muscle of the calf — the *gastrocnemius* — is the one most generally employed. This muscle is attached above to the lower end of the thigh bone (femur) and below, through a strong tendon called the tendon of Achilles (tendo Achillis), to the bone of the heel. In preparing the muscle for an experiment, it is removed from the animal together with its nerve supply, the sciatic, and the lower end of the femur. The preparation is then suspended by fixing the section of bone in a clamp, and fastening the lower tendinous end of the muscle to a light lever, as shown in Fig. 197. The lever is adjusted so as to make light contact with the surface of a revolving drum, motivated by clock-work and covered with smoked paper. This instrument is called a *kymograph*. As the drum revolves the soot is removed by the point of the lever, which thus traces a white horizontal line so long as the lever remains stationary. Any shortening (contraction) of the muscle causes an upward movement of the lever which then inscribes a curve on the rotating drum.

The simple muscular contraction or "twitch." Muscle, like nerve, responds to any one of the four types of stimulus — *electrical, mechanical, thermal* or *chemical*. Electrical stimulation, either by means of the induced (faradic) or the galvanic current, is most usually employed on account of its convenience and the accuracy with which its intensity can be controlled. The muscle may be stimulated directly, that

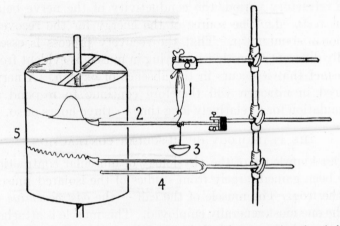

Fig. 197. Diagram showing method of recording the contraction of an isolated muscle. 1, frog's gastrocnemius preparation, bone held in clamp; 2, muscle lever; 3, scale pan for holding weights; 4, tuning fork (time marker); 5, kymograph drum.

is, by placing the electrodes in contact with its surface, or through its nerve. When stimulated in either of these ways and with a single stimulus, e.g., a make or break shock, the muscle contracts and, having raised the writing lever to a certain height, relaxes again and allows the lever to return to its original position. Thus a curve similar to that shown in Fig. 198 is inscribed. This simple brief contraction is called a muscle *twitch;* it is due, of course, to the shortening (contraction) in unison of the numerous fibers of which the muscle is composed. The curve shown in Fig. 198 is marked off into three parts to represent corresponding phases of the muscular response. The stimulus was applied at A. Shortening of the muscle commences at B and relaxation at C. The distance from A to B indicates the period elapsing from the application of the stimulus to the commencement of the contraction. This is called the *latent period;* its duration is about 0.01 second. The next period (B-C), during which the lever rises from the horizontal line (base line) to the summit of the curve, is the *contraction phase;* it lasts for approximately 0.04 second. The part of the curve from C to D represents the *relaxation phase*. This has a duration of about 0.05 second.

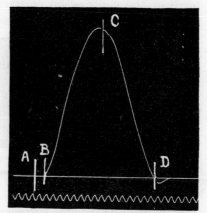

The total duration of the contractile process of the frog's gastrocnemius muscle, including the latent period, is therefore about a tenth of a second. The muscles of warm-blooded animals have considerably shorter contraction times.

These time relations of the muscle twitch are determined by having a tuning fork record its vibrations (100 per second) upon the

Fig. 198. Record of a muscle twitch. A-B, latent period; B-C, contraction phase; C-D, relaxation phase. Time indicated by lower tracing ($\frac{1}{100}$ sec.) caused by a vibrating tuning fork. (After Stirling.)

drum, while the contraction curve is being inscribed (see Fig. 198).

The effect upon the force of the contraction of increasing the intensity of the stimulus. If a series of stimuli of gradually increasing strength is applied directly to the muscle, contraction curves of graded heights will be obtained (see Fig. 199). The weakest stimulus which will excite the muscle is called the *minimal* or *threshold stimulus*. As the strength of each successive stimulus is increased, a greater and greater response is obtained from the muscle. Ultimately, a point is reached where the muscle contracts maximally, that is, no further increase in the height of the contraction curve results from increasing the strength of the stimulus. This is called the *maximal stimulus*.

It was stated on p. 391 that muscle, like nerve, obeys the "all or none" law. The grading of the muscular response to stimuli of graded strength, as just described, appears to contradict this statement. The explanation is that a muscle is composed of a number of units — the muscle fibers. The force of the contraction of the whole muscle is dependent upon the number of fibers excited by the stimulus. A

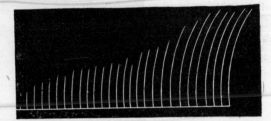

Fig. 199.   Record of a series of contractions caused by a succession of stimuli of graded strength. The muscle lever traced each of these lines while the drum of the kymograph was at rest, it being moved by hand to a fresh position after each contraction.

strong stimulus excites a larger number than a weak one, and with a maximal stimulus the current spreads to involve all the fibers. Studies made upon a single muscle fiber have shown that it does not respond by graded responses as the strength of the stimulus is increased. It responds maximally or not at all, that is, it obeys the "all or none" law.

Summation and tetanus. If a second stimulus is sent into an isolated frog's muscle within 0.01 second of the first, i.e., during the latent period, no obvious effect is produced. If, however, the second stimulus is applied while the muscle is contracting in response to the first stimulus, it contracts again; the second contraction is added to the first, the shortening of the muscle being then greater than that caused by a single stimulus. The greatest effect of the second stimulus is observed when it is applied to the muscle at the height of the contraction caused by the first. This phenomenon, whereby one contraction is added to a previous one to produce a greater total shortening of the muscle, is called *summation* (Fig. 200). A third contraction may be added to a second, a fourth to a third, and so on. When the stimuli sent into a frog's gastrocnemius muscle are at a slower rate

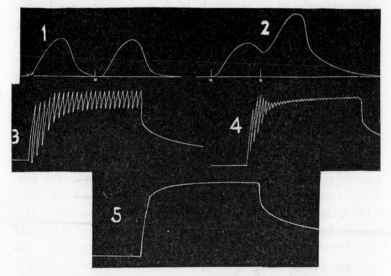

FIG. 200. Illustrating summation and tetanus. 1, the second stimulus X was applied after relaxation of the muscle, two separate contractions of equal amplitude result; 2, summation, the second stimulus being applied at a shorter interval after the first than in 1; 3 and 4, incomplete tetanus caused by a series of stimuli applied at short intervals apart; 5, complete tetanus resulting from a still more rapid rate of stimulation, the individual muscular responses being completely fused. (After Stirling and Howell.)

than from 15 to 30 per second the individual contractions can be distinguished, that is, they are not completely fused. The contraction curve shows smaller or larger waves synchronous with the rate of stimulation. At rates of stimulation higher than this the responses are completely fused, the contraction curve being perfectly smooth. The curve rises to a maximum height which is considerably greater than that caused by a single stimulus, and remains at this height as long as the stimulation lasts or until the muscle becomes fatigued. A sustained contraction of this nature is called *complete tetanus*. The contraction caused by slower rates of stimulation, and in which the individual responses are distinguishable, is referred to as *incomplete tetanus* (Fig. 200). Smooth muscle, which contracts and relaxes much more slowly than voluntary muscle, shows complete tetanus when stimulated at intervals of 5 seconds or so. In the rapidly acting wing muscles of insects, on the other hand, tetanus is not complete until the stimulation rate reaches 300 or so per second. In man, the contractions of the voluntary muscles are brought about by the discharge of impulses along the motor nerves at rates of from 5 to 50 per second. At the lower rates the contraction is an incomplete tetanus, but at the higher rates complete fusion of the contractions results (see also p. 394).

Contracture. Under certain conditions relaxation of the muscle takes place very slowly; it may remain in the partially contracted state for a considerable length of time. This state of the muscle is referred to as *contracture*. If a muscle in a state of contracture is stimulated at relatively long intervals it responds by further shortening, each contraction being then superimposed upon the sustained contraction caused by the previous stimulus. Contracture is brought about by the action of certain drugs, especially *veratrine*, and by *fatigue*. It also sometimes occurs in apparently normal muscle during the first of a series of contractions and then passes off (Fig. 202).

Treppe or the "staircase" phenomenon. When a muscle is stimulated repeatedly at regular intervals, the first few contractions of the series increase successively in amplitude. This phenomenon has already been described for heart muscle (p. 113). It is due, apparently, to the beneficial effect exerted upon the irritability of the muscle by the chemical products of the first few contractions, and the rise in temperature (Fig. 202).

Fatigue. If regular stimulation of a muscle be continued after the contractions have reached their maximum amplitude, the irritability of the muscle becomes depressed, the contractions diminish in height, and ultimately the muscle fails to respond (Fig. 202). The onset and development of this state of *fatigue* are more rapid, the higher the rate of stimulation. Isolated muscle, or one in the intact animal

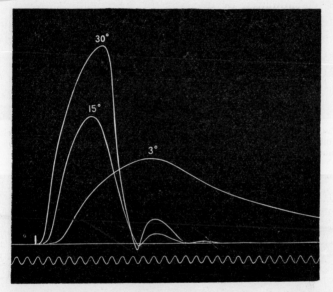

Fig. 201. The effect of temperature upon the contraction of a frog's gastrocnemius muscle. Tracing should be read from left to right. Figures are the temperatures (°C.) of the salt solution in which the muscle was immersed. (After Pembrey and Phillips.)

the blood supply of which has been occluded, also fatigues more rapidly than one receiving an adequate oxygen supply. Oxygen is required for the removal of the lactic acid produced during contraction. In the muscle deprived of its blood supply this, of course, does not readily occur. Lactic acid accumulates, and it is to such accumulation that the loss of irritability of the muscle is attributed (see p. 408).

The effect of temperature upon muscular contraction. Warming a muscle causes it to respond more rapidly and vigorously to stimulation. Contraction and relaxation phases are both shortened; the latent period is also of shorter duration. Lowering the temperature of the muscle exerts the opposite effect, the contraction being weaker and

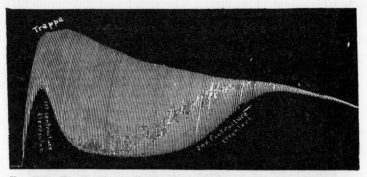

FIG. 202. *Tracing*, illustrating treppe, contracture and fatigue. The muscle was stimulated at intervals of one second. The contractions are very close together because the kymograph drum was moving slowly. (After Howell.)

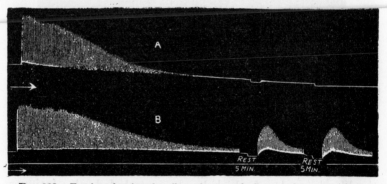

FIG. 203. *Tracing*, showing the effect of oxygen lack upon the onset of fatigue. Records from a pair of sartorius muscles of frog, stimulated at one second intervals. A, in nitrogen; B, in oxygen. (After Fletcher.)

all its phases lengthened. Cold-blooded animals, such as snakes and frogs, whose body temperature varies with that of the environment, move sluggishly therefore in cold water. The activity of mammals, on the other hand, whose muscles are maintained at a constant temperature of around 98.5° F., is not influenced by changes in the temperature of the environment. Nevertheless, the more efficient action of the muscles after the commencement of exercise is due, in part, to the local rise in temperature resulting from the earlier contractions. "Warming up" to one's work is a familiar expression (Fig. 201).

The effect of temperature upon the speed of muscular contraction conforms with Van't Hoff's law, which states that the velocity of chemical reactions, which, of course, are the basis of muscular contraction, is increased to between two and three times by a rise in temperature of 10° C.

Muscle is inexcitable at very low temperatures. Frog's muscle, for example, fails to respond at temperatures of from 32 to 35° F. On the other hand, at an excessively high temperature (105 to 110° F. for frog's muscle) the muscle proteins are coagulated, and death of the muscle results. At the same time, the muscle undergoes pronounced shortening and loses its natural translucency. This state is called *heat rigor*. It resembles *rigor mortis*, a term given to the stiffening of the muscles of the body generally which occurs in from one to seven hours after death.

Muscular work and efficiency. Work, as defined by the physicist, is the product of the load (expressed in grams, kilograms or pounds) and the vertical distance (in millimeters, centimeters, meters or feet) through which it is raised. According to the units of distance and weight employed, the work is expressed in grammillimeters, gramcentimeters, kilogrammeters or foot-pounds.

The isolated muscle can be made to perform work by stimulating it to contract and lift a weight. A load of a known weight is attached to the lever at the point of attachment of the muscle, which is then stimulated. The height above the base-line of the tracing inscribed by the lever is measured. This measurement, however, is not the actual distance through which the weight has been raised, for the shortening of the muscle has been magnified by the lever. The distance as measured must, therefore, be divided by the magnification of the lever, which is usually 5.

The work performed by the gastrocnemius muscle of the frog is most suitably expressed in grammillimeters. For example, a muscle which lifts a weight of 1 gram to a height of 2 millimeters does 2 grammillimeters of work. The muscle when loaded with a heavier weight may not raise it so high, yet may do more work. Thus, if it lifts a weight of 4 grams only 1 millimeter it does 4 grammillimeters of work. Starting with a light load and gradually adding to it for a number of successive contractions, it is found that the work performed increases up to a maximum and then falls off. There exists, therefore, an optimum load, that is, a load with which the muscle performs the maximum amount of work (see Fig. 204). Since the work, as just defined, is the prod-

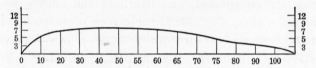

Fig. 204. Diagram to show the method of measuring muscle work. Heights of contractions along vertical lines, weights in grams along the horizontal line. (After McKendrick.)

uct of the load and the lift, no work is done by an unloaded muscle when it contracts; nor by one which contracts against a weight which it is unable to lift. In both these instances, however, there is an expenditure of energy which is derived from chemical processes taking place in the muscle; all of this energy appears as heat.

The fibers of a muscle contracting against a resistance, such as a weight which it cannot move or a stiff spring which it cannot bend, of course do not shorten. The tension within the muscles increases, however. Such a contraction is called *isometric* (G. *isos* = same, *metros* = measurement). An *isotonic* contraction, on the other hand, is one in which the muscle shortens, but its tension remains constant throughout. In the body both types of contraction take place. The isometric type is seen in those muscles which maintain the body's posture, such as the extensors on the front of the thigh. These exert a constant pull upon the leg, and thus hold the limb in the extended position to afford a firm support for the body. The movements of the limbs, as in walking, lifting objects with the hands, or throwing a ball are brought about by isotonic contractions.

Of the total energy expended by any machine, a part appears as mechanical work, the remainder being dissipated as heat. The efficiency of the machine is defined as the proportion of the total energy which appears as work. Thus,

$$\text{Efficiency} = \frac{\text{work}}{\text{total energy (work + heat)}}$$

As mentioned above, a muscle contracting isometrically or without a load performs no work, all the energy is transformed to heat. Contracting with an optimum load, on the other hand, muscle has an efficiency of from 25 to 30 per cent, which compares favorably with that of the best type of gasoline engine. By measuring the heat produced by a muscle during its contraction and the work done, its efficiency can be readily calculated from the equation given above. In making the calculation, the energy appearing as work and as heat must, of course, be expressed in the same units. We may express either the heat in work units (e.g., grammillimeters), or the work in heat units (e.g., microcalories). Now, the heat equivalent of a grammillimeter is .00235 microcalorie. Therefore, if the heat produced is 8.4 microcalories, and the work performed is 1200 grammillimeters, then the total energy expenditure expressed as heat can be calculated as follows;

Heat produced = 8.4 microcalories
Work   = 1200 grammillimeters
Heat equivalent of the work = 1200 × .00235 = 2.8 microcalories

The total energy expenditure is, therefore, 8.4 + 2.8 = 11.2 microcalories. The efficiency is,

$$\frac{2.8}{11.2} = 25 \text{ per cent}$$

The chemistry of muscular contraction. The isolated muscle derives the energy for its contraction ultimately from the combustion of carbohydrate. Oxygen is consumed and carbon dioxide produced. The actual contraction of the muscle, however, is brought about by the explosive breakdown of a compound of adenylic acid with two molecules of phosphoric acid, called *adenosine triphosphate*. Through the action of a ferment (enzyme) in the muscle, glycogen breaks down to glucose. The phosphoric acid liberated in the breakdown of adenosine triphosphate joins with the glucose molecules to form glucose phosphate. Through a series of reactions fructose diphosphate is ultimately formed. Phosphocreatine next breaks down into creatine and phosphoric acid. The phosphoric acid freed in this reaction rejoins the adenylic acid again to form adenosine triphosphate. The fructose diphosphate, through a sequence of chemical changes, forms lactic acid. The energy liberated in the breakdown of adenosine triphosphate is utilized for the recombination of phosphoric acid and creatine, i.e., for the resynthesis of the phosphocreatine. The foregoing chemical changes occur during the contraction and relaxation of the muscle, and do not require oxygen. The changes constitute the *non-oxidative* or *anaerobic* phase of muscular contraction. Following the relaxation of the muscle, $\frac{1}{5}$ of the lactic acid produced during the contraction is oxidized; the energy derived from this reaction is utilized in the resynthesis of the remaining $\frac{4}{5}$ of the lactic acid to glycogen. This series of reactions is called the *oxidative, recovery* or *aerobic* phase of contraction.

A muscle deprived of oxygen (i.e., in an atmosphere of nitrogen) is, therefore, capable of responding to stimulation for a considerable time. Lactic acid, however, is not removed by oxidation and resynthesis to glycogen, but, accumulating, reduces the irritability of the muscle. The concentration of lactic acid at which the muscle fails to respond is around 0.5 per cent. This is called the *lactic acid maximum*. When oxygen is supplied to a muscle fatigued by repeated stimulation in nitrogen, the lactic acid is removed and the irritability of the muscle restored.

The foregoing is a bare outline of the chemical changes occurring in a muscle during its contraction. It should be added that an intermediate step in the breakdown of glycogen to lactic acid is the formation of fructose diphosphate, that is, a sugar containing 6 carbon atoms, combined with 2 molecules of phosphoric acid.

It will be clear from the foregoing account that the breakdown of glycogen to lactic acid, though one of a series of chemical reactions occurring in active muscle, is not essential for the actual contraction. The production of lactic acid by the isolated muscle can be prevented by treating it with a drug called *sodium iodoacetate*, yet the muscle so treated responds to stimulation for some time, or until the phosphocreatine store of the muscle is exhausted. But phosphocreatine cannot be reformed, since the energy for the resynthesis is derived from the glycogen to lactic acid reaction. A muscle poisoned by iodoacetate obviously cannot continue to respond for as long a time as can a normal muscle. The glycogen to lactic acid reaction, therefore, though not directly responsible for the contraction, serves, as it were, to "re-wind" the contractile mechanism — to "set the trigger" for the next contraction. Carbohydrate, then, is the ultimate source of the energy for the activity of the isolated muscle.

The following table presents a summary of the chemical changes occurring during and immediately after its contraction.

(a) Adenosine triphosphate →	phosphoric acid + adenylic acid creatine	energy for contraction
(b) Phosphocreatine →	+ phosphoric acid	energy for resynthesis of adenosine triphosphate
(c) Glycogen to lactic acid		energy for resynthesis of phosphocreatine
(d) Oxidation of part of lactic acid (about ⅕)		energy for resynthesis of the remainder of the lactic acid to glycogen

Heat production in muscle. It has been mentioned that during the isometric contraction of muscle, the total energy expended appears as heat. The heat production is divided into two phases, termed the *initial* heat and the *recovery* heat. The initial heat comprises the heat produced during the contraction of the muscle by the breakdown of phosphocreatine (contraction heat), together with a smaller quantity which appears during relaxation (relaxation heat). The latter results from the conversion of the energy exhibited as

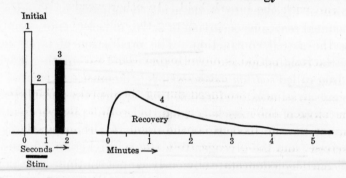

Fig. 205. Diagram showing the stages of heat production by muscle during and following a short tetanic contraction. The three rectangles represent the initial heat. 1, heat produced at the commencement of the contraction; 2, that produced during the maintenance of the contraction; 3, relaxation heat; 4, recovery heat. (After Evans, *Recent Advances in Physiology*.)

tension during the contraction phase. The initial heat is produced during the anaerobic phase of the contractile process; it, but not the recovery heat, is therefore generated by a muscle contracting in nitrogen. The recovery heat appears after relaxation is over, and is due mainly to the oxidation of lactic acid (Fig. 205).

The phases of heat production are summarized in the following table;

1. *Initial heat* = 45% of the total heat,
   a. Contraction heat 65% of the initial heat,
   b. Relaxation heat 35% of the initial heat.
2. *Recovery heat* = 55% of the total heat.

THE PHYSIOLOGY OF MUSCULAR EXERCISE

Oxygen debt. In strenuous muscular exercise only a fraction of the oxygen required for the recovery phase of the contracting muscles is breathed during the course of the exercise. For example, the oxygen requirement for a race of 100 yards, which takes only a few seconds to run, is 6 liters or more. Yet the quantity of oxygen which can be absorbed in this time is less than 1 liter. Indeed, a short race can be run with the breath held. In other words, the sprinter goes into debt for oxygen during the race, and pays up after the race has been run. Thus the oxygen consumption after the exercise period is much higher than during an ordinary period of rest. The extra oxygen is utilized in the removal of the lactic acid produced during the exercise. The size of the oxygen debt for any piece of work is determined by measuring the oxygen consumption of the after-period of exercise, and subtracting from the result the figure for the oxygen consumption of a corresponding period of rest. During very strenuous muscular effort the oxygen debt may amount to 15 liters or more.

The ability of the muscles to contract, without receiving the full oxygen requirement until the work has been completed, has an obvious advantage. Short periods of strenuous exercise can be undertaken which would otherwise be impossible, for the respiratory and circulatory systems are quite unequal to the task of furnishing, during the exercise, the great volume of oxygen which is ultimately used in the recovery process. The maximum quantity of oxygen that can be delivered to and consumed by the tissues of a large healthy man is not more than about 2 liters per minute and, of most persons, considerably less than this.

In light exercise no oxygen debt is incurred. The lactic acid is removed as it is produced; in other words, the body, in so far as oxygen consumption is concerned, "pays as it goes."

The source of the energy for muscular work. We have seen that the energy for the contraction of the isolated muscle is ultimately derived from carbohydrate. Glycogen is broken down through hexose diphosphate to lactic acid. In the numerous studies of the respiratory exchanges of the isolated gastrocnemius muscle of the frog during contraction, a respiratory quotient of 1 has been obtained. In the intact animal carbohydrate is also the fuel for short bouts of muscular exercise. After a sprint, for example, a fall in blood sugar may occur, and the ingestion of glucose prior to a race is now recognized as a valuable means of postponing fatigue and enhancing muscular performance. In prolonged and exhausting work the carbohydrate stores become depleted; fat is then burned to furnish the required energy. Protein apparently is not utilized in muscular exercise, or, if so, to a very small extent.

The adjustments in the respiratory and circulatory systems in muscular exercise. During strenuous muscular effort the quantity of air breathed is from 300 to 400 per cent greater than during rest. The greater pulmonary ventilation is brought about by an increase in the respiratory rate, as well as by an increase in the volume of each breath. The increased breathing occurs at the very outset of exercise; indeed, it has been shown in experiments upon man that it may actually anticipate the exercise by a brief interval, that is, an effect upon the respirations may be noted at the instant a signal has been given to start some muscular act, and before the muscles contract. Changes in heart rate and blood pressure may also anticipate the contractions of the muscles. The influence upon the respiratory and circulatory systems at the commencement of or preceding the exercise, is due to impulses from psychic levels of the brain, and probably also from the motor area of the cerebral cortex, upon the centers in the medulla. The efficiency with which the work is performed is also undoubtedly influenced by emotional factors. These act most likely by bringing about more perfect co-ordination of respiratory and circulatory mechanisms, but also, probably, through a direct effect upon the muscular contractions themselves. A man is spurred to greater effort, and is a more effective worker if the work interests him, than if he is bored with it, or does it as a matter of routine. In emergencies or during excitement — "in the heat of the moment" — feats of strength or endurance are accomplished which, in the absence of the emotional factor, would be impossible. It is likely that adrenaline liberated into the blood stream through nervous influences plays a role in some instances (p. 347).

If the exercise is severe, chemical factors soon come into play to increase the pulmonary ventilation. The production of lactic acid and carbon dioxide in the muscles causes a slight increase in the hydrogen ion concentration of the blood which acts as a stimulus to the respiratory center. The greater carbon dioxide produced by the exercise is thus eliminated.

The adaptations of the circulatory mechanism in exercise are of a highly complex nature. The blood pressure rises to from 160 to 180 mm. Hg, as a result of constriction of the vessels in the splanchnic region. The vessels in the muscles themselves dilate. A larger proportion of the blood volume than during rest is diverted, therefore, to the active muscles. The dilatation of the vessels in the muscles is brought about mainly by the action of chemical substances, namely, carbon dioxide and lactic acid, products of the contractile process. Not only do the muscles receive a greater proportion of the total blood volume during exercise than during rest, but as a result of the contraction of the spleen the volume of circulating blood may be increased by from 20 to 25 per cent. The blood also circulates more rapidly; the output of the heart and, consequently, the quantity of blood pumped per minute through the systemic and pulmonary vessels, is increased many fold. In a large robust man performing arduous work the output of the heart may amount to 35 liters (nearly 8 gallons) or more per minute. The greater cardiac output is the result of the greater venous return, that is, of the increased volume of blood flowing through the contracting muscles and carried along the great veins to the right side of the heart.

The effect of muscular exercise upon the heart rate varies in different persons. In those untrained to muscular work the heart accelerates markedly, a rate of from 110 to 120 per minute being not unusual, whereas the heart of the athlete may show little or no acceleration during muscular feats of a highly exacting character, such as sprinting or rowing. Through the respiratory and circulatory mechanisms just described, the maximum load of oxygen is delivered to the contracting muscles. The oxygen supply is further augmented through the effect which the carbon dioxide and lactic acid produced in the muscles, and the local rise in temperature, exert upon the oxyhemoglobin. As mentioned on p. 190, increased acidity and a rise in temperature cause the hemoglobin to give up a greater part of its oxygen load.

Athletic training causes a moderate enlargement of the normal heart. The enlargement is purely physiological, and is commensurate with the accompanying increased bulk of the skeletal muscles. Enlargement (dilatation and hypertrophy) of the heart occurs when the heart is damaged; and athletes, like anyone else, may be subjects of cardiac disease. Because some athletes have shown cardiac dilatation and hypertrophy or other evidence of heart disease, it used to be thought that athletics, if engaged in too enthusiastically, led to heart disease. It is now generally admitted, however, that the well-conditioned heart of the young adult is not damaged by even strenuous exercise. The skeletal muscles fatigue before a healthy heart. In other words, the heart free from disease can perform the greatest task which is ever demanded of it. The work of the heart consists in discharging the blood conveyed to it, and the skeletal muscles are not capable of driving enough blood along the veins to tax its powers. On the other hand, a person with a diseased heart, should he indulge in strenuous exercise, runs a serious risk, if not of inducing cardiac failure, of at least causing serious damage to his heart. In persons after middle age, the state of the heart is always an unknown quantity, and for this reason excessive muscular effort should be avoided.

CHAPTER X

THE CENTRAL NERVOUS SYSTEM

The structure of nervous tissue. The brain and spinal cord are composed of *nerve cells* with their processes — the

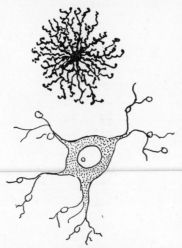

nerve fibers — and *neuroglial cells*. The bodies of the nerve cells, and their processes for a short distance from their origin, compose the *gray matter* of the central nervous system. The nerve fibers, collected into bundles or tracts, constitute the *white matter*. *Neuroglial cells* perform no essential nervous function; they form a supporting framework for the nervous elements proper (see Fig. 206).

The *nerve cell* or *neuron* is the structural unit of the nervous system. It consists of a *body* or *perikaryon* and two types of

Fig. 206. Showing two types of neuroglial cells.

process, the *dendrite* and the *axon*. The axon is usually single, but there are often two or more dendrites. The cell bodies in different parts of the nervous system vary widely in size (4 to 125 microns), and in shape (triangular, multangular, round, spindle- or pear-shaped). In respect to their internal structure, however, all possess certain characteristics in common. The typical nerve cell has a well-defined globular nucleus situated near the center of the perikaryon. Nerve cells, in the adult, are incapable of multiplication; the nucleus does not possess a centrosome. By special staining methods fine fibrils — the *neurofibrils* —

416

can be identified in the cytoplasm. These course through the cell body from dendrites to axis cylinder, sweeping around the nucleus. Their presence in the nerve fiber has been mentioned on p. 381. When stained with a suitable

basic dye the cytoplasm exhibits a mottled appearance, due to the presence of irregularly shaped particles, resembling the chromatic material of the nucleus. These particles are called *Nissl bodies* or (from their tendency to be arranged in rows, and thus suggesting a tiger's stripes) *tigroid bodies* or the *tigroid substance* (see Fig. 207).

At the point of origin of the axon, the contour of the cell body shows an elevation called the *axon hillock;* the cytoplasm here is devoid of Nissl bodies.

The axon conducts impulses *away from the cell body*. The dendrites, so named because they break up into nu-

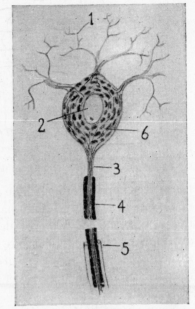

Fig. 207.   Drawing (semidiagrammatic) of a nerve cell. 1, dendrites; 2, nucleus; 3, axis cylinder showing neurofibrils; 4, myelin sheath; 5, neurilemma; 6, Nissl bodies.

merous branches (G. *dendron* = tree), transmit impulses *toward the cell body*. Those of most nerve cells are short, and branch close to the cell body. Other neurons, however, such as the cells in the ganglia of the posterior spinal nerve roots, have dendrites several feet long; these constitute the sensory fibers of the peripheral nerves. On the other hand, the motor fibers of the peripheral nerves, which arise from the anterior horn cells of the spinal cord, and the fibers composing the long tracts of the brain and cord (e.g., the corticospinal or pyramidal tracts) are axons. Structurally, there is nothing to distinguish these two types of long nerve

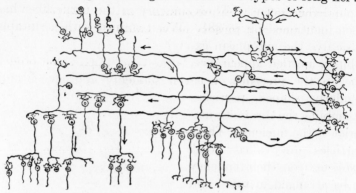

FIG. 208.   Diagram to show how a few nerve cells may communicate with a great number of others in different parts of the central nervous system.

fibers from one another. The distinction between dendrite and axon is a purely functional one; fibers which transmit impulses to the cell body are dendrites, those which conduct away from the cell body are axons. (For a description of the structure of the nerve fiber see p. 379.)

FIG. 209.   End feet (e) or pieds terminaux making contact with the body of a nerve cell.

Neurons are linked together in the central nervous system, axon to dendrite or to the cell body. Through the formation of chains of two or more links, long and often very intricate conducting paths are established in the nervous system (Fig. 208). A junction between the axon of one neuron with a dendrite or the cell body of another is called a *synapse*. There is no actual structural union of two neurons at the synapse — merely contact. The axon terminates in a small swelling called an *end-foot* or *pied terminal* which is applied to the neighboring neuron (Fig. 209).

REFLEX ACTION

A nervous reflex is an involuntary act brought about by the stimulation of a sensory nerve ending. Familiar examples of actions which are purely reflex in nature are the following: the quick closure of the eyelid when some object touches the eyelashes, or even suddenly approaches and threatens to strike the eye; the sudden withdrawal of the hand or foot when it is painfully stimulated; the sharp recovery of one's balance when, as a result of a slip, the body's center of gravity is suddenly shifted; and the jerk of the leg (knee jerk, p. 428) when the patellar tendon is tapped sharply. Though such reflex acts are brought about involuntarily, we are aware that they have occurred, but innumerable acts of which we are quite unconscious, e.g., the movements of the gastro-intestinal tract, variations in heart rate and respiration, changes in caliber of the small blood vessels, the secretion of glands, etc., are continually taking place in the body.

The reflex arc. The structural basis of reflex action is the *reflex arc*. The latter may be described in its simplest conceivable form as consisting of two neurons, linked together in the central nervous system, axon to dendrite (see Fig. 210). The two neurons are thus arranged, one with its axon, the other with its dendrite, directed toward the periphery. The latter receives the stimulus, and transmits impulses to the central nervous system; it is therefore called the *receptor neuron,* or the *afferent limb* of the reflex arc. The other neuron transmits impulses from the central nervous system to the peripheral organ, muscle or gland, and is called the *effector neuron* or the *efferent limb* of the reflex arc. The region in the central nervous system (brain or spinal cord) where the two neurons form their junction (synapse) is referred to as the *reflex center*. Thus a stimulus applied to the terminal of the receptor neuron sets up an impulse or a volley of impulses which is transmitted to the reflex center;

a discharge of impulses then occurs down the effector neuron to the peripheral organ.

For the sake of simplicity in illustrating the general principles of the reflex arc, one composed of only two neurons has been described, but it is unlikely that such exists in the central nervous system of higher animals. One nerve cell, at least, is interposed between the receptor and effector neurons. This is called the *connector, internuncial* or *intercalated* neuron. In the great majority of reflex arcs in the central nervous system of mammals, not one but a chain of such connector neurons is present.

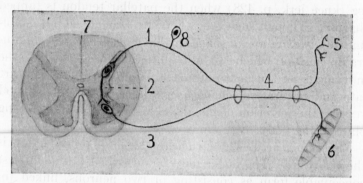

FIG. 210. Diagram of the spinal reflex arc. 1, receptor neuron; 2, connector neuron; 3, effector neuron; 4, peripheral nerve; 5, sense organ (receptor); 6, effector organ (muscle); 7, spinal cord; 8, posterior root ganglion.

A diagram of a reflex arc having its center in the spinal cord is shown in Fig. 210. It will be noted that the cell body of the receptor neuron is situated, not within the cord itself but just outside, namely, in the ganglion of the posterior root of a spinal nerve. The effector neuron has its cell body in the anterior horn of gray matter (anterior horn cell, p. 432), its axon leaves the cord in the anterior root of the spinal nerve, and is continued into a peripheral nerve. The connector neuron has its cell body in the posterior horn of spinal gray matter. Its axon synapses with the dendrite of the anterior horn cell, its dendrite with the central process (axon) of the receptor neuron.

In any reflex action of higher animals, a great number of reflex arcs are involved. For example, should a person's arm be given a sharp and unexpected slap, he would jerk the arm away; associated movements of the shoulder and trunk would probably occur; he would turn his head and eyes toward the source of the injury and, most likely, utter an exclamation of some sort. A large number of muscles — those of the arm, shoulders, trunk, neck, eyes, tongue, larynx and respiration — would therefore take part in the action. Each muscle is supplied in turn by a large number of nerve fibers — effector (motor) neurons — and the stimulus must have excited a large number of afferent nerve endings — receptor neurons — in the skin. If instead of slapping the skin, which stimulates a relatively large area, a stab were made with a pin, the reflex response would probably be the same. Yet, as compared with the slap, the pin must have stimulated much fewer sensory endings. The number of effector (motor) neurons must have been greatly in excess of the sensory endings which had been stimulated. Each receptor neuron must therefore be connected within the central nervous system with a large number of effector neurons. As a matter of fact, every receptor neuron is potentially in communication with motor neurons throughout the entire spinal cord and brain. The synapses, normally, offer a certain "resistance" to the passage of impulses which limits the spread of excitation within the central nervous system. In strychnine poisoning or in tetanus, however, synaptic resistance is greatly diminished; a very weak localized stimulus then sets up impulses which spread widely throughout the central nervous system, causing forcible convulsive contractions of all the voluntary muscles of the body.

Not only is each afferent fiber in communication with a number of effector neurons, but, conversely, each of the latter is connected with many afferent fibers. That is to say, stimulation of sensory nerves in widely separated parts of the body may bring about reflex contraction of one and the same group of muscles. An anterior horn cell of the cord is, therefore, a point of convergence of a number of afferent paths, each motor neuron serving as a pathway common to impulses from various sources (see Fig. 211). It is therefore called the *final common path*. For example, scratching the

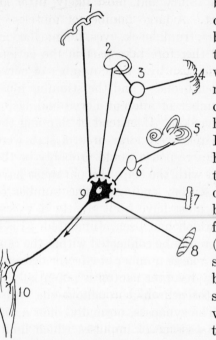

back of a spinal dog (i.e., one whose spinal cord has been severed in the upper thoracic region some weeks previously) causes rhythmical contractions of the flexor muscles of the hind limb (*scratch reflex*). Painful stimulation of the hind paw also causes contraction of the flexor muscles of the limb, the paw being thus withdrawn from the injurious agent (*flexor reflex*). If one should attempt to elicit both these reflexes at the same time there must obviously be a conflict between them. They are antagonistic and cannot both employ the final common path at the same instant. In such and in other instances of two an-

FIG. 211. Diagram to illustrate the final common path. 1, cerebral cortex; 2, corpus striatum; 3, red nucleus; 4, cerebellum; 5, semicircular canals; 6, vestibular nucleus; 7, skin; 8, muscle spindle; 9, anterior horn cell (final common path); 10, skeletal muscle.

tagonistic reflexes competing for the final common path, the one of less biological importance gives way. Thus, as compared with a painful stimulus which signals some injury to the animal, the momentary irritation of a flea is of little importance. It is otherwise with reflexes which are allied in nature; they can utilize the final common path simultaneously; one reflex tends to strengthen or reinforce the other. For example, stimulation of the toes of the hind paw causes flexion of the corresponding limb. If the opposite fore paw is stimulated simultaneously, the flexion of the hind limb is strengthened.

Receptors. Most types of afferent nerve terminate at the periphery in specialized structures, known as *receptors* or *sense organs*. There are various types of receptor, each being especially adapted to respond to a particular kind of stimulus. Those of the skin, for example, respond to mechanical or thermal stimuli, the rods and cones of the retina to light, the taste buds and olfactory cells to chemical stimuli, and those of the ear to sound vibrations. The energy of the stimulating agent is converted by the receptor, in each instance, into nerve impulses.

Receptors are divided into three main classes, namely, *exteroceptors*, *proprioceptors* and *interoceptors*. Exteroceptors are those which receive stimuli from the external environment. The receptors of the eye, ear and skin, and those of taste and smell, i.e., those of the five senses, come under this heading. The receptors of sight, hearing and smell are sometimes also called *distance receptors* or *telereceptors*, since they make possible perception at a distance (see Pl. 8 A).

Proprioceptors receive stimuli which arise within the body itself. The skeletal muscles, the tendons and joints, the lungs, heart and abdominal viscera, as well as certain arteries (carotid and aorta, see p. 153) and veins, contain receptors which respond to changes in the activity of their immediate surroundings (internal environment). Those situated in the skeletal muscles are stimulated by the contraction or stretching of the muscle fibers; they are called the *muscle spindles*. Of the impulses set up by the stimulation of proprioceptors in muscles, tendons and joints, some reach consciousness; to such impulses is due our sense of the movement and position of our limbs — *kinesthetic sense*. Many impulses set up by muscular movement end, however, in parts of the central nervous system, e.g., spinal cord and cerebellum, which carry out their activities beneath the level of consciousness. The tonic contractions of skeletal muscle, as well as the smooth and co-ordinated nature of voluntary movement, are dependent upon impulses, both sensory and non-sensory, arising in the muscle proprioceptors.

The interoceptors are situated in the mucous membrane of the respiratory and alimentary tracts. Though removed from direct influence by the external environment, these receptors, nevertheless, are stimulated by agencies originating in the outside world, namely, air and food.

Conduction over the reflex arc. Reflex conduction differs from conduction over nerve fibers in several particulars. In the first place, the *velocity of transmission of impulses* over the reflex arc is considerably less than that over the nerve fiber. For example, if a muscle is caused to contract reflexly, the time elapsing between the application of the stimulus to the afferent nerve and the response of the muscle is considerably greater than if the impulses had travelled the same distance over a nerve fiber. The difference is due to the synapse, where the impulses are delayed. Secondly, conduction in the reflex arc is always in *one direction* — to the center in the afferent limb, away from it in the efferent limb. When a nerve fiber is stimulated, impulses travel in *both directions*. If, for example, a motor nerve fiber is cut just after it leaves the spinal cord, and the central end stimulated, impulses are set up which travel along the efferent fibers to the spinal center. But these impulses, caused by the artificial stimulus, do not reach the afferent neurons; they are blocked at the synapse. The latter thus acts like a valve, permitting impulses to pass in one direction over the reflex arc, but not in the other.

Thirdly, reflex conduction is much more *susceptible to lack of oxygen, fatigue and the action of anesthetics*. We have seen that the nerve fiber has a very low metabolism (p. 396), and will continue to respond to stimulation for a considerable time when deprived of oxygen. The metabolism of nerve

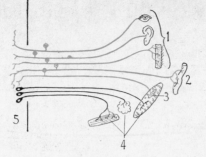

PLATE 8A

Diagram of receptor and effector organs. 1, exteroceptors; 2, interoceptors; 3, proprioceptors (muscle spindles); 4, effector organs, smooth muscle, gland and skeletal muscle; 5, central nervous system.

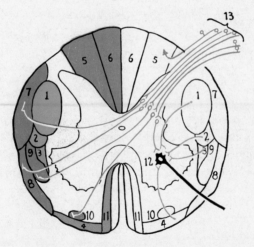

PLATE 8B

Diagram of a cross section of the spinal cord to show the main nerve tracts. Ascending tracts in blue, descending in red. 1, lateral (crossed) corticospinal tract; 2, rubrospinal tract; 3, lateral vestibulospinal tract; 4, anterior vestibulospinal tract; 5, fasciculus cuneatus; 6, fasciculus gracilis; 7, posterior spinocerebellar tract; 8, anterior spinocerebellar tract; 9, posterior spinothalamic tract; 10, anterior spinothalamic tract; 11, anterior (direct) corticospinal tract; 12, anterior horn cell (motor neuron); 13, fibers of posterior spinal nerve root connecting with secondary neurons in spinal gray matter.

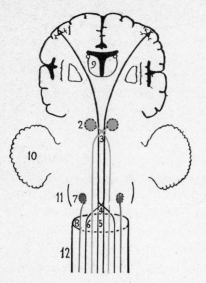

PLATE 9A

Diagram of the descending tracts of the cord. 1, Betz cell of motor area of the cerebral cortex; 2, red nucleus; 3, crossing of rubrospinal tracts (decussation of Forel); 4, decussation of pyramids; 5, anterior corticospinal tract (direct pyramidal tract); 6, lateral corticospinal (crossed pyramidal) tract; 7, vestibular nucleus; 8, vestibulospinal tract; 9, optic thalamus; 10, cerebellum; 11, medulla oblongata; 12, spinal cord.

PLATE 9B

Diagram of the ascending tracts of the cord. 1, optic thalamus (thalamus of left side not shown in order that the connections may be seen more clearly); 2, cerebellum; 3, nuclei gracilis and cuneatus in medulla oblongata; 4 (*red*), pathway for pain; 5, (*yellow*), fiber conveying sensations of touch, etc., to the opposite side of the cord; 6, (*blue*), fiber transmitting touch up the posterior columns; 7 and 8, (*black*), direct and indirect spinocerebellar tracts; 9, midline.

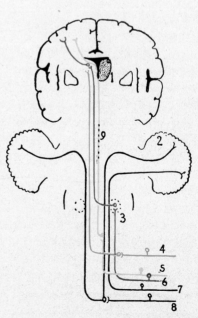

cells, on the other hand, is high and the cells soon lose their irritability when deprived of oxygen. The cells of the cerebral cortex, for example, are permanently injured if their blood supply is cut off for 10 minutes or so. Though the spinal cord will recover after a longer period of oxygen lack, its reflex responses commence to deteriorate within a short time after they have been deprived of blood. In the presence of oxygen the nerve fiber continues to respond to stimulation for long periods without showing fatigue, in marked contrast to the reflex arc, which is readily fatigued. In the intact animal, anesthesia (e.g., by ether or chloroform) quickly abolishes reflex action, whereas little effect is produced upon the excitability of the nerve fiber. Even after an animal has been killed by an anesthetic the nerves show little or no alteration in their responses to direct stimulation. Of course, when an anesthetic is applied to an isolated nerve, its excitability is very quickly abolished. Among other characteristic features of reflex action are *summation*, *after discharge* and *reciprocal inhibition*.

Summation. It has been pointed out that the magnitude of the nerve impulse cannot be increased by increasing the rate of stimulation. When a nerve receives stimuli in rapid succession, the impulses do not fuse and produce an impulse of greater magnitude, but always remain separate. Summation, on the other hand, is readily demonstrated in the reflex arc. A single stimulus, for example, applied to an afferent nerve, though it sets up an impulse, rarely causes a reflex response. If, however, two or more stimuli of the same strength as the single one are applied in rapid sequence, a response follows. Each impulse produces a state of some sort at the synapse which is capable of being added to, or summed with, that produced by other impulses. The nature of this state produced at the synapse — the *central excitatory state*, as it has been called — is not clearly understood, but evidently it must be raised to a certain threshold value before excitation of the effector neuron can occur.

After discharge. When a motor nerve is stimulated, the response of the muscle ends (i.e., impulses cease to be discharged along the fibers of the nerve) the moment that the stimulus is withdrawn. When, on the other hand, the muscular response is brought about reflexly, the muscle may continue to contract for a short time after the stimulus to

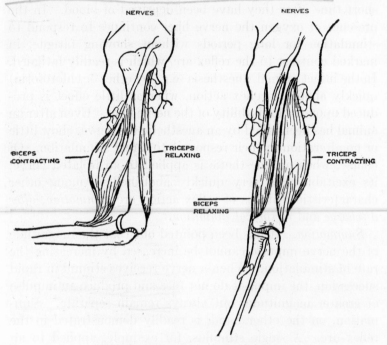

FIG. 212.   Illustrating reciprocal inhibition.

the afferent nerve has ceased.   This reflex phenomenon is explained upon the basis that the central excitatory state, which has been built up at the synapse, takes an appreciable length of time to be discharged along the effector neuron.

Reciprocal inhibition.   Stimulation of a motor nerve results in the contraction of all the muscles supplied by the nerve, irrespective of their actions; muscles having antagonistic actions (e.g., flexors and extensors) contract and oppose one another; no purposeful movement of the part is brought about. The motor nerve does not contain inhibitory fibers. In a reflex action, on the contrary, the muscular response consists of a co-ordinate movement, flexion of the knee joint, for example (see flexion reflex below). In such a movement, the flexors of the knee contract while the extensors undergo reciprocal inhibition (relaxation). The mechanism whereby the extensors are inhibited is not fully understood, but the inhibitory effect must be developed in the reflex center, i.e., at a synapse between the afferent and efferent neurons for, as just mentioned, the motor nerve itself does not contain inhibitory fibers. We therefore speak of a *central inhibitory state* as well as of a central excitatory state.

Reciprocal inhibition is also seen in voluntary movement. For example, in flexing the arm at the elbow the contraction of the biceps is accompanied by reciprocal inhibition of the triceps. On the other hand, when the elbow is extended the triceps contracts while the biceps relaxes (Figs. 212 and 213).

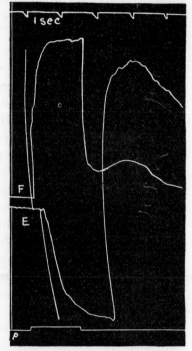

Fig. 213.   Reciprocal innervation. Record from the leg muscles of a decerebrate cat, showing contraction of flexors (F) and inhibition of the extensors (E). The two curves actually were inscribed synchronously but the lever for the extensor muscle is set a little to the right of that of the flexor muscle. (From Sherrington.)

Limb reflexes of special interest. *The flexion reflex.* This reflex consists of a strong contraction of the flexor muscles of the limb (together with inhibition of the extensors — reciprocal inhibition) when the efferent nerve of the *same* (*ipsi-*

lateral) limb is stimulated. The limb is flexed at ankle, knee and hip. The biological significance of this reflex is evident; in the intact animal the limb is withdrawn, automatically, from an agent which causes pain and, therefore, threatens injury. This and other reactions which are initiated by injury, and serve a protective purpose, are called *nociceptive reflexes*.

The crossed extensor reflex. This is a strong contraction of the extensors of the limb which results from stimulating an afferent nerve of the *opposite* (*contralateral*) limb. It is evident then, that this and the preceding reflex can be brought about simultaneously by the stimulation of a single afferent nerve. In the everyday life of the animal the two reflexes therefore compose a purposeful act, for, should one paw come in contact with something which stimulates it painfully, it is raised from the ground, while the body's support is strengthened by extension of the opposite limb.

The stretch reflex. Stretching a muscle causes it to contract. The response is purely reflex. Proprioceptors in the muscle — the *muscle spindles* — are excited by a stretch stimulus. The impulses thus set up are transmitted to the spinal reflex center, a discharge of impulses then occurring down the effector neurons.

The knee jerk and other tendon (*or deep*) *reflexes.* A light tap upon the tendon below the knee cap (patellar tendon), while the knee hangs limply in a semi-flexed position, causes a quick contraction of the extensor muscle on the front of the thigh (quadriceps muscle). The leg gives a sharp kick. This is called the *knee jerk* or *patellar reflex;* it is one type of stretch reflex, the tap upon the tendon causing a sudden stretch of the thigh muscle. In the investigation of a person with nervous disease the knee jerk is tested as a matter of routine. The reflex is abolished in any condition which interrupts the reflex arc, namely, disease or injury of the peripheral nerves (efferent or afferent fibers) to the quadriceps muscle, or of the reflex centers in the lumbar region of the spinal cord. It is exaggerated in disease or injury involving the corticospinal tracts (p. 435). Other tendon reflexes of clinical importance are the biceps and triceps jerks (tapping the biceps tendon in front of, or the triceps tendon behind the elbow) and the ankle jerk (tapping the tendo Achillis — the tendon above the heel). The state of the biceps and triceps jerks gives information concerning lesions involving the nerves of the arm, or of the thoracic region of the spinal cord; abolition or exaggeration of the ankle jerk tells of disease or injury involving the nerves to the leg muscles, or of the lumbo-sacral part of the spinal cord.

Though they do not come under the present heading, it is convenient to mention here two *cutaneous* or *superficial reflexes* of great clinical importance, namely, the *plantar response* and the *abdominal reflex*. The normal plantar response consists of a downward movement (plantar flexion) of the great toe, i.e., toward the sole, when the skin of the sole is stroked. In certain nervous lesions, e.g., injury to the corticospinal tracts, the great toe instead of being flexed toward the sole moves upward (dorsiflexion). This abnormal response is called the *sign of Babinski*.

The abdominal reflex consists in a contraction of the abdominal muscles caused by stroking the overlying skin. It is abolished in lesions of the corticospinal tracts, of the peripheral nerves or of the reflex centers in the thoracic part of the spinal cord.

Skeletal muscle tone. During consciousness the voluntary muscles, though not engaged in any movement, are always maintained in a state of slight contraction which is referred to as *tone* or *tonus*. All voluntary muscles show tonus to some extent, but it is seen pre-eminently in those muscles which maintain the posture of the body against the force of gravity — the so-called *antigravity muscles*. These are, chiefly, the extensor muscles of the lower limbs, trunk and neck. Muscle tonus is entirely reflex in character. The muscles are stretched between their attachments, thus the constant stimulus of stretch applied to the muscle spindles initiates the reflex. The reflex arc is broken by a lesion of the motor nerves, of the afferent nerves or of the reflex centers. For example, in injury or degenerative disease of the motor nerves, in locomotor ataxia (which involves the afferent paths in the spinal cord), or in infantile paralysis (which attacks the anterior horn cells), the tone of those muscles implicated by the disease is completely lost.

Higher centers of the brain (their precise location is unknown) exert an inhibitory influence upon muscle tone. Thus, in man a lesion of the corticospinal tracts, which connect the cerebral cortex with the spinal centers, results in an

exaggeration of the tonic contraction; this is manifested by the greater resistance offered by the limbs to passive movement. The physician, in describing the muscles whose tone is increased in this way, says they are *spastic*, and refers to the hypertonic state itself as

FIG. 214.   Decerebrate rigidity.
(After Pollock and Davis.)

spasticity. Muscle tone is increased to an extreme degree after complete separation of the lower centers from higher control. For example, section through the brain of an animal, anywhere between the upper part of the mid-brain and the vestibular nuclei (p. 512) in the medulla oblongata results in pronounced rigidity of the antigravity muscles. All four limbs are stiffly extended, the head is held erect and the tail elevated. The stiffened limbs support the animal when it is placed upon its feet. The condition is called *decerebrate rigidity* (Fig. 214). The hypertonus is at once abolished by destruction of the vestibular nuclei or section of the spinal cord. Destruction of the vestibular nuclei or section of the spinal cord of an animal not

previously decerebrated also abolishes the normal tone of
the muscles. The muscles become completely relaxed (*flac-
cid*) immediately after this operation. The limbs hang
limply like those of an animal immediately after death, and
no reflex activity can be elicited. Also, since the vasomotor
centers in the medulla oblon-
gata are separated from the
spinal centers, there is a profound fall in blood pressure
(p. 151). This state, called
spinal shock, persists for a
time which varies with the
species. Recovery from
spinal shock occurs within a
few minutes in the frog, but
not for several weeks in the
dog and never completely in
man.

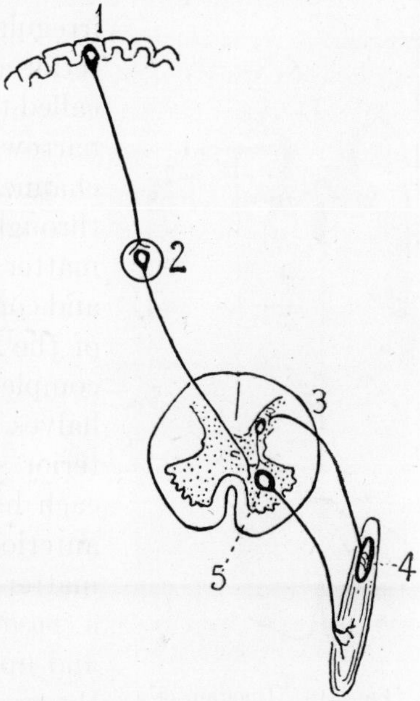

From these observations it
is concluded that the spinal
reflex arc, upon which muscle
tone is directly based, must
be reinforced by impulses discharged from the vestibular
nuclei. The latter, in turn,
are under an inhibitory influence from higher centers.
The vestibular nuclei, when

FIG. 215. Diagram of the factors
responsible for muscle tone. 1, cerebral cortex or other higher cerebral
region; 2, vestibular nucleus; 3,
spinal cord; 4, muscle spindle;
5, anterior horn cell of the spinal cord.

released by brain section from the restraint of the latter, become hyperactive, with consequent exaggeration of tonus.
Though the spinal centers are dependent, normally, upon impulses from the vestibular nuclei for the maintenance of
tonus they can, in animals at any rate, act independently
when isolated from the higher influence. This is evident from
the fact that spinal shock is recovered from after a time (see
diagram, Fig. 215).

THE SPINAL CORD

The spinal cord is composed of a central fluted column of gray matter, surrounded by white substance. The latter consists of bundles of nerve fibers (see Fig. 216). In a cross section of the spinal cord the gray matter appears as an irregularly H-shaped mass. The anterior and broader limbs of the H are called the *anterior horns;* the posterior narrow limbs, the *posterior horns.* A channel — the *central canal* — runs throughout the length of the gray matter; it contains cerebrospinal fluid, and communicates with the ventricles of the brain. The spinal cord is incompletely divided into two lateral halves by an anterior cleft and a posterior septum. The white matter of each half is marked off again by the anterior and posterior horns of gray matter into an *anterior,* a *lateral* and a *posterior column.* In the thoracic and upper lumbar regions of the cord the gray matter between the anterior and posterior horns shows a small projection called the *lateral horn;* it is composed of sympathetic nerve cells.

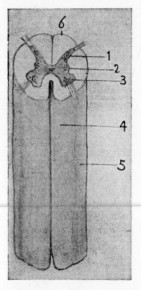

FIG. 216. Diagram of a section of the spinal cord to show the disposition of gray and white matter. 1, posterior horn; 2, lateral horn; 3, anterior horn; 4, posterior column of white matter; 5, lateral column; 6, anterior column.

The anterior horns of gray matter contain large multangular cells. These cells are points of convergence for impulses from various sources — from the periphery of the body along sensory nerves, and from the motor area of the cerebral cortex by the corticospinal tracts (p. 435), as well as from the cerebellum and other parts of the brain. The axons of the anterior horn cells of the cord constitute the only pathway (final common path, p. 422) from the spinal cord to the skeletal muscles; the anterior horn cells, therefore, relay the impulses which bring about voluntary movement, and are also the effector (motor) neurons of the spinal reflex arc. The posterior horns of gray matter contain the cell bodies of connector neurons; afferent impulses, after entering the cord, are relayed by these cells to the anterior horn cells, and to neurons which connect with higher levels of the central nervous system.

The spinal nerve roots. In man there are 31 pairs of spinal nerves. Each nerve arises from the cord by two roots, an anterior and a posterior. The anterior root is composed entirely of efferent fibers, the majority of which are derived from the cells of the anterior horn; other smaller fibers are efferents of sympathetic nerve cells in the lateral horn. The posterior roots contain only afferent fibers — sensory fibers from the skin, muscles, viscera, etc., and other afferent fibers which transmit non-sensory impulses, i.e., impulses which do not reach consciousness. The cell bodies from which the fibers of the posterior roots arise are situated in a small swelling upon the root itself; this is called the *ganglion of the posterior root* (Fig. 217). Both the dendrite and axon of each of these cells arise by a short common stem which divides into two fibers, one of which (dendrite) passes peripherally, the other into the cord, where it makes connection with intraspinal neurons or ascends to the medulla oblongata. The cranial nerves possess similar ganglia from which their afferent fibers originate (see Fig. 115, p. 230). The two roots of a spinal nerve unite within the intervertebral foramen. The trunk so formed divides again almost immediately into a large anterior and a small posterior branch, each of which receives fibers (sensory and motor) from both spinal roots. The posterior branches of the spinal nerves are distributed to the skin and muscles of the back. The anterior branches fuse with one another, redivide and combine again in a complicated way to form three plexuses — the *cervical, brachial* and *lumbosacral* plexuses — from which the periph-

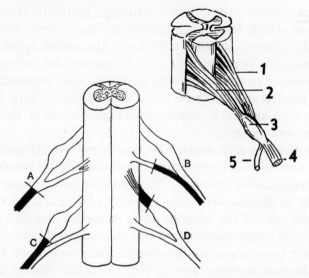

FIG. 217. *Right hand drawing*, the spinal nerve roots (after Allen Thomson). 1, anterior root; 2, posterior root; 3, posterior root ganglion; 4, anterior primary division; 5, posterior primary division. *Left hand drawing*, diagram to illustrate Wallerian degeneration (modified from Halliburton). Section at A causes degeneration of all motor and sensory fibers of the peripheral nerve beyond the point of section (black area). In B, section of the anterior root causes degeneration of the motor fibers since the motor cell bodies lie within the spinal cord; in C, section of the posterior root is followed by degeneration of the sensory fibers of the peripheral nerve because the cell bodies of the sensory fibers lie in the ganglion; in D, section of the posterior root between the ganglion and the cord causes degeneration of the sensory fibers of the spinal stump of the root and of ascending fibers within the cord as far as the next cell station.

eral nerves to the skin and muscles of the neck and limbs ultimately emerge. Thus, in the formation of the plexuses, the fibers of the original spinal nerve roots become intermingled, the peripheral nerve trunks containing both motor and sensory fibers.

The tracts of the spinal cord. The nerve fibers composing the spinal white matter have various origins and form definite bundles, usually referred to as *tracts* or *fasciculi*. The fibers of some of these tracts arise from higher levels of the nervous system and conduct impulses downwards; others arise from lower levels and conduct in an upward direction. They are therefore classed into *ascending* and *descending* groups. Each tract is further given a specific name derived from the origin and destination of its fibers (Pl. 8 B).

The descending tracts. The *corticospinal* or *pyramidal tracts* arise from the large cells of the motor area of the cerebral cortex (p. 441) on each side of the brain. The fibers of each tract synapse with the anterior horn cells of the opposite side of the cord. The tracts descend through the substance of the brain, traversing successively the internal capsule of the cerebrum (p. 443), the mid-brain, pons and medulla oblongata. They form two prominences on the anterior aspect of the medulla oblongata, called the pyramids. At the lower border of the medulla oblongata the greater proportion of the fibers of one side cross to the opposite side of the cord and descend in the lateral column. The remaining uncrossed fibers descend in the anterior columns, but these also ultimately cross to the anterior horn cells of the opposite side at various levels of the cord.

The corticospinal tracts transmit impulses which bring about voluntary movements of the limbs and trunk. A lesion involving these tracts in any part of their course, from the motor area of the central cortex to their terminations in the spinal cord, results in weakness or paralysis of the muscles on the opposite side of the body. The fibers conveying impulses to the muscles of the eyes, face, tongue and throat also arise from the motor area of the cerebral cortex, but they form connections with nerve cells in the motor nuclei of the cranial nerves (3rd to the 12th). These fibers, though they are strictly analogous to the corticospinal fibers and travel with the latter for a part of their course, are referred to as the *corticobulbar tracts*. Like the corticospinal tracts, they convey impulses from one side of the brain to the muscles of the opposite side.

Every pathway for the transmission of impulses governing voluntary movements, whether of the limbs and trunk or of the face, eyes, tongue and throat, consists, therefore, of two neurons. The one whose cell body lies in the cerebral cortex is called the *upper motor neuron*. The *lower motor neuron* is the anterior horn cell of the spinal cord or a cell in one or other of the cranial nuclei. The axons of the lower motor neurons form, of course, the peripheral motor nerves (cranial and spinal).

The effects following a lesion of the upper motor neuron differ in certain respects from those resulting from injury or disease of the lower. These differences are summarized in the following table.

Effects of lesions of the upper motor neuron	*Effects of lesions of the lower motor neuron*
(1) Paralysis of the spastic type. That is, the paralyzed muscles are hypertonic and offer a greater resistance to passive movements than normally.	The paralyzed muscles are flaccid. They are hypotonic, offering little resistance to passive movement.
(2) The tendon jerks are exaggerated.	The tendon jerks are absent.
(3) Normal response to electrical stimulation.	Reaction of degeneration.
(4) Little muscular wasting.	Marked wasting of muscles.
(5) Babinski response; abdominal reflexes lost.	Plantar response; abdominal reflexes lost.

The rubrospinal tracts. These descend in the lateral columns of the cord to synapse with the anterior horn cells. They arise from the red nucleus in the mid-brain (p. 448). After issuing from the red nucleus the fibers cross to the opposite side (*decussation of Forel*). Thus, the red nucleus of one side is connected with the anterior horn cells of the opposite side of the spinal cord.

The vestibulospinal tracts arise from the vestibular nuclei situated in the lower part of the medulla oblongata. The fibers of each tract connect with the anterior horn cells of the opposite side of the spinal cord. These tracts relay impulses transmitted to the vestibular nuclei from the labyrinth and cerebellum. They are of essential importance in the maintenance of equilibrium, correlating the tone and movements of the muscles with the position of the head in space.

The chief descending tracts of the brain and cord are indicated in the diagram, Pl. 9 A.

The ascending tracts. The *fasciculus gracilis (tract of Goll)* and *fasciculus cuneatus (tract of Burdach)* occupy the posterior column of each half of the cord. They are composed of the axons of cells of the posterior root ganglia. The fibers of these tracts transmit impulses of light touch and the sense of position and movement (*kinesthetic sense*) to the nucleus gracilis and nucleus cuneatus in the medulla oblongata; from here the impulses are relayed upwards by other neurons to the optic thalamus, and thence to the cerebral cortex. When these tracts are injured, the subject, since he is not informed of the movements and positions of his limbs, has difficulty in executing muscular acts with orderliness and precision; his movements are jerky and poorly controlled. Impaired muscular control of this type is called *ataxia*. The sense of touch is little affected, however, because touch impulses ascend also in the anterior spinothalamic tracts.

The spinocerebellar tracts. These are two in number on each side. One, the *dorsal spinocerebellar tract*, reaches the cerebellum via the inferior cerebellar peduncle; the other, the *ventral spinocerebellar tract*, ascends to the mid-brain, entering the cerebellum through its superior peduncle. They ascend in the lateral columns of the cord and transmit non-sensory impulses from the muscles to the cerebellum. Injury or disease of these tracts also results in ataxia, because the cerebellum does not receive the impulses which enable it to exercise its function in controlling voluntary muscular acts.

The spinothalamic tracts ascend one in the anterior column, the other in the lateral column of each half of the cord. The *anterior spinothalamic tract* conducts impulses of light touch from the skin of the opposite side of the body to the thalamus; from the thalamus the impulses are relayed by other fibers to the cerebral cortex. The *lateral spinothalamic tract* is the pathway for impulses of pain, heat and cold from the opposite side of the body (see Pl. 9 B).

The sensory pathways in the brain are described on pp. 451–453.

The brain is that part of the nervous system enclosed by the skull. It consists of the *cerebrum, mid-brain, pons, medulla oblongata* and *cerebellum* (see Fig. 218).

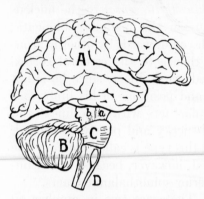

The cerebrum. The *cerebrum* is divided incompletely by a longitudinal fissure (the *superior longitudinal fissure*) into two halves called the *cerebral hemispheres*. These are the large ovoid masses lying in contact with the vault and walls of the skull. The hemispheres constitute by far the largest part of the human brain, and of the brains of apes and monkeys, but are less prominent structures in the brains of lower vertebrates. The most highly developed functions of the nervous system — memory, intelligence, moral sense, etc. — and the centers for sight, hearing, smell, taste and general body sensations, are seated in the cerebral hemispheres.

FIG. 218. Plan in outline of the brain as seen from the right side, ⅓ natural size. The parts are represented as separated from one another considerably more than is natural so as to show their connections. A, cerebrum; B, cerebellum; C, pons; D, medulla oblongata; a, cerebral peduncle; b, colliculi. a and b form the mid-brain. (After Quain.)

The hemispheres are composed of a covering of gray matter, called the *cerebral cortex* and a central mass of white matter. The latter is composed of tracts of nerve fibers ascending to the cortex and descending from the cortex to lower levels of the nervous system; these are referred to as

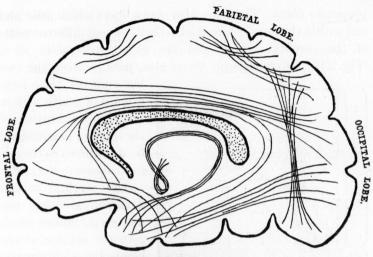

FRONTAL LOBE.

PARIETAL LOBE.

OCCIPITAL LOBE.

TEMPORAL LOBE

Fig. 219. Diagram to show the general course of the association
fibers of the cerebral hemisphere.

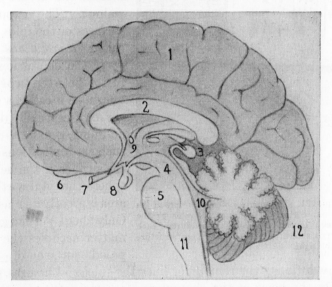

Fig. 220. Section through the brain in a plane passing between the cerebral
hemispheres. 1, right cerebral hemisphere; 2, corpus callosum; 3, pineal body;
4, mid-brain; 5, pons; 6, olfactory lobe; 7, optic nerve; 8, pituitary; 9, third
ventricle; 10, fourth ventricle; 11, medulla oblongata; 12, cerebellum, sectioned
surface shows the arborization of the white matter.

projection fibers. There are also many fibers which arise and end within the hemisphere itself; they connect different parts of the cerebral cortex and are called *association fibers* (Fig. 219). *Commissural fibers,* also, pass between the two hemispheres; these form a mass of white matter lying at the bottom of the superior longitudinal fissure, known as the *corpus callosum* (Fig. 220).

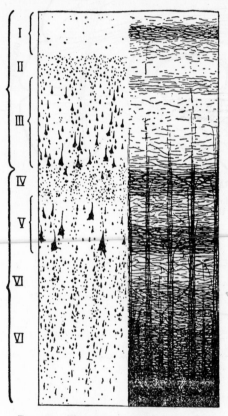

The cerebral cortex. The cortex shows numerous infoldings which give the surface of the hemispheres an appearance not unlike the surface of the kernel of a walnut. The exposed surfaces of the folds are called *convolutions* or *gyri;* the depression or furrow between two convolutions is called a *sulcus,* or if especially deep and long, a *fissure.* By such reduplications of the surface of the hemisphere the total cortical area is greatly increased. Only about $\frac{1}{3}$ of the gray matter occupies the exposed surface of the convolutions; the remainder lines the sulci and fissures.

FIG. 221. The microscopical structure of the cerebral cortex. The numerals refer to the different layers. The cellular structure of each layer is shown on the left, the fiber structure on the right. (After Economo.)

On the basis of the characters of their constituent cells, several well-defined layers can be distinguished in the gray matter. The respective cell layers, however, do not show

uniform characters throughout all regions of the cortex. On
the contrary, certain layers exhibit special characteristics in
certain areas, e.g., the motor area in the frontal lobe and the
visual area of the occipital lobe. Upon such characteristics
depend, undoubtedly, the special functions of the different
cortical areas (Fig. 221).

Localization of function in the cerebral cortex. For convenience of description each cerebral hemisphere is divided

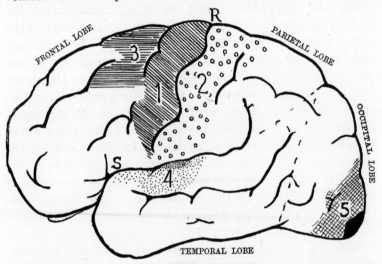

FIG. 222. Diagram illustrating the localization of function in the cerebral
cortex. 1, motor area; 2, sensory (somesthetic) area; 3, premotor area; 4, auditory area, the lighter stippling indicates the association area; 5, part of visual
area, the cross-hatching represents the association area; R, fissure of Rolando;
S, fissure of Sylvius.

into four parts called lobes. The *frontal lobe* is that part
in front of the deep cleft (*fissure of Rolando*) which runs
obliquely downwards and slightly forwards from the upper
border of the hemisphere (Fig. 222). The *parietal lobe*
lies behind the fissure of Rolando; the *temporal lobe* lies
below the well-marked horizontal fissure — *fissure of Sylvius*
— on the lateral aspect of the hemisphere. The *occipital lobe*
forms the posterior pole of the hemisphere lying behind the
parietal and temporal lobes. The cortex of the frontal, pari-

etal and occipital lobes extends on to the opposed aspects of the hemispheres, i.e., on to the walls of the longitudinal fissure.

A band of cortex lying in front of, and parallel to the fissure of Rolando contains large pyramidal cells (Betz cells). The axons of these cells descend through the brain to connect with the motor cranial nuclei and the anterior horn cells of the cord; they constitute the corticobulbar and cortico-spinal tracts (p. 435), along which are transmitted the impulses governing voluntary movement. This part of the cortex is, therefore, called the *motor area*. The voluntary movements of the various parts of the body are repre-sented in this area in the following order, from the upper border of the hemisphere downwards; toes, ankle, knee, hip, trunk, shoulder, elbow, wrist, fingers, neck, face, tongue, larynx. It has been mentioned elsewhere that the cortico-spinal fibers ultimately cross to the opposite side of the spinal cord. It follows that the muscles of one side of the body are controlled by the motor area of the opposite side of the brain. Injury to the motor area of one hemisphere, therefore, results in paralysis of the muscles on the opposite side of the body.

Situated in front of the upper part of the motor area is the so-called *premotor area*. The functions of this cortical area have not been fully elucidated, but it appears to exert a controlling influence over the motor area itself, probably synthesizing the more localized movements, represented in the latter area, into more complex acts. The premotor area is also connected by descending fibers with the *corpus stria-tum* (p. 444) and, through the *frontopontine tract*, with the gray matter of the pons. Through the former connection it is in indirect communication with the red nucleus, cere-bellum and spinal centers; through the frontopontine fibers a connection is also established between it and the cere-bellum.

Of the functions of the remaining and greater part of the

frontal cortex, that is, of the part not occupied by the motor and premotor areas, little is definitely known; this region is, therefore, spoken of as a "silent" area. It is sometimes the site of a tumor, and the surgeon in order to eradicate the growth is often forced to sacrifice a large part of the brain tissue. The frontal lobe of one side, except for the motor and premotor areas, has been excised in a number of instances, but such operations are followed by little or no functional defect. Even after the removal of both frontal lobes in front of the premotor areas, there is remarkably little disability. It has been thought that the frontal lobe was the seat of intelligence; the greater development of this part of the human brain has supported such an idea. However, in the light of the results just cited and of experiments upon animals, our views on the importance of this part of the brain must be revised. There is apparently no special region or center for intelligence. It depends upon the cortex as a whole; upon the degree of development of the various cortical sensory areas, and the richness of the association paths through which these areas are interconnected. The frontal cortex is simply a region of high associative ability, and as such contributes its share to the general intellectual capacity of the individual.

The parietal lobe. The area of cortex lying behind the fissure of Rolando is sensory in function. It is called the *somesthetic* area. Here sensations of touch, warmth and coolness, and of muscular movements (kinesthetic sensations), are perceived and interpreted (see also p. 423). The sensory representation of the various parts of the body show definite localization, following the same order as that already described for the motor area (see Fig. 222).

The temporal lobe. The cortex bordering the fissure of Sylvius, together with that buried in the fissure itself, is the region for the perception of sound. Here the fibers of the *auditory radiation* (p. 455) terminate; it is therefore called the *acoustic area* or the center for hearing. The acoustic area of each side of the brain receives impulses from both ears. Its unilateral destruction, therefore, does not cause deafness in either ear, though some dullness of hearing in both ears may result. The temporal cortex adjacent to the acoustic area is associative in function, being concerned with the interpretation of sounds, that is, with understanding the meaning and significance of the various kinds of sound, e.g., words, music, etc., and with the association of a particular sound with visual, tactile or other sensations.

The occipital lobe. The cortical area for vision — the *visual area* — is situated chiefly on the inner aspect of the occipital lobe, but it also extends around the posterior extremity of the lobe to a small part of its lateral surface. Impulses from the right halves of the retinas are transmitted to the visual area of the right hemisphere, impulses from the left halves of the retinas to the left visual area. Destruction of the visual cortex on one side of the brain, therefore, causes blindness in the corresponding halves of the retinas only (see p. 480). The remaining part of the occipital lobe is associative in function; upon its activity depend the recognition and interpretation of visual impressions, and the integration of these with other sensations.

The optic thalamus, corpus striatum and internal capsule. The *optic thalamus* is a mass of gray matter situated at the base of each hemisphere, just above the mid-brain. The third ventricle separates the thalami of the two sides (Fig. 238). The *corpus striatum* is an irregular mass of gray matter lying toward the outer side of the thalamus, but separated from it by the *internal capsule*. The latter structure is composed of bundles of ascending and descending nerve fibers (e.g., corticospinal and sensory tracts). It is a bottle-neck pass which all fibers must traverse in order to reach lower levels of the nervous system, and through which all sensory fibers destined for the cortex must ascend. An injury to the internal capsule, therefore, causes extensive damage to the conducting pathways; paralysis and often sensory loss on the opposite side of the body result. Paralysis confined to one side of the body is called *hemiplegia*. It most commonly follows rupture of a blood vessel supplying the internal capsule, with consequent interruption of the motor and sensory paths. The immediate effect of hemorrhage into the internal capsule is loss of consciousness and paralysis of all four limbs. This condition, called *cerebral apoplexy* or in popular parlance "a stroke" lasts for a variable time; the subject may die without regaining consciousness. If he survives, the paralysis on one side disappears as consciousness is regained, but loss of power in the muscles of the face and limbs on the side of the body opposite to that of the hemorrhage persists. The tone of the affected muscles is increased (spasticity), the tendon reflexes are exaggerated and the normal plantar reflex is replaced by the Babinski response (p. **429**). In other words, the signs are those of an upper motor neuron lesion (p. **436**).

The optic thalamus and corpus striatum are intimately connected by nerve fibers, and both are connected with the cerebral cortex, and with the spinal cord, cerebellum and other parts of the nervous system. All sensory paths conveying impulses of pain, temperature, touch and muscle sense enter the thalamus. The sensation of pain, of rough contact and extremes of temperature — heat above 45° C. and cold below 25° C. — are appreciated in the thalamus itself. The thalamus is therefore an organ of crude consciousness. The finer sensations, i.e., light touch, moderate changes in temperature — warmth and coolness — and muscle sense, are perceived by the somesthetic region of the cortex. The impulses subserving these sensations are relayed to the parietal cortex by fibers which arise in the thalamus and ascend in the internal capsule. The parietal cortex brings a discriminating and critical ability to bear upon the impulses which it receives, being capable of judging the lesser gradations in stimulus intensity, and of detecting minor qualitative differences in sensation. The thalamus possesses no such discriminating capability. The parietal cortex is believed also to send impulses to the thalamus which restrain its activity. When released from cortical restraint, the thalamus reacts in an "all or none" manner, a diffuse, ill-defined but intensely umpleasant sensation being aroused by painful stimuli or extremes of temperature.

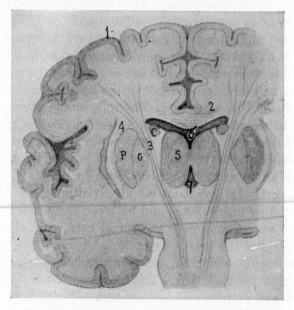

Fig. 223. Vertical and transverse section through the cerebrum to show its internal structure. 1, cerebral cortex; 2, corpus callosum; 3, internal capsule; 4, corpus striatum; P = putamen, G = globus pallidus; 5, optic thalamus; 6, lateral ventricle; 7, third ventricle.

The *corpus striatum* is a large gray mass curved upon itself in such a way that in a horizontal section of the brain it appears as two separate gray masses — the *caudate nucleus* [1] and the *lentiform nucleus* (Figs. 223 and 224). The latter consists of two parts; the outer and larger part is called the *putamen,* and the inner part the *globus pallidus.* The lenti-

[1] The term, *nucleus,* is used to denote any circumscribed group of nerve cells or isolated mass of gray substance within the central nervous system.

form nucleus is separated from the thalamus by the posterior limb of the internal capsule, and from the caudate nucleus by the latter's anterior limb. The striate body has numerous fiber connections with other parts of the nervous system, e.g., with the premotor area of the cerebral cortex, the thalamus and the red nucleus, and through the latter with the cerebellum and spinal centers. Of the functions of the corpus striatum little is definitely known. It is concerned in some way with the control of skeletal muscle tone; it probably also exerts a steadying influence upon muscular movements. In disease of the corpus striatum or of its connections, marked rigidity of the muscles — flexors and extensors — is seen. The resistance offered by a limb to passive movements has suggested a comparison with a lead pipe ("lead pipe" rigidity). Tremor or jerkiness of the limbs, upon attempting a voluntary movement, is also a common manifestation of disease of the corpus striatum. Both these signs, namely, rigidity and tremor,

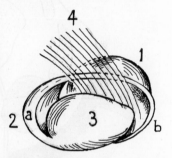

FIG. 224. The corpus striatum. 1, thalamus; 2, caudate nucleus, a, head, b, tail; 3, lenticular nucleus; 4, fibers of internal capsule. (2, 3 and 4 constitute the corpus striatum.)

are seen in *paralysis agitans*, the name given to one form of disease of the striate body.

The mid-brain or mesencephalon. The mid-brain is the short, narrow, pillar-like portion of the brain, lying immediately below the optic thalami. It is traversed by a narrow canal called the *cerebral aqueduct;* this communicates above with the third ventricle of the brain and below with the fourth ventricle. The greater part of the mid-brain lies in front of the aqueduct, and consists of the two *cerebral peduncles.* Anteriorly the latter are separated by a cleft, and appear as two stout columns which emerge from the pons below, and plunge into the substance of the cerebrum above.

Each column, which is termed the *base* of the peduncle, transmits the *corticospinal, frontopontine* and *temporopontine tracts* of the corresponding side of the brain. Posteriorly the peduncles are fused into a single structure called the *tegmentum* which contains, on each side of the mid-line, an ovoid mass of gray matter — the *red nucleus* — and two

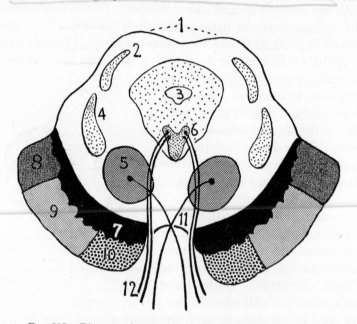

FIG. 225. Diagram of a transverse section through the mid-brain. 1, inferior colliculi; 2, lateral fillet; 3, cerebral aqueduct; 4, medial fillet; 5, red nucleus; 6, nucleus of oculomotor nerve; 7, substantia nigra; 8, temporopontine tract; 9, corticospinal tract; 10, frontopontine tract; 11, crossing of rubrospinal tracts (decussation of Forel); 12, fibers of oculomotor nerve.

smaller gray masses, the *nuclei of the oculomotor* and *trochlear nerves*. This part of the mesencephalon also transmits two bundles of sensory fibers — the *lateral* and *medial lemnisci*. The former is the pathway for auditory impulses, the latter for impulses of touch, pain, muscle sense, etc. (Fig. 225).

The part of the mid-brain lying posterior to the cerebral

aqueduct is called the *tectum*. It consists of two pairs of rounded eminences called, respectively, the *superior* and *inferior colliculi*. The superior colliculus receives impulses from the retina and is connected with the spinal centers through a tract of descending fibers — the *tectospinal tract*. It is a center for visual reflexes, e.g., movements of the head and eyes in response to retinal stimuli. The inferior colliculus receives auditory impulses, and serves as an auditory reflex center, e.g., pricking of the ears in response to sound.

A small oval eminence is seen on the outer side of each colliculus. These are called, respectively, the *medial* and *lateral geniculate bodies*. The former, which is connected by a strand of fibers called the *inferior brachium* with the inferior colliculus, receives the bulk of the fibers comprising the auditory pathway (the lateral lemniscus; see also p. 455). The lateral geniculate body receives most of the fibers of the optic tract (p. 453) and is connected by a band of fibers — the *superior brachium* — with the superior colliculus (see Fig. 226).

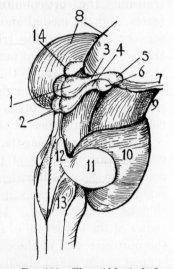

FIG. 226. The mid-brain looking from behind and to one side, cerebellum removed. 1, superior colliculi; 2, inferior colliculi; 3, superior brachium; 4, inferior brachium; 5, lateral geniculate body; 6, medial geniculate body; 7, optic tract; 8, optic thalami; 9, cerebral peduncles; 10, pons; 11, sectioned middle cerebellar peduncle; 12, superior cerebellar peduncle; 13, medulla oblongata.

The *red nucleus* (*nucleus ruber*) is connected by fiber tracts with the cerebral cortex, corpus striatum, thalamus, cerebellum and spinal cord. Its functions are imperfectly understood, but it appears to be an integral part of the nervous mechanism controlling the execution of skilled muscular movements. The fibers which descend to the spinal centers are called the *rubrospinal tracts*. Upon issuing from the lower part of the red nucleus these fibers cross with the fibers of the opposite side. This crossing is called the *decussation of Forel*.

The pons. The pons is that part of the brain stem lying below the mid-brain and above the medulla oblongata. It transmits the corticobulbar, corticospinal and rubrospinal tracts, and the medial and lateral lemnisci. It contains the sensory nucleus of the trigeminal nerve and the nuclei of the facial and abducent nerves. It is in communication with the cerebellum through the middle cerebellar peduncle, and with the cerebrum through the frontopontine and temperopontine tracts. The fibers of these tracts synapse with nerve cells in the substance of the pons called the *pontine nuclei*.

The medulla oblongata. The medulla oblongata is the continuation upwards of the spinal cord. It is somewhat conical in shape, broadening as it ascends, until at its junction with the pons its circumference is nearly double that of its lower end. A central canal runs through the center of the lower half of the medulla, but in the upper half the posterior wall of the canal opens out to form a lozenge-shaped space called the fourth ventricle. The floor of the fourth ventricle is composed of gray matter — the prolongation upwards of the anterior horns of the cord which, through the opening of the central canal, have become exposed. Upon the anterior aspect of the medulla are two vertical columns called the *pyramids*, formed by the corticospinal (pyramidal) tracts. At the junction of the medulla with the spinal cord, the pyramid of each side divides into a smaller and a larger part. The latter crosses (decussates) with that of the opposite side and descends in the lateral column of the cord. The smaller division descends uncrossed in the anterior column of the cord. The medial fillets (see below) cross (*sensory decussation*) a little above the decussation of the pyramids (*motor decussation*) and ascend behind the latter. The nuclei of the eighth, ninth, tenth, eleventh and twelfth cranial nerves are situated in

the medulla; it also contains the nucleus gracilis and the
nucleus cuneatus, and the so-called vital centers — cardiac,
vasomotor and respiratory. It is connected through the
inferior cerebellar peduncle with the cerebellum.

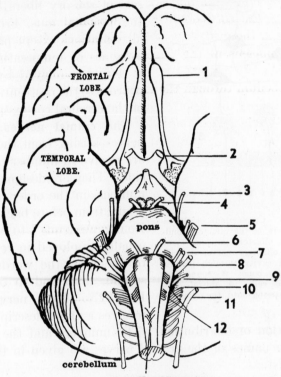

FRONTAL
LOBE.

TEMPORAL
LOBE.

1

2

3
4

pons

5
6
7
8
9
10
11

12

cerebellum

medulla oblongata

FIG. 227. The base of the brain showing the origins of the
cranial nerves, numbered from 1 to 12.

Summary of sensory pathways in the brain. As mentioned,
on page 437, impulses reaching the nuclei gracilis and cuneatus along the fibers of the posterior columns, are continued
upwards by secondary neurons. The axons of the latter,
after leaving the nuclei and crossing to the opposite side
(*sensory decussation*), ascend through the medulla, pons and
mid-brain forming a tract known as the *medial fillet* or

lemniscus. The medial fillet is joined by the anterior and lateral spinothalamic tracts, as well as by fibers carrying

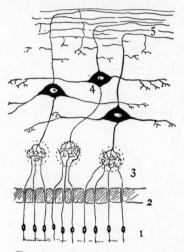

impulses from the face (*trigeminal lemniscus*). These four sets of sensory fibers lead to the optic thalamus. From here all sensations except pain and extremes of temperature (see p. 445) are relayed by other neurons to the postcentral area of the cerebral cortex (p. 443).

The cranial nerves. The nerves arising from the brain are twelve in number on each side. They are designated by numbers in the order of their origin, from before backwards. Roman numerals I to XII are usually employed in referring to them, or the words first, second, third and so on (see Fig. 227). Each nerve also receives a name descriptive of

FIG. 228. Connections of the olfactory fibers in the olfactory bulb. 1, cells of olfactory mucous membrane; 2, olfactory nerves entering the cranial cavity through perforations in the bone; 3, connections with mitral cells; 4, mitral cells; 5, fibers passing into the olfactory tract.

its function or distribution.   The numbers and the corresponding names of the cranial nerves are given in the following list.

List of the cranial nerves

I.	Olfactory	VII.	Facial
II.	Optic	VIII.	Acoustic (or auditory)
III.	Oculomotor	IX.	Glossopharyngeal
IV.	Trochlear	X.	Vagus
V.	Trigeminal	XI.	Accessory
VI.	Abducent	XII.	Hypoglossal

The olfactory nerves, or nerves of smell, are distributed to the olfactory mucous membrane covering the roof of the nose (p. 520).

They consist of some twenty short bundles of fibers, composed of the axons of the olfactory cells lying in the olfactory mucosa. They pierce the bone separating the cranial from the nasal cavity to reach the olfactory bulb. This is an oval mass of gray matter lying upon the floor of the skull beneath the fore and inner part of the frontal lobe of the brain. In the olfactory lobe, the axons of the olfactory cells form connections with the dendrites of secondary neurons; these are large pyramidal cells (*mitral cells*) whose axons compose the olfactory tract. The latter terminates in the center for smell situated in the hippocampal gyrus of the brain (see Fig. 228).

The optic nerve, or nerve of sight, is composed of the axons of the ganglion cells of the retina. A short distance behind the eyeballs, the optic fibers from the inner (nasal) half of the retina cross with the corresponding fibers of the opposite side. The fibers from the outer (temporal) halves of the retinas do not cross (see p. 480). From the chiasma the visual fibers (i.e., nasal fibers of one eye and temporal fibers of the other) proceed to the mid-brain, this part of their course being called the *optic tract*. The greater proportion of the fibers of the optic tract terminate within the *lateral geniculate body*, which is referred to as the *primary visual center*. From the lateral geniculate body the visual impulses are relayed by secondary neurons, through the internal capsule, to the visual area of the cerebral (occipital) cortex. The visual pathway from the lateral geniculate body to the occipital cortex is called the *optic radiation* (see Pl. 12 B).

The oculomotor nerve arises from a group of nerve cells — the *nucleus of the oculomotor nerve* — situated in the gray matter of the floor of the cerebral aqueduct (p. 447). The fibers course forward through the mid-brain, emerging from the inner aspect of the cerebral peduncle. The oculomotor nerve supplies all the eye muscles with the exception of the external rectus and superior oblique. It also conveys parasympathetic fibers to the constrictor muscle of the iris, and to the ciliary muscle.

The trochlear nerve has its nucleus in the floor of the cerebral aqueduct, a little behind the oculomotor nucleus. It emerges from the brain at the border of the pons. The trochlear nerve supplies the superior oblique muscle of the eyeball.

The trigeminal nerve contains both sensory and motor fibers.

Its *motor* fibers are the axons of a group of cells situated in the upper part of the pons. This collection of gray matter is called the *motor nucleus* of the trigeminal. The *sensory* fibers originate in the *trigeminal (semilunar) ganglion* which lies upon the floor of the skull, and is homologous with the posterior root ganglia of the spinal nerves. The central processes (axons) of the ganglion cells form a short trunk — the *sensory root of the trigeminal* — which enters the brain with the motor root. Within the brain, the fibers of the sensory root divide into ascending and descending groups. The former end in a collection of gray matter — the *superior sensory nucleus of the trigeminal* — situated in the pons close to the motor nucleus. These fibers convey the discriminative qualities of sensation, namely, light touch, localization, kinesthetic sense, etc., from the face. The descending fibers terminate in the *spinal nucleus of the trigeminal nerve* — an elongated mass of gray substance, extending from the lower part of the pons to the upper part of the spinal cord. The fibers entering the spinal nucleus transmit impulses of the crude forms of sensation from the face, namely, pain and extremes of temperature. The peripheral processes of the cells of the trigeminal ganglion are distributed to the skin of the face, forehead and anterior half or more of the scalp, to the eyeball and conjunctiva, to the mucous membrane of the nasal cavities, to the teeth and gums and to the anterior two-thirds of the tongue. The motor fibers supply the muscles of mastication.

The abducent nerve. The abducent nucleus is situated in the lower part of the pons beneath the floor of the 4th ventricle. The nerve emerges from the anterior aspect of the brain in the groove lying between the pons and the upper end of the pyramid of the medulla oblongata. It supplies the external rectus muscle of the eyeball.

The facial nerve has a large motor and a small sensory root. The fibers forming the *motor* root arise from the *motor nucleus*, which lies in the lower part of the pons. This root also transmits *secretory* and *vasodilator* (parasympathetic) fibers to the submaxillary and sublingual glands; these fibers arise from a separate group of nerve cells — the *superior salivary nucleus* — lying in close proximity to the motor nucleus. The motor root of the nerve leaves the anterior aspect of the brain at the lower border of the pons. The fibers of the *sensory* root (also called the *nervus intermedius*) are the axons of cells situated in the *facial (geniculate) ganglion* which lies within a canal in the temporal bone. The sensory root enters the brain in close association with the motor root. The peripheral processes of the ganglion cells are distributed to the anterior two-thirds of the tongue (see Fig. 115, p. 230). They transmit impulses of taste to a nucleus in the medulla oblongata named the *tractus solitarius*. From the latter the impulses are relayed to the thalamus and thence by tertiary neurons to the center for taste in the cerebral cortex (p. 520). Both taste and parasympathetic fibers (secretory and vasodilator) leave the facial trunk in its *chorda tympani* branch.

The motor fibers of the facial nerve form a stout trunk which leaves the cranial cavity through a small opening in the floor of the skull. The nerve curves forward below the ear to reach the face, where it breaks up into numerous branches. These supply the muscles of the face, lips, eyelids, forehead and anterior part of the scalp.

The auditory nerve is entirely sensory in function. It consists of two distinct sets of fibers, the *cochlear* and *vestibular nerves*. The cochlear nerve, or nerve of hearing, conveys impulses from the auditory part of the labyrinth (the cochlea, p. 502). It is composed of the central processes (axons) of cells situated in the *spiral ganglion* of the cochlea. The peripheral fibers (dendrites) terminate around the bases of the hair cells of the organ of Corti. The axons of the cochlear nerve enter the upper part of the medulla oblongata, and divide into two groups. One group of fibers terminates in the *dorsal cochlear nucleus*, the other in the *ventral cochlear nucleus*. From these nuclei the auditory impulses are relayed by the axons of secondary neurons across the mid-line of the medulla. They then ascend in the lateral lemniscus through the pons and mid-brain to the *medial geniculate body* — the *primary auditory center*. From here tertiary neurons transmit the impulses through the internal capsule to the auditory area in the cortex of the temporal lobe (p. 443). The fibers extending from the medial geniculate body to the cerebral cortex are referred to as the *auditory radiation*.

The vestibular nerve consists of the axons of neurons situated in the *vestibular (Scarpa's) ganglion*. The central connections are described on p. 512.

The glossopharyngeal nerve contains *motor, sensory, secretory* and *vasodilator* fibers. The motor fibers issue from the upper part of the *nucleus ambiguus* situated in the medulla oblongata, and are distributed to a single muscle (the stylopharyngeus). The sensory fibers conduct impulses of taste from the posterior third of the tongue to the lower part of the tractus solitarius. The taste impulses are relayed to the optic thalamus, and thence to the cerebral center for taste. Sensory fibers are also distributed to the mucous membranes of the pharynx, tonsil and palate; they convey impulses of ordinary sensation, touch, temperature, etc. The secretory and vasodilator (parasympathetic) fibers leave the glossopharyngeal nerve in the *tympanic branch* and are distributed to the parotid gland. The secretory and vasodilator fibers have their origins in the *inferior salivary nucleus*, which lies below the superior salivary nucleus (p. **454**).

The glossopharyngeal nerve appears as a slender strand attached to the side of the medulla oblongata just below the auditory nerve. It enters the neck through an opening (the jugular foramen) in the base of the skull. The nerve at its point of emergence from the skull shows two ganglia. The processes of the neurons of these ganglia constitute the sensory fibers of the nerve.

The vagus nerve is composed of *motor, sensory, secretory* and *vasodilator* fibers. The motor fibers are of two types — voluntary and autonomic. The fibers to voluntary muscle originate in the lower part of the nucleus ambiguus; they supply the cricothyroid muscle of the larynx, and the inferior constrictor muscle of the pharynx. The autonomic motor fibers are distributed to the muscle of the bronchi, heart, esophagus, stomach, gall-bladder, pancreas, small intestine and first third or so of the large intestine. The involuntary motor fibers, the secretory fibers (to the gastric glands and pancreas) and the vasodilator fibers belong to the parasympathetic division of the autonomic system. They arise from the *dorsal nucleus of the vagus*. This nucleus is a mixed one, for it is also a terminal for sensory fibers. Some of the latter connect with motor autonomic neurons within the dorsal nucleus, which thus functions as a reflex center.

The vagus emerges from the lateral aspect of the medulla oblongata as a series of rootlets which soon join to form a stout trunk. This leaves the skull through the jugular foramen, and passes down the neck in close relation to the internal and common carotid arteries. Two ganglia are situated upon the vagus trunk, the upper one lies within the jugular foramen, the other just below the point where the nerve issues from the skull. The sensory fibers of the vagus have their origin within these ganglia.

The accessory nerve is entirely motor in function, and consists of a *cranial* and a *spinal* part. The cranial fibers arise from a nucleus lying below, and continuous with the nucleus ambiguus. They leave the side of the medulla oblongata as four or five delicate strands, which after uniting, pass from the skull through the jugular foramen. The spinal fibers are the axons of anterior horn cells situated in the upper five cervical segments of the spinal cord. This part of the nerve enters the cranial cavity through the foramen magnum and re-enters the neck through the jugular foramen. Within the latter foramen it joins the cranial part, but becomes separate again almost immediately.

Most of the muscles of the pharynx, larynx and soft palate are supplied by the cranial part of the accessory nerve. The spinal part sends fibers to certain muscles of the neck and shoulder (sternomastoid and trapezius).

The hypoglossal nerve is distributed entirely to the muscles of the tongue. Its fibers arise from the hypoglossal nucleus in the medulla oblongata, and appear as a series of rootlets in the groove situated on the antero-lateral aspect of the pyramid. The rootlets leave the skull through the hypoglossal canal and unite just below the base of the skull. The trunk so formed curves forwards in the upper part of the neck to reach the cavity of the mouth.

The cerebellum. The cerebellum is situated behind the brain-stem (mid-brain, pons and medulla), and beneath the posterior portions of the cerebral hemispheres (Fig. 220, p. 438). It is composed of two lateral masses, the *cerebellar hemispheres* (Fig. 229) and a central elongated worm-like structure, called the *vermis* (L. *worm*). The white matter of the cerebellum forms a central branching framework within the substance of each hemisphere. The gray matter covering the terminal stems of this structure constitutes the cerebellar cortex. The cortex of the hemispheres

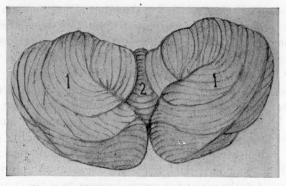

FIG. 229. The cerebellar hemispheres and vermis
from below. 1, hemispheres; 2, vermis.

is thus constructed of a number of leaves flattened against
one another with only their edges appearing on the surface.

The cerebellar cortex is composed
of several layers of cells, but unlike
the cerebral cortex is of uniform
structure throughout. Large cells
with flask-shaped bodies and extensive dendritic arborization —
the *cells of Purkinje* — are peculiar to the cortex of the cerebellum
(see Fig. 230).

Each half of the cerebellum is
connected with the rest of the central nervous system through three
compact bundles of nerve fibers,
called the *cerebellar peduncles*. The
superior cerebellar peduncle (or
brachium conjunctivum) plunges
into the mid-brain and transmits
impulses from the cerebellum to
the red nucleus and thalamus and,
through the latter, to the motor area
of the cerebral cortex (see Fig. 231).

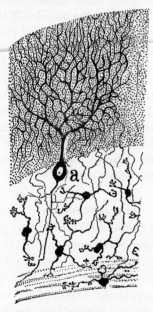

FIG. 230. Section of the cerebellar cortex showing minute
structure. a, Purkinje cell.

It also transmits the ventral spinocerebellar tract which con-

veys impulses to the cerebellum from the spinal cord (p. 437).
The impulses which leave the cerebellum by its superior peduncle originate in the cerebellar cortex. They pass first to
one or other of three masses of gray matter — the *cerebellar
nuclei* — embedded in the white matter of the hemispheres.
From here the impulses are relayed by secondary neurons.
The largest of the cerebellar nuclei is called the *dentate*

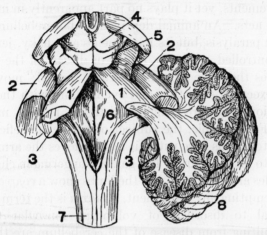

Fig. 231. Showing the three pairs of cerebellar peduncles. 1, superior peduncle;
2, middle peduncle; 3, inferior peduncle; 4, superior colliculus; 5, inferior colliculus; 6, floor of fourth ventricle forming posterior aspect of pons and medulla oblongata; 7, spinal cord. (Redrawn after Hirschfeld and Leveillé.)

nucleus; the axons of cells composing this gray mass make up
the bulk of the fibers leaving the cerebellum by the superior
peduncle.

The *middle* peduncle (or *brachium pontis*) transmits impulses from the pons *to* the cerebellum; its fibers arise from
the pontine nuclei which, as stated elsewhere, receive impulses from the frontal and temporal regions of the cerebral
cortex (frontopontine and temporopontine tracts).

The *inferior* peduncle (or *restiform body*) connects the
cerebellum with the lower part of the medulla oblongata.
It is composed, mainly, of fibers of the dorsal (direct) spinocerebellar tract and of fibers arising in the vestibular nuclei

in the medulla oblongata (*vestibulocerebellar tract*). Thus, through the inferior cerebellar peduncle the cerebellum receives proprioceptive impulses from the labyrinth (p. 510) and the skeletal muscles. The inferior peduncle also transmits impulses *from* the cerebellum to the vestibular nuclei (*cerebellovestibular tract*).

The *functions* of the cerebellum are concerned with voluntary movements, yet it plays no part apparently in initiating muscular acts. An animal deprived of its cerebellum shows no actual paralysis, but its movements are shaky, jerky and poorly controlled. In man, injury or disease of the cerebellum causes the same lack of muscular control; movements are not executed smoothly and evenly, and with the nicety of direction and force characteristic of normal muscular action. For example, the subject of cerebellar deficiency if asked to touch his nose with his finger moves the arm jerkily and fails to hit the mark. The gait is staggering in character; the muscles are hypotonic and the limbs show a coarse tremor upon attempting any movement. *Ataxia* is the term applied in general to disorders of voluntary muscular control; those resulting from disease of the cerebellum are therefore grouped under the designation *cerebellar ataxia*.

As a result of numerous experiments upon animals and of studies of cerebellar deficiency in man (gunshot wounds or disease), it is now generally believed that the chief function of the cerebellum is to *synergize* the actions of the different muscles engaged in a given movement. Through cerebellar activity the contractions of the individual muscles, or groups of muscles, are so timed and graded in force that their combined action results in a smooth and effective movement. The anatomical basis for such function has been outlined above. Its superior peduncles connect the cerebellum with the motor area of the cerebral cortex on the one hand, and on the other hand, through the red nucleus and the rubrospinal tracts, with the anterior horn cells of the spinal cord. Through the spinocerebellar tracts the cerebellum is kept constantly informed of the position of the limbs and movements of the muscles. Through the vestibulocerebellar tracts it receives impulses from the labyrinth acquainting it with movements of the head in space.

The impulses reaching the cerebellum give rise to no sensation; the cerebellum carries on its activities entirely beneath the level of consciousness.

THE AUTONOMIC NERVOUS SYSTEM

The autonomic or involuntary nervous system governs those functions which are carried out automatically, and which under ordinary circumstances do not obtrude upon consciousness. These functions include the movements of the heart and gastro-intestinal tract, the control of the smooth muscle of the blood vessels, urinary bladder, bronchi and skin, and the activities of the various glands.

The efferent nerves of the autonomic nervous system arise from groups of cells situated at different levels of the central nervous system, from the mid-brain to the sacral region of the spinal cord. The fibers, after issuing from the brain or cord, make connections with nerve cells situated either in a ganglion or in the innervated organ itself (muscle or gland). Thus, every autonomic pathway consists of two neurons. The axon, whose cell body lies within the central nervous system, is called the *preganglionic fiber*, that of the outlying nerve cell, the *postganglionic fiber* (see Pl. 11 A).

The autonomic nervous system is divided upon an anatomical as well as upon a physiological basis into two parts, called the *sympathetic* and the *parasympathetic* divisions (see Pl. 10).

The parasympathetic division. The parasympathetic division is divided into a *cranial* and a *sacral* part or *outflow*. The preganglionic fibers of the cranial outflow arise from groups of cells situated in the mid-brain, pons and medulla oblongata. The mid-brain fibers originate in the oculomotor nucleus and connect with cells in the ciliary ganglion; postganglionic fibers are distributed to the iris, and transmit impulses which constrict the pupil. The cells in the pons are in close association with the nucleus of the facial nerve, the preganglionic fibers are conveyed in the chorda tympani branch of the facial nerve to ganglion cells situated in, or in close relation to the submaxillary and sublingual (salivary) glands. From here the impulses are transmitted by post-ganglionic fibers to the gland cells. The fibers in the chorda tympani nerve are vasodilator as well as secretory in function.

In the medulla, the cells giving rise to the parasympathetic fibers are situated in the glossopharyngeal and vagus nuclei. The former enter the glossopharyngeal nerve and pass to the otic ganglion; from here postganglionic fibers conveying vasodilator and secretory impulses are relayed to the parotid gland.

The vagus nerve is composed in the main of parasym-pathetic fibers; these have a very wide distribution — to the heart, bronchioles, esophagus, stomach, small intestine and first third of the large intestine, and to the pancreas, liver, gall-bladder and bile ducts. The preganglionic fibers of the vagus may, therefore, be two feet or more in length, whereas the postganglionic fibers are very short. The lat-ter form a rich plexus — *Auerbach's plexus* — in the walls of the gastro-intestinal tract, bronchioles and biliary ducts. Groups of nerve cells are scattered throughout the plexus of fibers.

The cells of the *sacral outflow* are situated in the 2nd, 3rd and 4th sacral segments of the spinal cord. The fibers leave the cord by the anterior spinal nerve roots. Separating again from the other anterior root fibers, they combine to form the *pelvic nerve*. This nerve supplies motor fibers to the distal two-thirds of the large bowel and to the wall of the urinary bladder, and vasodilator fibers to the penis and clitoris. It also contains inhibitory fibers to the internal anal sphincter and to the internal sphincter of the bladder. The postganglionic fibers of the sacral outflow arise from small ganglia situated in close proximity to, or in the walls of the innervated organ.

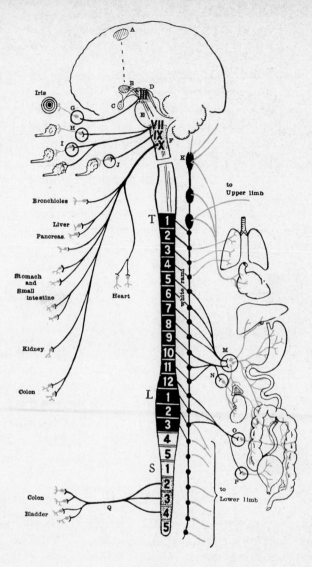

PLATE 10

Plan of the autonomic nervous system. Parasympathetic fibers on left, sympathetic on right; preganglionic in *black*, postganglionic in *red*. Parasympathetic centers in stippled shading. The Roman numerals refer to the respective cranial nerves. A, cerebral cortex; B, hypothalamus; C, pituitary gland; D, mid-brain; E, pons; F, medulla oblongata; G, ciliary ganglion; H, sphenopalatine ganglion, postganglionic fibers to lachrymal gland. I, submaxillary ganglion, postganglionic fibers to sublingual gland, submaxillary gland below, ganglion cells within the gland substance; J, otic ganglion, postganglionic fibers to parotid gland; K, superior cervical ganglion, postganglionic fibers to iris, blood vessels, sweat glands and smooth muscle of head. The middle and inferior cervical ganglia are shown below. M, N, O, P, celiac, superior mesenteric, inferior mesenteric and hypogastric ganglia, respectively; Q, pelvic nerve. The large letters T, L and S indicate, respectively, the thoracic, lumbar and sacral segments of the spinal cord.

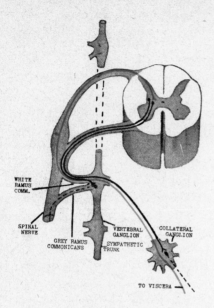

WHITE RAMUS COMM.

SPINAL NERVE

GREY RAMUS COMMONICANS

VERTEBRAL GANGLION

SYMPATHETIC TRUNK

COLLATERAL GANGLION

TO VISCERA

PLATE 11A

Diagram of the connections of the sympathetic fibers. Efferent fibers in black; preganglionic, solid lines; postganglionic, interrupted lines; afferent visceral fiber in red. Collateral ganglion = prevertebral ganglion. (After Best and Taylor, *The Physiological Basis of Medical Practice.*)

PLATE 11B

Diagram to illustrate the division of the autonomic nervous system into cholinergic and adrenergic types of fiber. P, parasympathetic; S, sympathetic; 1, preganglionic fibers; 2, postganglionic fibers; cholinergic fibers, *red;* adrenergic, *black.* (The figure 2 has been omitted in error from the postganglionic parasympathetic fiber.)

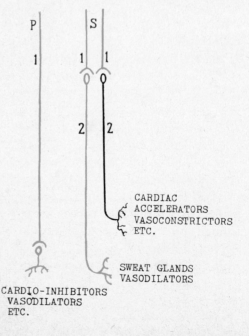

P   S

1   1   1

2   2

CARDIAC ACCELERATORS VASOCONSTRICTORS ETC.

SWEAT GLANDS VASODILATORS

CARDIO-INHIBITORS VASODILATORS ETC.

The sympathetic division. The preganglionic fibers of the sympathetic nerves are the axons of cells in the lateral gray horns of the spinal cord, from the first thoracic to the second or third lumbar segments. The sympathetic is, therefore, commonly referred to as the *thoracicolumbar outflow* of the autonomic nervous system. The preganglionic fibers leave the anterior roots of the corresponding spinal nerves. The ganglia of the sympathetic are in two main groups, the *vertebral* and the *prevertebral*. The vertebral ganglia are situated on either side of the vertebral column (Pl. 10.) They appear as a series of 22 swellings on each side, connected together to form a long, beaded cord. This extends from the base of the skull to the coccyx, and is called the *gangliated cord of the sympathetic*. The prevertebral ganglia are larger than the vertebral; they lie in front of the spinal column and in close relation to the aorta and its branches.

The sympathetic fibers destined for the supply of the limbs (blood vessels, sweat glands and smooth muscle of the skin) soon separate from the anterior nerve roots and enter the vertebral ganglia. These fibers (preganglionic) are seen as delicate white strands connecting each anterior spinal nerve root from the 1st thoracic to the 2nd or 3rd lumbar segments with the corresponding lateral ganglion (Pl. 11 A). They are called the *white rami communicantes*. Their constituent fibers do not necessarily terminate in the ganglion which they first enter, but may pass up or down the gangliated cord to end around ganglion cells at a higher or lower level. The postganglionic fibers leave the ganglia as yellowish-pink strands known as the *gray rami communicantes*, which join the spinal nerves. The sympathetic fibers are thus distributed to the periphery with the ordinary motor and sensory fibers. All the spinal nerves receive postganglionic fibers, though the anterior roots of only a proportion of the spinal nerves (1st thoracic to 2nd or 3rd lumbar) give rise to white rami (preganglionic fibers).

The sympathetic fibers to the viscera and blood vessels

of the abdomen do not connect with the vertebral chain of ganglia, but pass to the prevertebral ganglia — *celiac, superior mesenteric*, etc. The postganglionic fibers form plexuses around the branches of the abdominal aorta, from which the vessels and viscera receive their sympathetic supply. The fibers passing from the spinal cord to the prevertebral ganglia are collected on each side into three well-defined strands called the *greater, lesser* and *least splanchnic nerves*.

The sympathetic nervous system exerts a regulating influence on a great number of structures. Through the cardiac accelerator nerves it increases the rate of the heart; through the splanchnic nerves it inhibits the movements of the intestinal tract, maintains the tone of the arterioles of the abdomen, hastens the formation of glucose from glycogen by the liver, and causes the liberation of adrenaline from the adrenal medulla. Sympathetic impulses cause relaxation of the wall of the urinary bladder, but contraction of the internal sphincter of this organ. Sympathetic fibers in the cutaneous nerves transmit motor impulses to the smooth muscle of the skin and secretory impulses to the sweat glands.

Many structures, such as the iris, heart, intestines, urinary bladder, salivary glands and pancreas, receive fibers from both divisions of the autonomic nervous system. The actions of the two upon a given organ are antagonistic and balanced one against the other, the activity shown by the organ at any moment being the resultant of the two opposing influences. The parasympathetic fibers (vagus) to the heart, for example, are inhibitory, the sympathetic excitatory. On the other hand, motor fibers to the wall of the intestine are derived from the parasympathetic, the inhibitors from the sympathetic. The walls of the urinary bladder and intestine receive their motor innervation from the parasympathetic (vagus and pelvic nerves), whereas the sympathetic is inhibitory. The internal sphincters of the bladder and anus are innervated in a reverse manner; they are excited by the sympathetic and inhibited by the parasympathetic.

A summary of the actions of the parasympathetic and sympathetic fibers upon a number of structures is given in Table 18.

TABLE 18

Organ	Parasympathetic effects *	Origin of sympathetic postganglionic fibers	Sympathetic effects
Heart	Inhibition	Superior middle and inferior cervical ganglia	Acceleration
Vessels:			
Cutaneous		Various vertebral ganglia	Constriction
Muscular		Various vertebral ganglia	Dilatation
Coronary	Constriction	Cervical ganglia	Dilatation
Salivary glands	Dilatation	Superior cervical ganglion	Constriction
Pulmonary	Constriction	Thoracic vertebral ganglia	Constriction and dilatation
Cerebral	Dilatation	Superior cervical ganglion	Constriction
Abdominal and pelvic viscera		Prevertebral ganglia	Constriction
External genitalia	Dilatation	Prevertebral ganglia	Constriction
Eye:			
Iris	Constriction	Superior cervical ganglion	Dilatation
Ciliary muscle	Contraction	Superior cervical ganglion	Relaxation
Smooth muscle of orbit and upper lid		Superior cervical ganglion	Contraction
Bronchi	Constriction	Thoracic ganglia	Dilatation
Glands:			
Sweat		Vertebral ganglia	Secretion
Salivary	Secretion	Superior cervical ganglion	Secretion
Gastric	Secretion	Celiac ganglion	Inhibition? Secretion of mucus
Pancreas			
Acini	Secretion	Celiac ganglion	
Islets	Secretion	Celiac ganglion	
Liver		Celiac ganglion	Glycogenolysis
Adrenal medulla		No postganglionic fibers	Secretion
Smooth muscle:			
Of skin		Vertebral ganglia	Contraction
Of stomach wall	Contraction or inhibition	Celiac ganglion	Contraction or inhibition
Of small intestine	Increased tone and motility	Celiac and superior mesenteric ganglia	Inhibition
Of large intestine	Increased tone and motility	Inferior mesenteric and hypogastric ganglia	Inhibition
Of bladder wall (detrusor muscle)	Contraction	Inferior mesenteric and hypogastric ganglia	Inhibition
Of trigone and sphincter	Inhibition	Inferior mesenteric and hypogastric ganglia	Contraction

* With certain exceptions, e.g., those supplying the sublingual and parotid glands and the sphincter pupillae, the postganglionic fibers of the parasympathetic arise from cells situated in, or in close proximity to, the innervated organ itself.

The sympathetic and the hormone of the adrenal medulla are closely similar in their actions. The two, acting in conjunction, constitute what is referred to as the *sympatho-adrenal* mechanism and play an important role in the regulation of the internal environment of the body, i.e., the composition and temperature of the fluids bathing the cells of the tissues. Thus, through its effect upon the blood vessels, sweat glands and smooth muscle of the skin, the sympathetic controls heat loss; through its action upon the blood vessels it also varies the distribution of water between the vascular system and the tissues. Through an action upon the liver, either through sympathetic nerve impulses or the liberation of adrenaline, the sugar of the blood is raised. The sympatho-adrenal system through its various activities increases the body's efficiency in times of stress. Many manifestations of an animal when in danger or when its powers are being taxed to the utmost, are those of sympathetic stimulation, e.g., dilated pupils, rapid heart action, contraction of the spleen, and the erection of hair or ruffling of feathers (due to contraction of cutaneous smooth muscle; see also p. 347).

The sympatho-adrenal system, highly important though it is, can nevertheless be dispensed with. It is not essential to life nor even to well-being, provided the animal is not exposed to some environmental hazard. Animals from which the entire sympathetic and the medulla of both adrenals have been excised live in perfect health in the sheltered surroundings of the laboratory. They cannot, however, withstand cold and are less well equipped than a normal animal to meet an emergency which demands the marshalling of its resources, either to defend itself or to fly from the threatened danger.

The transmission of autonomic effects by chemical substances. Research of recent years has disclosed the amazing fact that sympathetic and parasympathetic effects are not brought about by the nerve impulses themselves, but by chemical substances which the impulses cause to be liberated from the nerve endings. In treating of the control of the heart, it has been mentioned that, when the vagus is stimulated, *acetylcholine* is liberated, and is the direct cause of the inhibitory effect upon the heart muscle. Similarly, an *adrenaline-like substance* is liberated from terminals of the cardiac accelerators, and from other nerves of the sympathetic system (see pp. 145 and 348). These facts, which have led to a revolutionary change in our ideas of peripheral nervous action, have been supplemented within the last few years by a number of observations of great interest and importance.

It has been shown, for example, that acetylcholine is liberated from such parasympathetic nerves as those going to the iris (in the oculomotor nerve), to the salivary glands (in the chorda tympani), to the stomach and intestines (in the vagus) and to the bladder (in the pelvic), as well as from certain sympathetic nerves, e.g., from those to the sweat glands and from those which cause dilatation of the vessels of the skeletal muscles. It has been shown further that the transmission of nervous effects across parasympathetic and sympathetic synapses, i.e., from the preganglionic fiber to the ganglion cell, is due to the liberation of acetylcholine from the preganglionic terminal. More extraordinary still, the contraction of skeletal muscle has been shown to be due to the liberation of acetylcholine from the voluntary motor nerve endings.

Following the suggestion of Sir Henry Dale, the English physiologist, it is now customary to speak of those fibers which liberate an adrenaline-like substance as *adrenergic*, and those which liberate acetylcholine as *cholinergic*. All preganglionic fibers (sympathetic or parasympathetic), all postganglionic parasympathetic fibers and certain postganglionic sympathetic fibers (e.g. to sweat glands), as well as the fibers of voluntary motor nerves are cholinergic (see Pl. 11 B).

CONDITIONED REFLEXES

The type of reflex which has been considered (pp. 418 and 426) is carried out entirely through centers situated in the spinal cord or lower (subcortical) levels of the brain. In conditioned reflexes, on the other hand, the activity of the cerebral cortex plays an essential role. Conditioned reflexes were first demonstrated and studied by Pavlov, the Russian physiologist, and most of the knowledge which we possess of this type of response is the outcome of his investigations. An understanding of the conditioned response can best be gained by giving a few examples of the results of Pavlov's experiments.

When a newborn puppy is given milk to drink there is a secretion of saliva, due to the stimulation of the taste buds in the mouth. The reflex arc in this instance is constituted of the nerves of taste, the salivary centers in the medulla and the secretory fibers (chorda tympani or glossopharyngeal) to the salivary glands. This is a simple or *unconditioned reflex*. It is inborn, and quite independent of previous experience gained through any of the organs of special sense. Now, as the puppy grows older it associates the appearance or smell of the milk, or both, with its taste and the pleasure of gratifying the appetite. The mere sight or smell of the milk will then elicit a secretion of saliva; such a response is called a *conditioned reflex*. Pathways have become established in the brain between the cortical center for sight or for smell, with the salivary center. In other words, the visual and olfactory stimuli — *conditioned stimuli* — set up impulses which, impinging upon the salivary centers, are capable alone (i.e., without stimulating the nerves in the mouth) of exciting them (see diagram, Fig. 232). If, on the other hand, a puppy which has never tasted meat is offered some (but is not allowed to taste it), there is no secretion of saliva. The association paths between the higher centers of the brain and the secretory centers have not been developed.

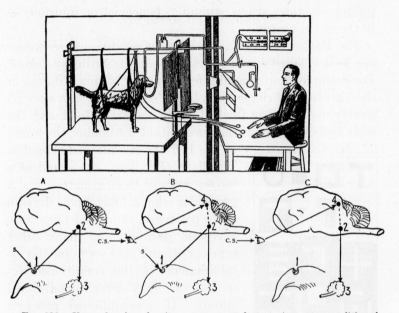

FIG. 232. *Upper drawing*, showing arrangement for carrying out a conditioned reflex experiment. The opening of the parotid duct has been transplanted to the skin of the cheek so that the saliva as it is secreted may be collected and measured. The animal is separated from the experimenter by a partition in order that extraneous types of stimulation (e.g., movements or sounds made by the experimenter) shall not arouse the animal's interest and thereby interfere with the conditioning process. (From Pavlov, *Lectures on Conditioned Reflexes*, International Publishers, N. Y.) *Below*, diagram to illustrate the theory of the mechanism underlying conditioned reflexes. 1, taste buds; 2, salivary center; 3, salivary gland; 4, occipital (visual) cortex; S, unconditioned stimulus; C.S., conditioned stimulus. In A the animal is fed and a stimulus thus applied to the taste buds. In B a conditioned visual stimulus (e.g., a flash of light) is applied at the same time as the unconditioned stimulus. A pathway from the occipital cortex to the salivary center is thus established. In C the conditioned stimulus is applied alone. Impulses pass from the visual cortex to the salivary center and evoke salivary secretion.

Conditioned reflexes become established not only with respect to feeding, and the secretion of saliva, but in many other similar ways in the everyday life of the growing animal. Such processes are essentially psychic in character and dependent upon experience. They therefore form the basis of training, and are of the greatest biological importance. The animal through the conditioning process reacts appropriately to the various stimuli — beneficial or injurious — in the environment.

The Pavlov school has shown that conditioned responses can be developed experimentally to an extraordinary degree. For example, if an animal is fed a number of times, during or shortly after the ringing of a bell, a secretion of saliva occurs merely upon ringing the bell. The contact of food with the taste buds constitutes the unconditioned stimulus, the sound of the bell the conditioned stimulus. The flash of a light, the sound of a buzzer, horn or ticking metronome, a particular odor, a touch upon the skin or the passive movement of a limb into a certain position, and many other types of stimuli may serve for the establishment of the conditioned response, i.e., may act as conditioned stimuli. If a conditioned reflex is evoked repeatedly, it becomes progressively weaker and finally fails. It is said to be *extinguished*. In order to maintain the reflex at full strength, the unconditioned stimulus (i.e., the giving of food in the case of a salivary conditioned reflex) must be applied after every few repetitions of the conditioned response. This is referred to as the *reinforcement* of the conditioned reflex.

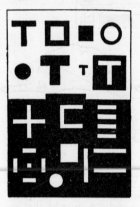

Fig. 233. Examples of different figures which were successfully differentiated in experiments upon a dog. The letter T, shown in the upper left-hand corner of the figure, served for the positive stimulus, the other black figures and the white letter T were differentiated from the positive stimulus. In another dog the white cross was the positive stimulus from which the other white figures were differentiated. (From Pavlov, *Conditioned Reflexes*, Oxford University Press.)

The conditioning process can be so developed that stimuli closely similar in character can be *differentiated* with astonishing precision. A dog in which a conditioned salivary reflex has been established to a sound of a certain pitch will not respond to a sound of the same quality and intensity, but varying in pitch from the original by only two or three double vibrations per second.

Differentiation of *visual* stimuli can also be developed to a phenomenal degree. Figures of various shapes — a cross, square or circle — are readily differentiated (see Fig. 233). A circle can be differentiated by the dog from an ellipse, whose diameters have a ratio no greater than 9 to 10. That is, if a salivary conditioned reflex has been established to a circular object, such as an unilluminated disc, it alone evokes a response. A disc precisely the same in all respects except that it is not quite circular but has diameters in the ratio of 9 to 10 will not cause a secretion of saliva. Olfactory, tactile and proprioceptive stimuli can likewise be differentiated with remarkable precision.

It is evident that conditioned reflexes afford a valuable means for studying perception in animals. It has been established, for example, that the dog possesses the ability of discriminating between slight variations in the intensity, quality and pitch of a musical note, between various odors, and by sight between objects of different sizes and shapes, and between lights of different intensities. Colors, on the contrary, cannot be differentiated, nor can a colored object be distinguished from a colorless one of the same size and shape. It is concluded, therefore, that color vision is lacking in the dog.

CHAPTER XI

THE SPECIAL SENSES

THE PHYSIOLOGY OF VISION

General description of the eye. The adult human eye is almost spherical, and about an inch in diameter. A transparent circular area, called the *cornea,* is situated in its anterior wall. The posterior wall is lined by a light-sensitive tissue called the *retina.* A rounded bundle of nerve fibers — the *optic nerve* — passes from the posterior pole of the globe to the brain. The eye, except for the anterior fifth or so of its circumference, is enclosed in a bony case, the eye socket or *orbital cavity,* but a thick layer of areolar tissue is interposed between the eyeball and the bone which serves as a cushion to buffer it against external violence. The eyeball is also protected from injury by the eyelids which, as we know, close reflexly in an instant to prevent dust or other particles from coming into contact with its surface. The exposed part of the eyeball is covered by a delicate membrane called the *conjunctiva* which is continued forward on to the inner surfaces of the lids. When the lids open and close, the apposed conjunctival surfaces slide over one another. The surfaces are lubricated by a thin film of tears secreted by the *lachrymal gland,* which lies under the shelter of the

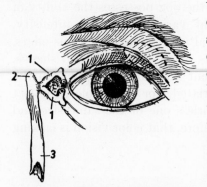

Fig. 234. The lachrymal apparatus. 1, lachrymal ducts; 2, lachrymal sac; 3, nasolachrymal duct. Region marked off by interrupted line indicates the position of the lachrymal gland.

bone forming the upper and outer part of the wall of the eye
socket. The tears, after flowing over the surface of the eye,
are drained from its inner angle into the nose by two small
tubes — the *lachrymal ducts* (see Fig. 234). If it were not for
the continual washing and lubrication of the eyeball by the
tears, the delicate protective membrane would soon become
dry and inflamed; ulceration of the corneal surface would
result.

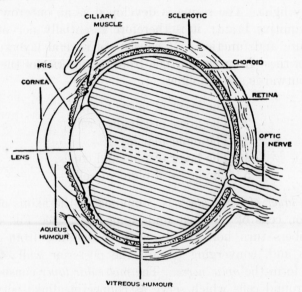

FIG. 235. Showing the different parts of the eye and the
coats of the eyeball.

The coats of the eyeball. The wall of the eye is composed
of three layers or coats — an *outer,* a *middle* and an *inner*
(see Fig. 235).

The outer layer or sclerotic coat is fibrous in character; it
preserves the form of the eyeball and protects the more delicate vascular and nervous coats within. The sclerotic is
transparent in front where it forms the cornea. It also composes that opaque exposed part of the eyeball surrounding
the cornea, and commonly called the *white of the eye.*

The middle layer or choroid coat is richly vascular, containing the main arteries and veins of the eyeball. It completely surrounds the globe, except for a small circular opening in front called the *pupil*. The circular band of choroid immediately surrounding the pupil and colored blue, gray, brown or hazel, is called the *iris*.

The inner layer or retina contains the receptors for sight, i.e., those elements highly specialized to respond to stimulation by light. The retina is developed as an outgrowth of the primitive brain; it is therefore essentially nervous in structure and function. It consists of several layers; the chief of these from within (i.e., from the interior of the eyeball) outwards are as follows:

1. The layer of nerve fibers,
2. The layer of ganglion cells,
3. The molecular layer,
4. The layer of rods and cones,
5. The layer of pigment cells.

The *layer of nerve fibers* is composed of the axons of the ganglion cells of the next underlying layer (see Fig. 236). The fibers turn horizontally a short distance from their origins and, converging toward the posterior wall of the globe, form the *optic nerve*. The *molecular layer* consists of small round cells which serve as connecting links between the rods and cones and the ganglion cells.

The rods and cones are the receptors of sight. They are modified nerve cells. When light strikes them, impulses are set up and transmitted by the nerve cells of the molecular layer to the ganglion cells, and thence by the axons of the latter (which constitute the optic nerve) to the visual area of the cerebral cortex (see p. 444). It is evident from their position that light, in order to reach the rods and cones, must penetrate all layers of the retina except the outermost one of pigment cells. It should also be mentioned that, though the visual receptors are stimulated most effectively by light they respond also to mechanical stimuli. A blow, or even light pressure upon the eyeball will cause a visual sensation in the form of a flash, circle or star of light.

Vision in bright light is dependent upon the cones; upon the rods depends the ability to see in dim light. In well-lighted surroundings the rods apparently play no part in vision. Most birds, for example, though they possess very acute vision have few or no rods in their retinas, and the most sensitive part of the retina in man, namely, the *fovea centralis* (see below) contains only cones; the rods become progressively more numerous, and the cones less so, from the fovea to the periphery of the retina.

The outer parts of the rods contain a red pigment called *visual purple* or *rhodopsin*. The visual purple is bleached by light, but in the living animal regenerates in darkness. If the eye is removed from an animal in the dark and then placed in front of a bright object, such

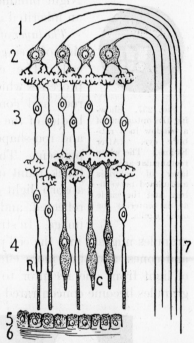

Fig. 236. Showing the chief layers of the retina. 1, layer of nerve fibers; 2, layer of ganglion cells; 3, molecular layer (composed of bi-polar nerve cells); 4, layer of rods and cones; R, rods; C, cones; 5, pigment cell layer; 6, the choroid; 7, fibers of optic nerve.

as a window against the sky, the outlines of the window frame can be made out upon the retina, when the eye is opened and examined in a dim light. Where the light fell upon the retina the visual purple is bleached, but is unchanged where the bars of the window cast their shadow (Fig. 237). The excised eye can thus be made to behave as a camera, the visual purple acting as the chemical in the coating on the film. The crude picture so formed is called an *optogram*. The visual purple is essential for the functioning of the rods. When it is lacking, as in vitamin A deficiency (p. 312) the subject is almost or quite blind in dim light.

FIG. 237. Showing the optogram of a window in a rabbit's eye. (After Kühne.) The white rectangular area is a layer of colorless medullated nerve fibers and the circle at its center is the optic papilla.

Night blindness is also occasionally due to an inherited absence of visual purple.

The layer of pigment cells. This layer consists of a single row of hexagonal epithelial cells. The cells send out protoplasmic processes which are insinuated between the rods and cones. The inner zones of the bodies of the cells contain numerous round and rod-shaped granules of a dark brown pigment. The pigment serves, like the black paint on the inside of a camera, to absorb light which, otherwise, would be reflected, and cause blurring of the retinal image. In strong illumination, the pigment granules migrate into the cell processes surrounding the rods and cones, and thus more effectually prevent the diffusion of light from one receptor to another. In dim light, the granules become concentrated toward the cell centers.

FIG. 238. The blind spot. Close the left eye, hold the figure about six inches in front of the right eye and look steadily at the white disc. Move the book slowly toward the eye until the cross disappears. When this occurs the image of the cross has fallen upon the entrance of the optic nerve from which rods and cones are absent; it is therefore insensitive to light.

The fundus oculi, as the posterior part of the interior of the eyeball is called, can be examined in the living subject by means of an instrument called an *ophthalmoscope* which throws a beam of light through the pupil on to the retina. The *optic papilla* is situated in the center of the posterior wall (see Pl. 12 A). It appears as a white disc, and is produced by the convergence of the visual fibers to form the optic nerve. The retinal blood vessels pierce the papilla near its center, and cross its face to reach the retina. The papilla is composed entirely of nerve fibers, the rods and cones and other retinal layers being absent. It is, therefore, insensitive to light, that is, an object is invisible, if its image falls upon this small area. The optic papilla is, for this reason, called the *blind spot* of the retina. The reader is referred to Fig. 238 for a demonstration of the blind spot in his own eye.

The macula lutea (yellow spot) is a small yellowish area of the retina situated a little to the outer side of the optic papilla (see Pl. 12 A). Its color is due to the presence of a yellow pigment. In the center of the yellow spot is a minute depressed area known as the *fovea centralis*. All the layers of the retina, except the rod and cone and pigment layers, are extremely thin in this area; it is about half a millimeter in diameter ($\frac{1}{50}$ inch). The fovea is the region of acute vision; when we look at an object the eyes are directed so that an image of the object falls upon the fovea of each eye. The rest of the retina (called the peripheral retina) is much less sensitive, and enables us to gain only a dim, ill-defined impression of our surroundings.

The crystalline lens is a transparent biconvex disc, about $\frac{1}{3}$ inch in diameter, situated within the globe of the eye immediately behind the iris. Its center coincides with the center of the pupil. It is suspended in this position by a delicate annular ligament — the *suspensory ligament* — which blends with the lens capsule, and is attached circumferentially to the interior of the globe through the *ciliary body*. The latter also connects the iris with the choroid, and consists of involuntary muscle fibers and a number of processes — the *ciliary processes*. These latter are arranged in the form of a circle to which the suspensory ligament is attached (see Fig. 239). The iris and ciliary body divide the part of the eyeball in front of the lens into an anterior and a posterior chamber. Both chambers are filled with a clear limpid fluid called the *aqueous humor;* a gelatinous transparent substance called the *vitreous body* fills that part of the eyeball lying behind the lens.

Though the healthy crystalline lens is perfectly transparent, in the condition known as *cataract* it becomes semi-transparent or opaque, causing blindness in the affected eye.

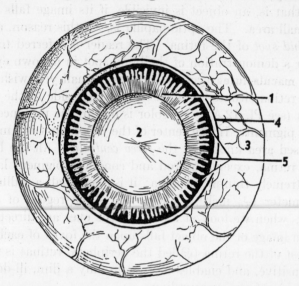

FIG. 239. The eyeball from in front, cornea and iris removed. 1, suspensory ligament; 2, lens; 3, choroid; 4, iris, cut edge; 5, ciliary processes. (Redrawn and modified from Schultze.)

The refracting media of the eye — the formation of an image upon the retina. There is a very close resemblance between the eye and a camera. In both, the rays of light are refracted (bent) and brought to a focus upon a light-sensitive surface — the photographic film and the retina, respectively. The refracting medium in the camera is, of course, the lens. In the eye, light rays are refracted by the cornea, and the aqueous and vitreous humors, as well as by the crystalline lens. The image of an object falls upon the photographic film in an inverted position; the retinal image is inverted similarly. But, of course, we do not see objects

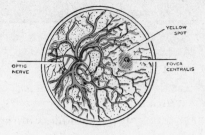

PLATE 12A

The interior of the posterior half of the left eyeball showing the entrance of the optic nerve (optic papilla), retinal vessels, macula lutea and fovea centralis.

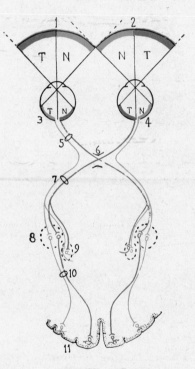

PLATE 12B

Illustrating the course of the visual fibers from the retina to the occipital cortex. 1, left visual field; 2, right visual field; 3, left retina; 4, right retina; T = temporal, N = nasal; 5, optic nerve; 6, optic chiasma; 7, optic tract; 8, lateral geniculate body; 9, superior colliculus; 10, optic radiation; 11, visual area of the occipital cortex.

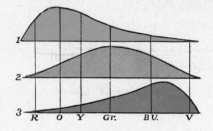

PLATE 13A

Diagram of the three primary color sensations (Young-Helmholtz theory). 1 represents the red, 2 the green and 3 the violet color sensation. The lettering along the base line indicates the colors of the spectrum. The diagram indicates by the height of the curve at which it is cut by the vertical lines the extent to which the several primary sensations of color are excited by vibrations of different wave lengths. (After Helmholtz.)

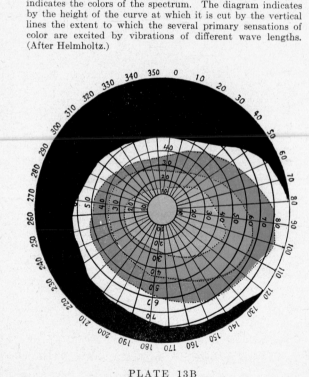

PLATE 13B

Chart showing color fields of the right retina. The entire area of the retina circumscribed by the periphery of a given colored band is sensitive to that color. (After Howell.)

upside down, because experience has taught us to interpret the retinal messages in accordance with reality. In other words, the visual area of the cerebral cortex through a psychological process which it is useless to try to explain, again inverts the image in consciousness, so that objects are seen in their true positions. (See Fig. 240, lower sketch.)

In Fig. 240 (upper sketch) are shown the paths taken by rays of light coming from an object (represented by the large

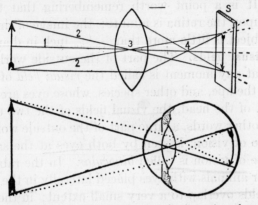

FIG. 240. *Upper drawing,* diagram showing the formation of an image by a convex lens. 1, principal axis; 2, secondary axes; 3, optical center of lens; 4, principal focus; S, screen. *Lower drawing,* the formation of an inverted image upon the retina.

arrow) placed a little in front of a biconvex lens. The diverging rays are refracted by the lens, and brought to a focus on the screen S, which may be taken to represent the retina. Rays from each point on the object are brought to a point upon the screen, but in a reversed position, those from the upper part of the object being directed to the lower part of the screen and vice versa. Similarly, those from the lateral halves of the object pass to opposite sides of the screen. Thus, a small inverted image of the object is formed. It will be noted that the peripheral part of the lens refracts more strongly than parts more centrally placed, and that rays of light passing through either the *principal* axis or the *secondary* axes are not refracted. The principal axis is represented by a line drawn horizontally through the center of the lens, a secondary axis by any oblique line passing through the lens' center. In the lower sketch in Fig. 240 the formation of an image upon the retina is illustrated.

The retinal image can be observed in the excised eye of an albino rabbit. When the eye is directed toward a lighted candle and viewed from behind, an inverted image of the flame is seen shining through the unpigmented wall of the globe. It is a point worth remembering that the image formed upon the retina is minute; the image of the smallest visible object is little more than $\frac{1}{10,000}$ inch in diameter.

The visual fields. The part of the outside world seen by one eye at any moment is called the *visual field* of that eye. In man, the ape, and other species, whose eyes are placed in the front of the head, the visual fields of the two eyes overlap. In other words, a large part of the outside world within the range of vision, is seen by both eyes at the same time. This type of vision is called *binocular*. In the rabbit, horse and other animals with eyes placed laterally in the head, the visual fields overlap to a very small extent; in these, vision is almost entirely *monocular*.

In those species possessing binocular vision, light rays from the *outer* or *temporal* half and from the *inner* or *nasal* half of either visual field, fall upon the *nasal* half and *temporal* half, respectively, of the corresponding retina (see Pl. 12 B). Now, the optic nerves come together a short distance behind the eyeballs to form the *optic chiasma*. Here, the fibers which have arisen from the nasal half of one retina cross with those coming from the nasal half of the other; that is, fibers from the nasal half of the right retina cross to the left side of the brain, those from the nasal half of the left retina to the right side of the brain. Fibers from the temporal halves of the retinas continue uncrossed. Thus, the visual pathway, on each side, from the optic chiasma to the cortex of the occipital lobe (visual center) transmits impulses from the nasal half of one retina and the temporal half of the other. Owing to this peculiar course taken by the visual fibers, the loss of sight following injury or disease of one optic nerve differs from that resulting from a lesion of the fibers anywhere between the chiasma and the occipital cortex, or of the visual center itself. If the function of the optic nerve is destroyed, complete blindness of the corresponding eye results, but the sight of the other eye is unaffected. Interruption of the fibers in their course from the chiasma to the visual area (optic tract), or a lesion of the visual area itself causes blindness in one half of each retina. For example, if the injury involves the left optic tract or left visual cortex, blindness of the nasal (left) half of the right retina and of the temporal (right) half of the left (opposite halves of the visual field) results. Blindness in one half of each eye is called *hemianopia* (half blindness). The nasal half of one retina and the temporal half of the other are called *homonomous* halves. The type of blindness just described is therefore called *homonomous hemianopia*. Rarer types of hemianopia result from bilateral involvement of the temporal fibers alone at the chiasma, or of the nasal fibers alone; these types are given the qualifying terms of *binasal* and *bitemporal*, respectively (the designation binasal and bitemporal refer to the visual fields, not to the retinas).

Objects in the binocular field of vision must, obviously, cast an image on each retina. Yet the two retinal images do not cause a double sensation; we do not see things in duplicate. The explanation for this fact is based upon the theory of *identical* or *corresponding retinal points*. Points in the nasal half of one retina are paired with corresponding points in the temporal half of the other. The ocular muscles direct the axes of the eyes so that an image falls upon each of these corresponding points. As mentioned above, the optic fibers from the homonomous halves of the retinas proceed to one side of the brain, the *left* halves (nasal of right eye and temporal of left) to the *left* visual area, the *right* halves (nasal of left eye and temporal of right) to the *right* visual area. The two images are fused in consciousness into a single sensation.

If, for any reason, the eyes are not directed in such a way that the two images fall on corresponding retinal points, double vision — *diplopia* — results. Diplopia as a permanent condition occurs most commonly as a result of paralysis or weakness of the ocular muscles. It is seen as a temporary state in alcoholic intoxication, being then due to imperfect control, and, in consequence, to unbalanced action of the muscles of the two eyes. One can cause double vision in himself by simply pressing upon the outer side of one eye, and thus displacing the eyeball slightly from its normal position. Two images are also seen if an object, such as a pencil, is held about three inches in front of the root of the nose, or if the pencil is held at arm's length, and the eyes then directed to look at a point some distance beyond it. In the first instance mentioned, it is not possible to converge the eyes sufficiently to bring the two images on to corresponding points on the retinas; in the second instance, images of the near object fall upon non-corresponding points of the retina, because the convergence of the eyes when looking at distant objects is less than that required for near vision.

Accommodation of the eye. Rays of light coming from a distant object are nearly parallel; those from a near object are divergent. Therefore, with a convex lens of a given refracting power, rays from a near object cannot be focused at as short a distance behind the lens as can those coming from a distance. In order to obtain a clear, sharp image of a near object, either a stronger lens (i.e., one with a greater convexity) must be used or the screen moved to a greater distance from the original lens.

The latter means is employed in photography. In order to take a photograph of a view less than 12 feet or so from the camera, the lens must be moved forward so as to increase the distance between it and the film. Though the eyes of certain species of fish have a mechanism for accommodating the eye to near vision based upon this principle, in man and the higher animals the first-mentioned method is adopted. Ac-

commodation of the eye for near vision is brought about by
increasing the convexity of the lens, and thereby raising its
refracting power.   The lens is a yielding elastic structure.
When the eyes are directed to a view, distant more than 15
feet or so, the suspensory ligament (which, as already stated,
extends outwards from the capsule of the lens to be attached
to the ciliary processes, and through these and the ciliary
muscle to the inner coat of the eye) is taut.   The tension thus
exerted upon the lens reduces its curvature.   When the eye
accommodates for near vision, the ciliary muscle contracts

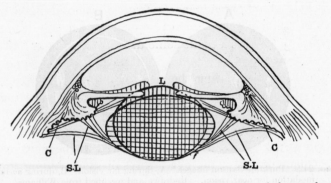

Fig. 241.   Illustrating the mechanism of accommodation of the eye for near
vision.   The horizontally shaded lens and the unshaded iris show the position
of the parts when at rest; the vertically shaded lens and iris show the position
during accommodation for a near point.   C, ciliary muscle; S.L., suspensory ligament.   (Redrawn from Landolt.)

and draws the choroid forward; the ciliary processes are
brought closer to the lens, i.e., they form a smaller circle.
The suspensory ligament is slackened thereby, and the tension on the lens diminished.   The lens by virtue of its inherent elasticity bulges forward (Fig. 241).   The convexity
of the central part of the anterior surface is increased to a
much greater extent than the more peripheral part.   Little
change in the curvature of the posterior surface occurs.
    The change in the form of the lens during accommodation
can be demonstrated by a simple experiment.   If one looks
into a person's eye in a dark room, while a lighted candle is

held a little in front and to its outer side, one sees three reflected images of the flame (Fig. 242). Of these images, one
is bright and upright; it is formed by the anterior surface of
the cornea which acts as a convex mirror. A larger but
dimmer upright image is formed by the anterior surface of
the lens. The third image is inverted, bright and smaller
than the others; it is formed by the posterior surface of the
lens which acts as a concave mirror. If the positions of the
images are noted while the subject gazes at a distant point,
and he then accommodates for near vision, the image re-

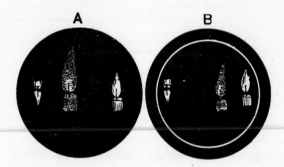

FIG. 242. Purkinje-Sanson images. A, during far vision; B, during accommodation for near vision. (Redrawn and modified from Williams.)

flected from the anterior surface of the lens will be observed
to become smaller, and to move toward that reflected from
the cornea which, of course, does not alter in size or position.
As a rule, no change can be observed in the reflection from
the posterior surface of the lens. The change in the image
on the anterior surface during accommodation can only mean
that this surface becomes more convex.

The other adjustments for near vision are *convergence of
the eyes,* which is necessary in order to bring the retinal images
on to corresponding points (p. 481), and *constriction of the
pupil.* The narrowing of the pupil permits light to pass only
through the central part of the lens which, as just mentioned,
is increased in its convexity to the greatest degree during
accommodation.

The appreciation of distance and depth — stereoscopic vision (Gr. *stereos* = solid, *skopeo* = I view). Our visual judgment of solidity, that is, our recognition that an object has depth as well as height and width, is due largely to the fact that the two retinal images are slightly dissimilar. If the reader will look at some object in front of him, first closing one eye and then the other, he will find that the view seen by the right eye is slightly different from that seen by the left. The right eye is able to see more of the right side of the object, the left eye more of the left side. The two slightly dissimilar images are fused in the brain, yet the composite image has, hidden within it, something of each separate one; upon this the stereoscopic effect largely depends. The fusion of the dissimilar images by the brain, and the impression of depth and solidity produced thereby, lies in a field of psychology of which little is known.

The instrument known as a stereoscope produces an illusion of solidity by making use of the principle of simultaneous stimulation of the retinas by dissimilar images. A photograph taken with an ordinary camera appears flat because identical images are formed upon the retinas. A stereoscopic photograph, on the other hand, is taken by a camera provided with two lenses which are set, like the eyes, a short distance apart. Thus, two slightly dissimilar views are taken, which, when looked at through the stereoscope, are projected by means of prisms, one to each eye, so as to fall on corresponding retinal points.

Stereoscopic perception cannot, however, be explained entirely upon the basis of dissimilar retinal images, for the sensation of depth (or distance) is not abolished when one eye is closed; other factors are concerned. (1) *The apparent size of various objects in our field of vision.* We know from experience the approximate size of the objects which we see, but the image which an object casts upon the fovea diminishes as its distance increases. For example, a church steeple at a distance casts an image upon the retina no larger, perhaps smaller, than a pencil held a few inches from the eyes. We know the relative sizes of the two objects, and therefore infer that the steeple must be far away and the pencil near.

2. *The apparent change in color of an object with distance.* The atmosphere is not perfectly transparent or equally so for all wave lengths. Tree-clad hills, which we know to be green, appear blue in the distance; the colors of many other objects appear to fade with distance, their detail and outline being dimmed by haze.

3. *The blocking out of parts of a distant view by objects between it and the eyes* gives a sensation of depth.

4. *Mathematical perspective.* Straight lines running into the distance which are actually parallel (or objects along imaginary straight lines) are convergent in the retinal image. When we look down a railway track, for example, the rails appear to converge toward some point beyond the horizon. This arrangement of lines in the image formed upon the retina we have come to associate with distance. Perspective is an elementary principle in drawing, used to create an illusion of depth or distance. The artist draws objects along imaginary lines which run toward a point in the background of his picture.

5. *Parallax.* When one moves in any direction, near objects appear to move in the opposite direction, those in the background in the same direction as ourselves. This apparent movement of near objects in relation to ones farther away, is called parallax; it is also produced by a movement of the head or eyes, even though the body remains stationary. Now, involuntary movements of the eyes are continually taking place with the production of parallax; this is believed to be one of the most important factors in giving us a sense of depth.

6. *The distribution of light and shade over the surface of an object and the shadow which it casts upon its surroundings* is also an important factor in the production of the stereoscopic effect.

Color vision. White light is in reality a combination of several colors — red, orange, yellow, green and blue — which can be separated by means of a glass prism. The prism refracts the long red rays less than it does the orange, the orange less than the yellow, the yellow less than the green and, so on, in the order of diminishing wave lengths. A beam of white light is thus split into its constituent colors. The separated colors can be recombined to produce white. But, in order to obtain a white light it is not necessary to employ all the prismatic colors; not only white, but all colors can be produced from three, namely, *red, green* and *violet.* If we were to set up three lanterns, one of which emitted red light, another green, and a third violet, we could, by blending one, two or all three of them upon a screen, produce white or any colored light we chose. For example, the three colors in nearly equal proportions would produce white; green and violet would give blue; red and green and a very little violet would give yellow or orange.

Several theories of color vision have been proposed. According to Young's theory three kinds of cones exist in the retina. One kind is stimulated by red rays, one by green and another by violet; white light falling upon the retina stimulates all three nearly equally. When a yellow color is seen, the sensation is due to the stimulation of equal numbers of the red and green, and a very few of the violet elements; if violet and green sensitive cones are stimulated, a sensation of blue results, and when the red, green or violet type of receptor is excited exclusively, we see red, green or violet, respectively (see Pl. 13 A).

Retinal areas sensitive to color. The greater part of the retina, i.e., the peripheral regions devoid of cones, is insensitive to color. Its sensitivity to color is confined to its more central region. The area sensitive to blue is the largest, that sensitive to red is next in order of size, and that to green the smallest (see Pl. 13 B). The three areas may be compared to three glass saucers of different colors, and of graded sizes, placed one inside the other. Light passing through the small green saucer must pass through the red and blue ones as well. The area of the retina represented by the green saucer is thus sensitive to green, red and blue; this area presumably contains all three types of cone. Light transmitted through the rim of the larger red saucer will pass through the blue as well but not through the green. The area of the retina so represented is therefore sensitive to red and blue, but not to green. The rim of the largest saucer transmits only blue light; the retinal area which it represents contains only blue-sensitive cones.

Color blindness. In some persons the retina is totally insensitive to color; to such their surroundings are seen in black and white and various tones of gray. Such a condition, called *achromatism,* is rare. In the common type of color blindness, known as *dichromatism,* the subjects are blind to red and green, seeing only yellows and blues and blends of these two colors. Such red-green blind persons see red, orange and green as various tones of yellow; green-blue as a bluish gray, and purple as blue. This type of color blindness is usually hereditary, and affects males almost exclusively. It follows the same mode of inheritance as hemophilia (p. 63).

Contrast effects. It is well known that when black is placed against white or vice versa they "set one another off," the black looks blacker and the white a purer white than if either were placed against a colored ground. It is also true that blue against a yellow ground (or yellow against a blue ground) is more vivid than if placed against any other color. Also green is enhanced by red and red by green. These phenomena are examples of *simultaneous contrast.*

The maximum effect of contrast is obtained when *complementary colors* are paired. Any pair of colors which, when fused as lights, produce white are said to be complementary to one another. Examples of complementary color pairs are the following.

Red and greenish blue
Orange and cyan blue
Yellow and indigo blue[1]
Violet and greenish yellow
Purple and green

Not only those listed above, but every color and shade of color has its complementary (Fig. 243). There are, consequently, a great number of complementary colors, and the contrast effect is produced when the colors of such a pair are

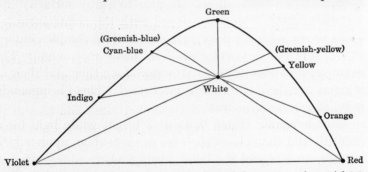

FIG. 243. Complementary colors. The colors of the spectrum from violet to red are marked upon the curve (roughly triangular). Other colors would fall upon intermediate points on the curve. The base line of the figure (from violet to red) represents the non-spectral purple. Any two points upon the curve intersected by a straight line drawn through the point marked *white* indicate complementary colors. (After Hall.)

placed side by side. Furthermore, when two colors which are not complementary to one another are placed in juxtaposition, each takes on a tint which is complementary to the other. For example, a lemon or other yellow object, placed in a bright light, casts a shadow which is tinged with blue — the complementary of yellow. The shadow cast by a red

---

[1] A distinction must be drawn here between lights and paints; we know that yellow and blue paints when mixed give green, not white. The color of a paint is due to its reflecting certain wave lengths in white light and absorbing the remainder. Even the bluest paint is not pure blue; it absorbs all light but blue and a little green. These it reflects. A yellow paint is not pure yellow; it reflects a little green with the yellow. When the two paints are mixed, blue light is absorbed by the yellow paint, and yellow light by the blue. The green rays, of which a little is reflected by each separate paint, are doubly reflected when the two are mixed.

object would be tinged with greenish blue, and one cast by a purple object with green. These principles are applied in art. The artist makes a yellow flood of sunshine more brilliant by painting blue into the shadows which, in turn, are given depth and an appearance of reality which they would otherwise lack.

FIG. 244. Zollner's lines. The long diagonal lines appear to converge; actually, they are parallel.

When one stares for a time at a colored surface in a strong light and then directs the gaze to a gray surface it appears tinged with the complementary color, and objects of the complementary color itself are made more vivid. For example, if one looks at a red surface for a time and then at a green one the latter color is intensified. This phenomenon is called *successive contrast*.

After images. If one looks at a bright white light for a moment and then closes the eyes or turns them upon a dark surface, an image of the light slowly floats into view, becomes more distinct for a time, and then gradually fades. Similarly, if the eyes are stimulated by a colored light or a brightly colored object of any sort, and then darkened, an image of the same color appears. These are called *positive after images*. If, instead of closing the eyes or turning them to a dark surface after looking at a white light, the retinas are stimulated a second time and diffusely by white, e.g., directing the eyes to a sheet of paper, one then sees a dark image against a white ground. This is called a *negative after image*. If the first stimulus was colored, then the after image is in the complementary color. Negative after images of colored objects are the cause of successive contrast described in the last paragraph.

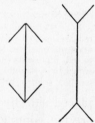

FIG. 245. Illusion of size. The vertical lines are the same length.

Positive after images are due apparently to chemico-physical changes in the receptors of the retina, caused by, and

outlasting the stimulus.   Negative after images are thought
to be due to a state comparable in certain respects to the
refractory period of nerve.   Cones which have responded to
a stimulus will not for a time respond again.   White light
stimulates all three types of cone (p. 487).   The negative
after image which appears upon applying a circumscribed
and then a diffuse white stim-
ulus to the retina is, therefore,
a dark patch against a white
background.   When the object looked at is colored, and

A ● ● ● ● ● ● ● B   C ●

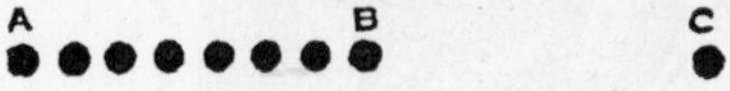

Fig. 246.   Illusion of distance. The distance from A to B appears to be greater
than that from B to C; they are the same.

the retina is then stimulated by directing the eyes to a white
surface, the image is in the complementary color, because only
those cones which had not previously been stimulated can
respond.   For example, if the object looked at is red, the red-
sensitive cones are not excited by a subsequent stimulus of
white; those sensitive to green and
to violet alone respond, giving the
complementary of red, namely, a
bluish green.

Fig. 247.   Illusion of size.
The figure of the man is actually smaller than that of the
child but the effect of distance
produced by the converging
lines causes it to appear larger.

Optical illusions.   The brain may
be deceived by imitations of certain
effects upon which our visual judgment of the size, shape and distance
of objects is based.   Visual errors
of this nature are called optical illusions or optical deceptions.   Some
interesting examples are shown in
Figs. 244–247.

Movements of the eyes.   The eyeballs are rotated in their sockets by
small muscles, attached, on the one
hand, to the walls of the orbital cav-
ity and, on the other, to the sclerotic coat at a distance of
from a third to half an inch behind the circumference of
the cornea (Fig. 248).   There are six muscles for each eye,

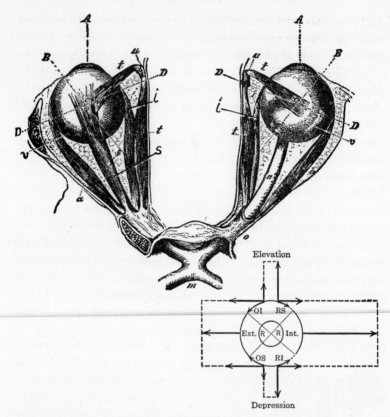

FIG. 248. The eye muscles. *Upper drawing*, *a*, external rectus; *s*, superior rectus (cut away on right side); *i*, internal rectus; *t*, superior oblique; *m*, optic chiasma; *n*, optic nerve; *u*, pulley of superior oblique. (The inferior rectus and inferior oblique muscles are not shown; the former runs parallel to and underneath the superior rectus. The latter originates at the nasal, anterior corner of the orbit and runs transversely on the posterior, temporal surface of the eye.) (Redrawn from Helmholtz.) *Lower drawing* is a diagram of the actions of the muscles of one eye. (From Fuchs after Marquez.) OI, inferior oblique; RS, superior rectus; R.ext., external rectus; R.int., internal rectus; OS, superior oblique; RI, inferior rectus. The arrows indicate the direction in which each muscle tends to move the eyeball. It will be noted, however, that the actions of some muscles are antagonized by those of others. For example, the eye is turned outward by the combined actions of the external rectus, inferior oblique and superior oblique. The upward and rotary movement caused by the inferior oblique is neutralized by the opposing action of the superior oblique.

the four *recti* muscles (*internal*, *external*, *superior* and *inferior*) and the two *obliques* (*superior* and *inferior*). The internal rectus muscle turns the eye inward, i.e., toward the nose; the external rectus turns it outward. The superior rectus rotates the eye upward and inward, the inferior rectus downward and inward. The superior oblique rotates the eyeball downward and outward, the inferior oblique upward and outward (see diagram, Fig. 248).

The muscles of the two eyes act in unison. For example, the eyes are turned to one or other side — *conjugate deviation* — by the contraction of the external rectus of one eye and the internal rectus of the other. *Convergence* of the eyes, i.e., turning both eyes inward, is brought about by the contraction of both internal recti. In any movements of the eyes the muscles which bring about the opposite movement, i.e., the antagonistic muscles, are inhibited. Thus, the principle of reciprocal inhibition (p. 426) applies to the ocular muscles as well as to other muscles of the body.

Strabismus or *squint* is due to the unbalanced action of the eye muscles. As a consequence, the axes of the two eyes do not bear the normal relationship to one another; they may be converged too sharply ("cross-eyes"), or not enough, or they may diverge.

The structure and functions of the iris. The iris is a circular diaphragm or curtain lying behind the cornea, and in front of the lens. Laterally, it is attached to the ciliary body. It is composed of two sets of smooth muscle fibers. One set of fibers is arranged circularly; it causes narrowing of the pupil, and is therefore called the *sphincter* or *constrictor pupillae*. The fibers of the other set run radially from the pupillary margin; they dilate the pupil and constitute the *dilator pupillae* muscle (see Fig. 249).

The control of the muscle of the iris is purely reflex. The receptors for the constrictor reflex are in the retina, the afferent pathway is over the visual fibers to the mid-brain; here, connections are made with the nucleus of the third nerve. The efferent fibers belong to the parasympathetic division of the autonomic nervous system. They issue from the nucleus of the third nerve, and are conveyed in the trunk of this nerve to the ciliary ganglion (see diagram, Pl. 14 A); from here postganglionic fibers pass to the iris. The dilator pupillae is supplied by the sympathetic. Light falling upon the retina of either eye causes both pupils to constrict, the constrictor pupillae being excited, the dilator pupillae inhibited; thus, the retina is shielded from the injurious action of very bright light. In the dark or in dim light, the pupil dilates, thus permitting the greatest illumination possible;

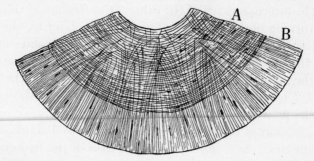

FIG. 249. Segment of the iris, enlarged, showing sphincter muscle, A, and dilator muscle, B.

the tone of the dilator pupillae is increased while the constrictor muscle is inhibited. The diameter of the pupil at any moment depends upon which of these two opposing actions is dominant. Constriction of the pupil occurs also during accommodation of the eye (p. 484). The pupil is altered in size by certain emotional states, constricting in anger and dilating in fear. It is constricted during sleep, and during ether or chloroform anesthesia. Drugs such as atropine (the active principle of belladonna) and adrenaline cause dilatation of the pupil; morphine and pilocarpine cause constriction.

Optical defects. *Spherical aberration.* The convergence point of rays passing through the peripheral parts of an ordinary convex lens is closer to the lens than that of rays

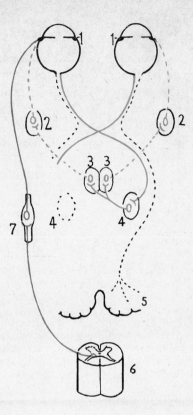

The nerves of the iris. Constrictor pathway (afferent and efferent) in *red*, dilators in *blue*, visual fibers *black* interrupted lines. 1, iris and ciliary muscle; 2, ciliary ganglion; 3, nucleus of oculomotor nerve; 4, superior colliculus; 5, visual area of the cortex; 6, spinal cord; 7, superior cervical ganglion.

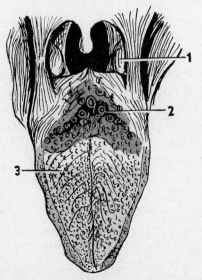

Map of tongue, showing distribution of the fundamental taste sensations. *Yellow*, sweet and salty; *blue*, acid; *green*, bitter. 1, tonsil; 2, circumvallate papillae; 3, fungiform papillae.

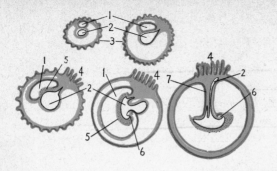

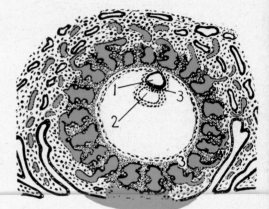

PLATE 15A

Diagram showing a series of stages in the growth of the ovum and development of the embryo. (Redrawn and modified from Gray.) 1, amnion; 2, yolk sac; 3, chorion; 4, placental villi; 5, embryo; 6, heart; 7, umbilical cord.

PLATE 15B

Very early human ovum embedded in uterine wall. Note the interlocking of the tissue of the ovum (chorionic villi) with the uterine tissue (decidua). The red areas are blood sinuses. 1, amnion; 2, yolk sac; 3 embryo. (After Bryce.)

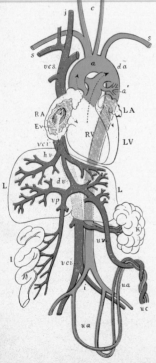

PLATE 15C

Diagrammatic outline of the organs of circulation in the fetus of six months. (After Allen Thomson.) RA, right auricle of the heart; RV, right ventricle; LA, left auricle; Ev, Eustachian valve; LV, left ventricle; L, liver; K, left kidney; I, portion of small intestine; a, arch of the aorta; a', its dorsal part; vcs, superior vena cava; vci, inferior vena where it joins the right auricle; vci', its lower end; s, subclavian vessels; j, right jugular vein; c, common carotid arteries; four curved dotted arrow lines are carried through the aortic and pulmonary opening and the auriculo-ventricular orifices; da, opposite to the one passing through the pulmonary artery, marks the place of the ductus arteriosus; a similar arrow line is shown passing from the vena cava inferior through the fossa ovalis of the right auricle, and the foramen ovale into the left auricle; hv, the hepatic veins; vp, vena portæ; x to vci, the ductus venosus; uv, the umbilical vein; ua, umbilical arteries; uc, umbilical cord cut short; i, i', iliac vessels.

transmitted more centrally. The two groups of rays cross, resulting in a blurred image. This is an inherent defect of convex lenses and is called *spherical aberration*. In the making of a high quality camera lens, special means are employed to correct this defect; the lens is built up of separate

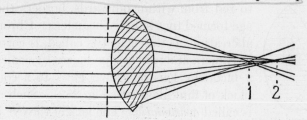

Fig. 250. Illustrating spherical aberration. Note that the outer rays come to a focus (1) in front of the more central rays (2). The vertical broken lines in front of the lens show how a "stop" of a camera or the iris of the eye cuts off the outer rays.

pieces of glass of different refractive indices cemented together so that all rays are converged to the same point (Fig. 250). Spherical aberration is corrected in a similar manner in the crystalline lens; the central part of the lens has a greater optical density, that is, a higher refractive index; thus the effect of the greater refracting power of

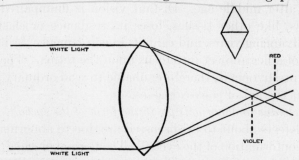

Fig. 251. Illustrating chromatic aberration. The small figure shows how a simple convex lens is essentially two prisms placed base to base.

the more peripheral parts of the lens is neutralized. The iris, since it covers the outer part of the lens and blocks the peripheral rays, also serves to correct spherical aberration. The diaphragm of a camera serves a similar purpose.

Chromatic aberration. The colors composing white light

are refracted to different degrees according to their wave lengths. The long red rays are refracted least; the violet rays most; the other colors of the spectrum are refracted in progressively greater degree from orange to blue (see Fig. 251). For this reason, a series of fringes, colored from violet to red from within outwards, borders the image formed by a simple cheap lens. Chromatic aberration, as this defect is called, is corrected in camera and microscope lenses by cementing a biconvex lens of crown glass to a concave block of flint glass (see Fig. 252). Such a lens is called *achromatic*. The lens of the eye is not corrected for chromatic aberration. A red and a violet object at the same distance from the eye, therefore, cannot both be seen sharply at the same time. If, for example, the eyes are focused upon a violet light, they must accommodate, in order to maintain the focus, when the light is changed to red. In ordinary vision, the colors surrounding the images on the retina are not perceived; we have come to ignore them.

FIG. 252. Diagram showing the structure of an achromatic lens. 1, flint glass; 2, crown glass.

Presbyopia. This is a defect of accommodation which develops after middle age. Distant vision is unimpaired, but the lens, like other tissues, loses its resilience or elasticity with advancing years, and cannot, in consequence, bring the image of a near object into focus upon the retina. The subject of presbyopia is, therefore, unable to read ordinary print without the aid of convex glasses.

Defects due to abnormalities in the form of the eyeball. The three defects about to be discussed are due to abnormalities in the conformation of the eyeball. The normal or *emmetropic* eye is nearly spherical, the vertical and transverse diameters being only about a millimeter shorter than the anteroposterior (see Fig. 253, A).

Myopia or shortsightedness. In this defect of the eye, the refracting power of the lens is the same as in the normal eye, but the anteroposterior diameter of the globe is abnormally

long. The image is, therefore, brought to a focus a little in
front of the retina. In other words, the lens is too strong for
the length of the eyeball. The rays after coming to a focus
disperse again, and a blurred image is formed upon the retina,
just as when the film of a camera is adjusted at too great a
distance from the lens. Myopia
is corrected by fitting the subject
with concave lenses which, by *diverging* the rays before they enter
the eye and thus counteracting
the converging power of the crystalline lens, bring them to a focus
upon the retina (Fig. 253, B).

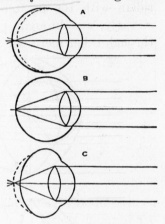

*Hypermetropia or longsighted-
ness.* This defect is due to the
anteroposterior diameter of the
eyeball being too short. Since the
refracting power of the crystalline
lens is the same as in the normal
eye, the rays cannot be converged

Fig. 253. Illustrating myopia
(A); emmetropia (B); hypermetropia (C).

acutely enough to form a clear image upon the retina. Hypermetropia is corrected by means of convex lenses which
converge the rays before they enter the eye, thus aiding the
crystalline lens (Fig. 253, C).

Astigmatism. This is probably the commonest of all defects of the eye. In astigmatism, as the name itself implies
(Gr. *a, privative + stigma,* a point), rays of light are not
brought to sharp points upon the retina, but form, instead,
short lines. The defect is present in all eyes to a certain
degree, and it is only when well marked that it can be considered abnormal. The stars, for example, which should
appear to us as small dots of light, seem to radiate short lines
of light. For the same reason a light shining through the
dark appears to emit radiating beams.

It must be remembered that rays of light pass through all
meridians of a lens; in converging to a focus they, therefore,

form a cone of light, not simply a flat, pennant-like beam. If, as in the normal eye, all meridians of the lens have approximately the same curvature, then rays in all planes will be refracted to the same degree and come to a focus together. If the curvatures differ, the rays transmitted through a meridian with the greater curvature will be refracted more strongly, and brought to a focus in front of rays passing through other meridians. For example, should the vertical

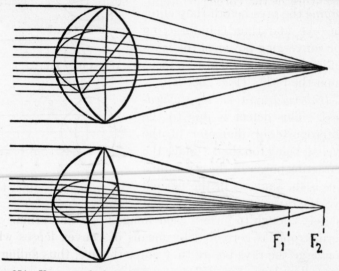

Fig. 254. *Upper cut*, the horizontal curvature of the lens is the same as the vertical; rays of light passing through the horizontal and vertical diameters (meridians) are therefore focused to the same point. *Lower*, the horizontal curvature is greater than the vertical. Rays passing through the horizontal meridian are focused at F_1 and those passing through the vertical meridian at F_2 (see text).

meridian be more curved than the horizontal, then when the rays passing through the vertical meridian are in focus those in the horizontal will form, not a point, but a horizontal line (see Fig. 254). Such inequalities of curvature in the meridians of the cornea or, less commonly, of the crystalline lens, are the cause of astigmatism. The greater curvature may be in either the vertical, horizontal or an oblique meridian. When the subject of astigmatism looks at a clock face, the straight lines in the vertical numerals XII and VI may be clearly seen, while the horizontal lines in IX and III are blurred, or vice versa. Again, the diagonal numerals may be out of focus while the vertical and horizontal are sharply defined.

Astigmatism is corrected by the use of spectacle lenses convex in the meridian corresponding to that of the cornea (or crystalline lens) having the lesser curvature. Thus, if the curvature of the cornea is greater in the vertical meridian, the subject is fitted with a cylindrical lens having its convexity in the horizontal meridian.

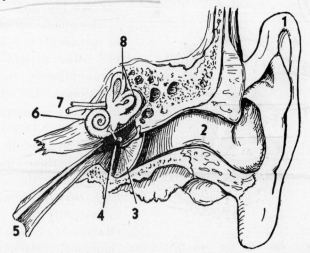

Fig. 255. Plan of the ear. (Redrawn and modified from Arnold.) 1, the auricle (or pinna); 2, external auditory canal (or meatus); 3, the tympanic membrane (sectioned); 4, the tympanic cavity (middle ear), the chain of ossicles lies just above the pointer; 5, Eustachian tube; 6, cochlea; 7, acoustic nerve, showing cochlear and vestibular divisions; 8, semicircular canals.

THE EAR

The structure of the ear. The ear consists of three distinct parts, called the *outer, middle* and *inner ears,* each of which has a special part to play in the mechanism of hearing.

The *outer ear* consists of an appendage of cartilage and skin situated on the side of the head and known as the *auricle* or *pinna,* together with a short funnel-shaped passage called the *external auditory canal*. The latter leads into the temporal bone of the skull, and is closed at its inner end by a flexible membrane called the *drum* or *tympanic membrane*.

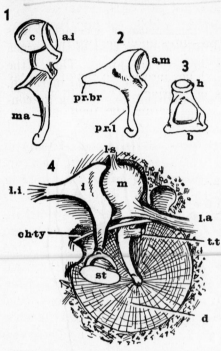

The auricle and auditory canal serve simply to collect and direct the sound waves to the drum membrane; the latter separates the outer from the middle ear (see Fig. 255).

The *middle ear, drum* or *tympanum* is a small chamber within the temporal bone. As just mentioned, the drum membrane is interposed between it and the outer ear. The middle ear contains three miniature bones (the *auditory ossicles*) named individually from their shapes, the *malleus* (hammer), the *incus* (anvil) and the *stapes* (stirrup) (see Fig. 256). The handle of the malleus is attached to the tympanic membrane; its head is connected by a small joint with

FIG. 256. The auditory ossicles. 1, left malleus viewed from outer side (Helmholtz), c, head, a.i, articular surface for incus; ma, handle. 2, left incus, pr.br, short process; pr.l, long process which articulates with stapes; a.m, articular surface for malleus. 3, left stapes, h, head; b, base or "footplate"; 4, the middle ear viewed from the inner aspect and showing ossicles in position; d, drum membrane; i, incus; m, malleus; st, stapes; ch.ty, chorda tympani nerve; l.s, ligament of malleus; l.i, ligament of incus; t.t, tendon of tensor tympani muscle.

the body of the incus. A process of the incus is joined to one end of the stapes; the other end or foot-plate of the stirrup-like bone is fitted into a small opening in the inner wall of the middle ear, called the *oval window*. Situated a little lower in the inner wall of the tympanum is the *round window;* this is closed by a thin membrane.

A narrow canal — the *Eustachian tube* — which connects the middle ear with the posterior part of the nose, serves for the passage of air between the middle ear and the atmosphere. Thus equality of pressures upon the two sides of the drum membrane is maintained.

The *inner ear* or *labyrinth* lies internal to the middle ear; it contains the receptors of hearing. The auditory sense organs lie in a spiral passage within the temporal bone, known as the *cochlea*, from its resemblance to a snail's shell. The spiral canal makes $2\frac{1}{2}$ turns around a central pillar of bone called the *modiolus*. The larger turns of the spiral are at the *base* of the cochlea, the smaller turns at the *apex* or *cupula*. A ledge of bone, which winds around the modiolus like the thread of a screw-nail, divides the spiral canal incompletely into two. The partition is completed by a thin membrane — the *basilar membrane* — which extends from the tip of the ledge of bone to the outer wall of the canal (see Fig. 257). A second membrane — *Reissner's membrane* — stretches from the upper surface of the bony ledge to a point in the outer wall of the canal, a short distance above the attachment of the basilar membrane. These two membranes thus divide the original canal into three spiral compartments. The compartment below the basilar membrane is called the *scala tympani*, the one enclosed between the basilar membrane and Reissner's membrane is called the *scala media, cochlear duct*, or *membranous cochlea*, and the one lying above Reissner's membrane, the *scala vestibuli*. The scala media is filled with a fluid called *endolymph;* the fluid within the scala tympani and scala vestibuli is known as the *perilymph*.

The scala vestibuli communicates with the middle ear through the oval window which, as already stated, lodges the foot-plate of the stapes.

The membrane of the round window is interposed between the commencement of the scala tympani and the middle ear.

The auditory sense organ or *organ of Corti* rests upon the basilar membrane which, as just stated, forms the outer part of the floor of the scala media. It contains a row of elongated cells — the *hair cells;* these are the auditory receptors. About twenty hair-like processes project from the free end

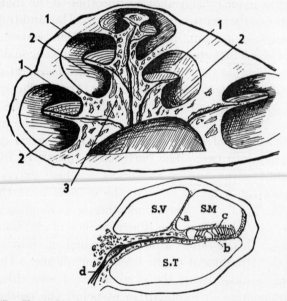

FIG. 257. *Upper drawing*, a view of the osseous cochlea divided through the middle. (After Arnold.) 1, scala vestibuli; 2, scala tympani; 3, modiolus, showing tunnels transmitting branches of auditory nerve. *Lower drawing*, enlarged sketch of one turn of the cochlea (redrawn after Quain). S.V, scala vestibuli; S.M, scala media (cochlear duct); S.T, scala tympani; a, Reissner's membrane; b, basilar membrane; c, organ of Corti; d, auditory nerve.

of each cell. The tips of the hairs are attached to a thin elastic membrane — the *tectorial membrane* — which extends outwards from near the attachment of Reissner's membrane to cover the organ of Corti.

The cochlear nerve enters the base of the modiolus of the cochlea. Traversing the modiolus, it gives off branches which radiate outwards in the floor of the scala media, and end in fine arborizations around the bases of the hair cells.

Only the auditory part of the labyrinth has been described in the foregoing paragraphs. The inner ear contains, also, the semicircular canals and otolithic organs. These, which have no auditory function, will be described later.

The physiology of hearing. The structure of the auditory apparatus having been sketched, we are in a position to understand the manner in which the energy of sound waves is transmitted to the auditory receptors. The outer and middle ears serve merely to transmit the sound waves to the inner ear in which the receptors are contained. The waves set up in the air by a sounding body strike the ear drum and

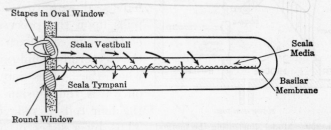

FIG. 258. Diagram of the passages of the cochlea straightened out to show the manner in which vibrations are transmitted from the oval to the round window through the scala media. The wavy line represents the organ of Corti.

set it into vibration. In man the pinna, and the somewhat funnel-like shape of the auditory meatus have only a slight effect in concentrating the sound waves upon the drum membrane. In many animals, however, the pinna serves an important function in this regard, being a large funnel-shaped structure which can be turned toward the source of the sound.

The vibrations set up in the tympanic membrane are transmitted across the middle ear by the auditory ossicles. The head of the malleus is connected to the body of the incus in such a way that a movement inward or outward of the tympanic membrane causes a corresponding movement of the handle of the malleus, of the long process of the incus and of the foot-plate of the stapes. The latter is lodged in the oval window between the middle ear and the scala vestibuli of the cochlea. Thus, movements of the tympanic membrane are transmitted through the ossicles to the inner ear. The series of inward and outward movements of the foot-plate of the stapes, acting like a plunger in the oval window, set up corresponding movements in the fluid contents of the scala vestibuli. These movements are transmitted freely through Reissner's membrane to the fluid in the scala media, and through the basilar membrane in turn, to the scala tympani (Fig. 258). Thus, each time the foot-plate of the stapes is

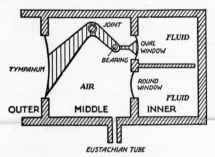

FIG. 259. Model illustrating the method of transmission of vibrations from the outer to the inner ear. (From Beatty modified by Lythgoe.)

pressed into the oval window the basilar membrane moves downwards and pulls upon the processes of the hair cells fixed to the tectorial membrane; when the stapes moves outwards the tension on the hair cells is relieved. Thus, by a series of mechanical stimuli, impulses are set up in the terminals of the auditory nerve. The round window, situated between the scala tympani and the middle ear, permits free movements of the contents of the inner ear. Since liquids are incompressible no movement of the stapes could occur, of course, were there no other part of the bony wall of the cochlea which yielded to pressure.

The auditory ossicles are connected to one another in such a way as to constitute a small lever (see Fig. 259). The handle of the malleus, attached to the tympanic membrane, forms the long arm of the lever; the long process of the incus is the short arm. The long arm is one and a half times the length of the short arm. The movement of the long process of the incus (and of the stapes with which it connects) is, therefore, only two-thirds as great as that of the tympanic membrane. We should expect, on the other hand, that the force exerted by the stapes at the oval window would be one and a half times greater than that applied to the handle of the malleus. But, on account of a large proportion of the energy being lost in transmission (due to inertia of the ossicles and friction of the air surrounding them), only about half of the force exerted upon the handle of the malleus reaches the oval window. However, the area of the tympanic membrane is nearly 20 times that of the oval window; this fact alone, were there no loss of energy in transmission, would cause the force exerted at the oval window to be increased twenty-fold over that of the vibrations of the tympanic membrane. Now, as just mentioned, the force reaching the oval window is only one-half of that applied to the malleus; the net magnification of the force exerted by the movements of the foot-plate of the stapes, brought about through the mechanism of the middle ear, is, therefore, about ten.

The appreciation of pitch. Sound is transmitted from a vibrating body to the ear as a series of alternating condensations and rarefactions of the atmosphere. The disturbance in the air travels as a succession of waves. A complete wave, i.e., from the crest or trough of one wave to the corresponding phase of the other, is referred to as a *double vibration* (d.v.) or a *cycle*. The pitch of a tone depends upon the frequency of the waves, i.e., upon the number of double vibrations or cycles reaching the ear per second. For example, a tuning fork which vibrates at a frequency of 100 d.v. per second emits a note of higher pitch (by an octave) than one vibrating at 50 d.v. per second.

Sounds ranging in frequency from 40 to 20,000 d.v. per second are audible to the human ear. The range of audible frequencies varies, however, between individuals, and between different species of animals. The cat, for example, can hear the very high-pitched sounds made by a mouse, which are usually quite inaudible to human ears. The bat also makes a cry which, of course, can be heard by its kind, and probably also by other animals, but which is of a pitch too high to make an impression upon the human ear.

There has been no little discussion as to the mechanism whereby variations in the frequency of the sound waves striking the ear are converted into messages which the brain interprets as differences in pitch. The two classical theories are, *the resonance theory of Helmholtz* and *the telephone theory of Rutherford*.

The resonance theory states that the basilar membrane, like the wires of a piano, is a scale of resonators. If the dampers of a piano are raised and a note sung near it, a tone of the same pitch is given out by the instrument. Those wires of the piano alone vibrate which, if struck, would themselves have emitted the same note. This well-known phenomenon is called *sympathetic resonance*. The basilar membrane contains some 24,000 fibers. These so-called *auditory strings* increase progressively in length from the base to the apex of the cochlea. Each fiber, or a group of fibers of a given length, vibrates in unison, it is supposed, with vibrations of a particular frequency transmitted to them from the drum membrane, the short tense fibers at the base of the cochlea to high notes, and the longer, more lax fibers at the apex to low notes. Of course, only those hair cells overlying the fibers which are set into sympathetic vibration are stimulated.

The resonance theory, therefore, *claims that the analysis of sound is a function of the cochlea, the particular region of the latter from which the impulses are discharged being the sole basis upon which the brain rests its faculty of pitch discrimination.* The resonance theory is supported by a number of facts. (a) When the ears of animals, e.g., guinea-pigs and rabbits, are subjected to prolonged stimulation by a high- or a low-pitched tone, degenerative changes are produced in the basal or the apical portion, respectively, of the organ of

Corti. (b) Boiler-makers or others who work among clanging noises sometimes become deaf to high tones (*boiler-maker's disease*); the organ of Corti in the basal turns of the cochlea is found to have degenerated. (c) Destruction of the apical part of the cochlea in animals results in deafness to tones of low frequency, of the basal part, in deafness to high tones. (d) The structure of the cochlea itself strongly suggests that it acts as a resonator, and recent experimental work has provided direct evidence of such a function.

When the ear is stimulated by a sound, the vibrations of the organ of Corti set up rhythmical changes in electrical potential within the cochlea (*Wever and Bray effect*). When amplified and recorded graphically, these are found to have exactly the same frequency as that of the sound. Indeed, if the electrical currents are conducted to a loud speaker the original sound is faithfully reproduced.

The cause of the potential changes is unknown, but they are not simply action currents picked up from auditory nerve fibers. Yet they are dependent upon movements of the organ of Corti, varying in magnitude with the amplitude of the latter's vibrations. With low notes the potential changes are greatest in the apical turns of the cochlea, with high notes, in the basal turns, thus demonstrating clearly the resonating function of the cochlea.

The telephone or frequency theory. In a telephone system the transmitting instrument converts the sound waves into electrical impulses of the same frequency. Upon reaching the receiver, the electrical impulses set up vibrations which reproduce the original sound. The telephone theory of hearing postulates that the basilar membrane does not vibrate selectively in the manner demanded by the resonance theory, but as a whole, in unison with the vibrations transmitted to it from the drum membrane. The frequency of the impulses resulting from the stimulation of the hair cells corresponds with that of the vibrations of the basilar membrane, and, consequently, with that of the sound waves.

The telephone theory *claims, therefore, that the cochlea possesses no power of sound analysis, and that such is purely a function of the brain, the frequency of the impulses received by the auditory center being the basis for the discrimination of pitch.*

The telephone theory as originally proposed is faced with the objection that the maximum frequency at which impulses can be transmitted by a nerve fiber is about 1,000 per second, whereas, sounds with frequencies up to 20,000 d.v. per second are audible. But the auditory nerve consists, of course, of a large number of fibers, and it has been proposed that the impulses are discharged over the separate fibers, not synchronously, but in a scattered volley. That is, some fibers are in their refractory phase (p. 391) while others are conducting. Thus, it is possible for a group of fibers to transmit impulses in "broken step" at frequencies as high as, or even higher than 20,000 per second. Nevertheless, the *volley theory*, as this amplification of the telephone theory is called, does not fit all the facts; it fails to explain the *appreciation* of tones having a vibration frequency higher than about 3,000 per second. For example, the action potentials set up by a sound and recorded (see p. 388) from the auditory tracts in the brain have exactly the same frequency as that of the sound up to 1,000 d.v. per second. Between 1,000 and 2,000 d.v. per second, one impulse occurs for every two sound vibrations, and one for every three between 2,000 and 3,000 d.v. per second. At higher frequencies (between 3,000 and 20,000 d.v. per second) there is no relationship.

By way of a summary to the discussion in the foregoing paragraphs, it may be stated that the resonance theory is essentially true. The telephone theory is also to a certain extent supported by experimental work for, as just stated, at and below 3,000 d.v. per second, the frequency of the impulses corresponds with that of the sound, frequencies between from 1,000 to 3,000 per second being explained upon the assumption that the refractory periods of the separate fibers of a group are not coterminous. The modern theory of

the mechanism of hearing is, therefore, a composite of the
two older ones, and is generally referred to as the *resonance-
volley theory.*

Intensity and loudness of sound. The power transmitted
through the atmosphere from a sounding body is referred to
as the intensity of the sound. Sound intensity is expressed
as the quantity of energy, in microwatts, passing per second
through an area of one square centimeter. The greater the
intensity of the sound the greater, of course, will be the amplitude of the movements of the drum membrane and, generally speaking, the louder will be the sound. But the ear

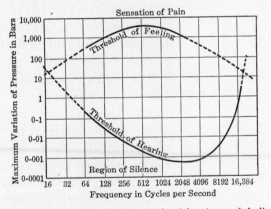

FIG. 260.   Chart showing the thresholds of hearing and feeling of
sound at different frequencies.   (After Wegel.)

does not possess the same sensitivity at all frequencies.
Within the range of from 1,000 to 2,000 double vibrations
per second the lowest intensity (*intensity threshold*) is required to arouse an auditory sensation, and a sound of any
given intensity is loudest. The sensitivity of hearing, i.e.,
the loudness of a sound of a given intensity, diminishes progressively as the frequency is increased above 2,000 d.v. per
second or reduced below 1,000 d.v. per second (see Fig. 260).
In other words, the *threshold of hearing* is lowest for sounds
with frequencies around 2,000 d.v. per second. It will be appreciated from these remarks that intensity and loudness are

not synonymous terms. The intensity of sound is an absolute physical value, whereas the loudness of sound is a matter of auditory perception.

As the intensity of the sound increases, other sense organs than those of hearing are stimulated. We *feel* the sound and, if very intense, it arouses the sensation of pain. For

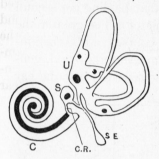

example, the report of a rifle fired at a distance is heard, but at short range is felt as well, and if too close to the ear causes pain. It will be seen from the chart in Fig. 260 that, in contrast to that of hearing, the *threshold of feeling* is highest at frequencies around 500 d.v. per second.

FIG. 261. Diagram of the right membranous labyrinth. U, utricle, into which the three semicircular canals open; S, saccule, communicating with the cochlea (C) by C.R., the canalis reuniens, and with the utricle by a canal having on it an enlargement, the saccus endolymphaticus (S.E.). The black shading represents the places of termination of the auditory nerve, namely, in the maculae of the utricle and saccule, in the cristae of the ampullary ends of the three semicircular canals and in the whole length of the canal of the cochlea. (After Schafer.)

The non-auditory part of the labyrinth — the organ of equilibrium. The inner ear contains another organ besides the cochlea, consisting of three *semicircular canals* and two small sacs, called, respectively, the *utricle* and the *saccule*. The semicircular canals and the utricle have no auditory function, being concerned solely with the maintenance of the equilibrium of the body (see Fig. 261).

The semicircular canals are membranous tubes filled with fluid known as the *endolymph*. They are contained within semicircular tunnels in the temporal bone — the osseous canals — but separated from the bone by *perilymph*. The three canals lie approximately at right angles to one another, one in each of the three dimensions of space. Two canals are vertical, one horizontal. The two vertical canals are placed diagonally in relation to the antero-posterior diameter of the skull; the convexity of one is directed outward and backward, of the other outward and forward (see Fig. 262), and of the horizontal canal, outward. One end of each canal is dilated into a fusiform swelling called the *ampulla*. A small elevation, called the *crista*, is situated in each of the three ampullae. This is composed of cells with bristle-like processes — the *hair cells* — surmounted by a cap of gelatinous material called the *cupula*. The cristae are the sense organs (proprioceptors) of the canals. Both ends of each canal open into the utricle.

The utricle and saccule are oval membranous sacs measuring (in man) about $\frac{1}{8}$ inch in their longest diameters. They are contained within an oval cavity in the bone, called the *vestibule*, situated between the cochlea and the semicircular canals. The utricle, as just mentioned, communicates with the semicircular canals, the saccule connects through a narrow canal with the scala media of the cochlea. The utricle and saccule are indirectly

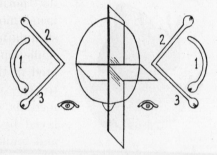

FIG. 262. Showing the positions of the semicircular canals in relation to the vertical planes (anteroposterior and transverse) of the skull. 1, horizontal canals; 2, posterior vertical canals; 3, anterior vertical canals.

connected through a narrow Y-shaped tube (Fig. 261). The entire membranous labyrinth, auditory and non-auditory, thus forms a continuous system of communicating passages and chambers. The utricle and saccule each contains a sense organ called the *macula;* this is a plaque of hair cells covered by a layer of a gelatinous substance. Adherent to the latter are a number of crystals of carbonate of lime, known as *otoliths* (ear-stones) or *otoconia* (ear-dust).

The terminations of the vestibular division of the eighth (auditory) nerve ramify around the hair cells of the cristae of the semicircular canals and of the maculae of the utricle and saccule.

The functions of the semicircular canals. If a frog is rotated rapidly on a turntable, the limbs on the side toward which the movement is made are extended; the limbs of the opposite side are flexed, and the head turned toward this side (see Fig. 263).   Thus displacement of the body is prevented. If the table is tilted forward, the animal avoids being thrown upon its face by extension of its forelimbs; a backward tilt causes extension of the hind limbs; and tilting laterally is followed by extension of the limbs on the corresponding side, accompanied by flexion of the opposite pair of limbs.   These reflex reactions, whereby the animal resists being upset from

its "normal" position by some unusual movement, are the result of stimulation of the end organs of the semicircular canals. Impulses initiated in the cristae are transmitted to the vestibular nucleus in the medulla oblongata, and thence relayed by the vestibulospinal tracts and motor nerves to the muscles. The reactions resulting from rotation in the horizontal plane are due

Fig. 263.   Position taken up by a frog during rotation to the left.   (After Ewald.)

to stimulation of the horizontal pair of canals; those caused by tilting forward or backward, or laterally (i.e., by a rotary movement in the plane, approximately, of one or other pair of vertical canals), are due to stimulation of the cristae of the corresponding canals.   The movement causes a mechanical stimulus to be applied to the hair cells of the cristae. When the head is rotated in the plane of one or other pair of canals, the endolymph, owing to its *inertia*, exerts a momentary pressure upon the hair cells of the canal on the side away from which the rotation is made. For the same reason, the pressure upon the hair cells of the canal of the opposite ear is reduced.   The effects upon the two ears, though opposite in nature, act conjointly in initiating the reflex muscular movement.

Stimulation of the semicircular canals also causes movements of the eyes. When, for example, a person is rotated rapidly with the head erect, i.e., approximately in the plane of the horizontal canals, the eyes are observed to make a series of rhythmical side to side movements after the rotation has ceased. These to and fro movements, which are termed *nystagmus*, are due to the *momentum* of the endolymph. That is, the endolymph movement continues for

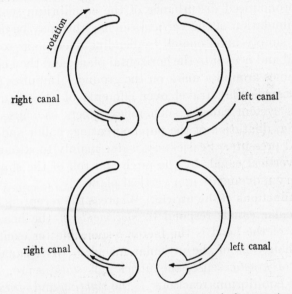

FIG. 264. Showing endolymph movement during and after rotation. *Upper drawing*, during rotation, large arrows indicate the direction of rotation, small arrows the endolymph movement. *Lower drawing*, after rotation. (After Best and Taylor, *The Physiological Basis of Medical Practice*.)

an instant after the rotation of the head has ceased, and thus exerts pressure upon the crista of the canal on one side (see Fig. 264); the pressure on the hair cells of the canal of the opposite ear is diminished. It is clear that the effects following rotation will be the reverse of those during rotation. If the head is bent forward, backward or on to one shoulder during the rotation, the vertical canals are stimulated. The nystagmus which follows rotation in these positions of the head is not horizontal; the eyes move either up and down (vertical nystagmus) or show a rotary movement (rotary nystagmus), according to which particular pair of vertical canals were in the plane of the rotation.

Other effects follow stimulation of the semicircular canals by a rapid rotary motion. Everyone is familiar with the sensation of dizziness or *vertigo*, and the staggering gait, which result from spinning (stimulation of horizontal canals). A more pronounced disturbance of the equilibrium sense follows stimulation of the vertical canals; this may be demonstrated simply upon oneself by bending over, so as to bring the head and neck into the horizontal plane, and then circling a few times around a mark on the ground. Impulses set up in the canals may travel over efferents of the autonomic nervous system causing such reflex effects as nausea and vomiting, dilatation of the pupil, sweating, pallor and a fall in blood pressure. Seasickness is due mainly to stimulation of the vertical canals by the pitch and roll of the ship, i.e., by rotary movements in a vertical plane.

The functions of the utricle. Whereas the receptors of the semicircular canals respond to *movements* of the head, the *position* of the head is the factor responsible for excitation of the hair cells of the utricular maculae. The canals are organs of *kinetic* sense, the utricles of *static* sense. Two types of equilibrium reactions — the *righting* and *attitudinal* reflexes — are dependent upon the utricles.

The righting reflexes. When an animal is placed upon its back it immediately rights itself. The head is first brought into its "normal" position in space by a contraction of the neck muscles, the body follows, being brought into its normal relationship with the head by contractions of the trunk and limb muscles. The movement of the neck muscles, whereby the head is righted, is dependent upon the sense organ of the utricle; it is, therefore, called the *labyrinthine righting reflex;* its center is in the mid-brain. When the head is in the wrong position, mouth looking upward, the otoliths adhering to the maculae hang downward; the tension which their weight exerts upon the hair cells acts as a stimulus to the sensitive hair cells. The movement of the neck stimulates, in turn, proprioceptors in the neck muscles, through which the reflex righting movements of the trunk and limbs are initiated. These movements of the trunk and limb muscles, caused by stimulation of proprioceptors in the neck muscles, are termed *neck reflexes*. Their center is situated in the upper cervical segments of the spinal cord.

The importance of the righting reflexes in man is evident if one considers how a swimmer after diving into deep water orients himself without difficulty and rises to the surface. The other senses, e.g., vision or touch, can give him little or no information of his position in space. He relies upon his utricles to bring his head "right side up." Deaf mutes whose labyrinths as a whole are not developed run a grave risk, even though they be good swimmers, if plunged into deep water.

Attitudinal reflexes. When a decerebrate animal, with its neck immobilized in a plaster cast (in order to exclude the neck reflexes) is placed in different positions, variations in the tone of the limb muscles will be observed. When the animal is placed back down with the cleft of the mouth at an angle of 45° above the horizontal plane, the tone of the muscles of all four limbs is maximal; in the opposite position (feet down with mouth cleft at 45° below the horizontal plane) the tone of the muscles is minimal. In positions of the head between these two extremes, gradations in muscle tone result, in accordance with the position of the head in relation to the horizontal plane (Fig. 265). These tonus reactions are the result of variations in the activity of the utricular proprioceptors (maculae). The sense organs are stimulated most strongly when the otoliths are hanging from the maculae, i.e., when the animal is on its back or on its feet with snout pointing upward (neck extended); when the otoliths are resting upon the maculae, i.e., with snout pointing downward (neck flexed) the hair cells are not stimulated.

The tone of the limb muscles is also influenced reflexly by movements of the neck muscles. When the neck is extended the tone of the extensor muscles of the *forelimbs* is increased, while the extensor tone of the *hind limbs* is reduced. Flexion of the neck causes the reverse effects, namely, decreased tone of the forelimb extensors together with increased tone of the extensors of the hind limbs. The neck reflexes are studied best after the vestibular nerves have been severed and the utricular reflexes thus abolished.

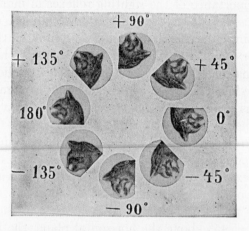

Fig. 265. Diagrammatic representation of the positions of an animal's head, each marked with the angle which the labial cleft makes with the horizontal plane. (After Magnus.)

Though the attitudinal reflexes are most readily demonstrated in the decerebrate preparation, they constitute an important mechanism controlling the posture of the normal animal. Otolithic and neck reflexes cooperate to facilitate various postural adjustments. When a cat, for example, turns its head to look upwards at a piece of food on a shelf, the otolithic organ is stimulated with a consequent tendency for the extensor tone of all four limbs to increase. The neck reflex initiated by the extension of the neck reinforces the otolithic influence on the forelimbs; but the effect of the neck movement upon the hind limbs is the reverse of that of the utricle. The influence of the neck movement upon the hind limbs, however, predominates so that the animal assumes a sitting posture with forelimbs extended and hind limbs flexed. On the other hand, when the animal lowers its head to look beneath a cupboard, the otolithic influence reduces the extensor tone in all four limbs; but the neck

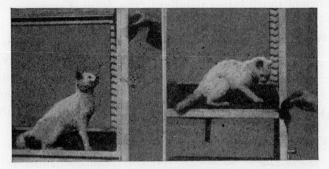

Fig. 266. Photographs of a normal cat, showing the animal's posture (*on left*) when its attention is attracted by an object placed above it. Photograph of the same animal (*on right*) when its attention is drawn to an object below it. The difference between the two positions of the forelimbs is very marked, because in them the neck and labyrinthine reflexes reinforce one another; the difference in the position of the hind limbs is not so great, since the two sets of reflexes oppose one another. (After Magnus.)

movement, though it also reduces the extensor tone of the forelimbs, and thus acts in conjunction with the labyrinthine effect, antagonizes and predominates over the labyrinthine influence upon the hind limbs. The animal, therefore, assumes an attitude with flexed forelimbs and extended hind limbs — an appropriate posture of the body for that particular position of the head (see Fig. 266).

TASTE

Smell and taste are chemical senses; that is, the receptors (chemoreceptors) respond to chemical stimuli. In order for a substance to arouse the sensation of taste, it must first be dissolved — either taken in solution or dissolved in the saliva; a solid placed in a perfectly dry mouth cannot be tasted.

The organs and nerves of taste. The surface of the tongue is beset with numerous small projections of the mucous membrane, called *papillae*. The papillae at the edges, tip and anterior two-thirds of the tongue's surface are minute conical or mushroom-shaped structures. They give a velvety character to this part of the lingual mucosa. The posterior third of the surface of the tongue is rougher, due to the presence of much larger papillae. These are of peculiar construction; each is surrounded by a groove, and beyond the groove by a ridge, the whole structure resembling a little squat tower encircled by a moat. From this appearance they have received the name of the *circumvallate papillae* (Pl. 14 B).

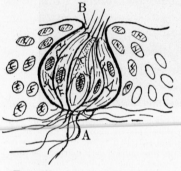

FIG. 267. A taste bud. A, taste fibers; B, taste pore.

Embedded in the covering of the papillae (both large and small types) are groups of slender cells provided with hair-like processes, packed lengthwise into bundles. The cells are the receptors of taste, the bundles which they compose are called *taste buds* (Fig. 267). Each cell receives a filament from one of the nerves of taste. The taste bud opens upon the surface of the papilla through a small pore. The ends of the cells converge toward this point where their processes become massed together. Substances in solution enter the pores and act as chemical stimuli.

The fundamental sensations of taste are four in number, *sweet, bitter, sour* and *salty;* two others, namely, *alkaline* and *metallic* tastes are sometimes included with these. The various other tastes which we experience are due (a) to the blending of some one or other of the fundamental sensations, or (b) to the combination of the latter with sensations caused by the stimulation of the ordinary nerves of the mouth. For example, ginger is recognized not only by its actual taste (i.e., by the stimulation of the taste buds) but from the burning sensation which results from excitation of the ordinary sensory nerves of the mouth. Oils are unpleasant to take, largely because of their "feel." Acetic and many other acids, as well as having a sour taste, give rise to an astringent or burning sensation which is confused in consciousness with taste.

Many of the finer flavors are in reality sensations of smell (p. 519), and smell enters largely into the many sensations which we attribute generally to taste. For this reason, when the nose is held or the nasal mucous membrane is inflamed, as by an ordinary cold, the sense of taste seems blunted. On the other hand, certain substances which we think we detect by smell are actually recognized by the sense of taste. The sweetish smell of chloroform is an example, the vapor reaching the taste buds in the inspired air.

The four fundamental taste sensations are not aroused with equal intensity over all parts of the surface of the tongue. Each type of taste sensation is served by its own kind of taste bud. Taste receptors sensitive to sweetness and to saltness are most numerous at the tip and forepart of the tongue, whereas those responding to sourness are found along the edges. Bitterness is tasted most strongly over the back of the tongue and epiglottis. A bitter-sweet substance, such as sodium salicylate, when first taken into the mouth tastes sweet, the bitter element being noticeable only after the substance has passed over the posterior part of the tongue.

The sense of taste is much less sensitive than the sense of smell. Sweetness, for example, is detected in a dilution of 1 part in 200, saltness (common salt) 1 part in 400, sourness (hydrochloric acid) 1 part in 130,000 and bitterness (quinine) 1 part in 2,000,000.

The chief *nerves of taste* are the *chorda tympani* branch of the facial nerve, and the *glossopharyngeal* nerve.[1] The chorda

[1] The mucous membrane in the region of the epiglottis contains a few sense organs which receive taste fibers through the vagus nerves.

tympani supplies taste fibers to the anterior two-thirds of
the tongue, the glossopharyngeal to the posterior third. The
fibers of the chorda tympani nerve are conveyed to the
tongue in the trunk of the lingual nerve (a branch of the inferior maxillary division of the trigeminal nerve). The center for taste has not been located precisely, but is believed
to lie in the hippocampal gyrus close to that for smell.

SMELL

Smell is very closely allied to taste and has been aptly described as "taste from a distance." In many animals the
sense of smell is almost incredibly acute; a large proportion
of the brain being concerned with this sense. In such species
the sense of smell is of paramount importance, warning the
animal of the approach of its enemies, and guiding it in the
quest for food. Even in man, in whom the sense of smell is
comparatively rudimentary, certain substances, such as mer-
captan, can be detected in a dilution of 1 part in 30 billion
or more parts of air.

An odorous material continually emits particles of molecular size which are carried in the air to the olfactory receptors. Substances which pass readily into the gaseous state
such as turpentine, gasoline and the essential oils have, in
general, strong odors; whereas non-volatile materials, e.g.,
the heavy metals, are relatively inodorous. A substance in
order to be smelled must reach the nose in gaseous form.

The mucous membrane on each side of the nose is raised
into three ridges by three spurs of bone (the *superior*, *middle* and *inferior turbinates*) which spring from the outer nasal
wall. The interior of the nose is thus divided incompletely
on each side into four compartments placed one above the
other (see Fig. 84, p. 166). The lower three of these serve
as air passages; they communicate with the outside through
the nostrils and behind with the pharynx. The uppermost
compartment is a narrow cleft lying immediately beneath
the anterior part of the floor of the skull. The olfactory re-

ceptors are embedded in a small patch of mucous membrane situated on each wall of this narrow space, which is a blind pocket from which the main air currents are excluded. Air containing the odorous particles must, therefore, be carried to the olfactory mucous membrane either by diffusion or by convection currents set up when the inspired air meets the warmer air within the nose. When, for example, we wish to smell some particular scent, we make a quick short inspiration or "sniff." This sharp indrawing of the cooler outside air creates ascending (convection) currents which convey the scent to the sensitive area. The material does not act directly upon the olfactory receptors, but is first dissolved in the layer of fluid covering the mucous membrane — a fact which emphasizes the similarity between the senses of taste and smell.

There are an almost infinite variety of odors, and it is very difficult to make a satisfactory classification; nevertheless, an attempt has been made to group them under the following eight headings.

1. *Ethereal odors*, e.g., of fruits.
2. *Aromatic* or *resinous odors*, e.g., of camphor, bitter almonds.
3. *Fragrant* or *balsamic odors*, e.g., of flowers, extracted or artificial perfumes.
4. *Ambrosial odors*, e.g., of musk.
5. *Garlic odors*, e.g., of garlic, onions and of sulphur and selenium compounds.
6. *Burning odors*, e.g., of burning feathers, tobacco, roasted coffee and meats.
7. *Goat odors*, e.g., of caproic acid, sweat and ripe cheese.
8. *Foul odors*, e.g., of excrement, decaying meat and vegetable matter.

It is not possible to correlate the chemical nature of substances with the odors which they emit, for materials quite different in their chemical constitution may have similar odors, while others closely similar chemically may smell quite different. Certain sensations which we usually class as olfactory, such as those aroused by pungent and acrid substances, are in fact due to the stimulation of the common nerves of the nasal mucous membrane.

The olfactory epithelium is composed of spindle-shaped nerve cells distributed evenly among other elongated cells which are purely supporting in function. Both types of cell lie perpendicular to the epithelial surface (see Fig. 268). The

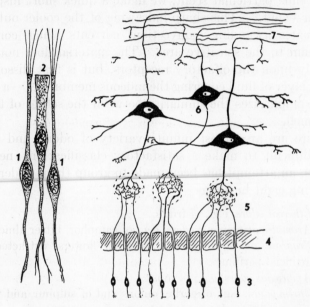

Fig. 268. *On left*, cells from olfactory mucous membrane separated from one another and highly magnified. 1, olfactory receptors; 2, supporting cells. *On right*, central connections of the olfactory nerves. 3, cells of olfactory mucous membrane; 4, olfactory nerve fibers piercing the floor of the skull to reach the olfactory bulb; 5, connections of olfactory nerves with processes of mitral cells in olfactory bulb; 6, mitral cells; 7, fibers passing into the olfactory tract.

nerve cells, or *olfactory receptors*, give rise to two types of process — an axon and a modified dendrite. The axons spring from the deep aspects of the cells and, combining in groups, form a number of slender bundles called the *fila olfactoria*. The dendrites are thick cylindrical processes; they penetrate, individually, to the surface through small gaps between the free ends of the supporting cells; except for these gaps the supporting cells are joined together to form a continuous covering. Each dendrite, after emerging from between the supporting cells, divides into a tuft of some 6 or 8 straight filaments which project a short distance beyond the epithelial surface. The fila olfactoria pass upwards through perforations in the floor of the skull and enter the olfactory bulb (p. **452**), the *primary olfactory center*. Here, the axons of the olfactory receptors synapse with other neurons which convey the impulses to the cortical center for smell situated in the hippocampal gyrus.

The olfactory receptors adapt rapidly; that is, they soon cease to respond to some particular stimulus. It is common experience that an odor, though strong when first smelled, becomes imperceptible after a short time. This phenomenon of adaptation — a property which the olfactory sense organs exhibit in common with several other types of receptors — should not be confused with fatigue. That it is not simply a matter of fatigue of the olfactory mechanism is evident from the fact that, when some particular odor is no longer smelled, another odor is readily perceived. Some persons are unable to smell certain odors at all, though there is no general impairment of the olfactory sense. Hydrocyanic gas, for example, a powerful poison used in the extermination of vermin, has a strong odor of bitter almonds, but is quite inodorous to some persons.

SKIN SENSATIONS

The sensations which can be aroused by stimulating the skin are five in number, namely, *touch*, *pressure*, *pain*, *heat* and *cold*. Touch may be defined as the sensation elicited by lightly brushing the skin with a wisp of cotton wool, or by pressing a stiff hair vertically upon the skin. The sensitivity to touch of a particular cutaneous area is tested by using hairs of graded thicknesses (von Frey's hairs), and finding the one which arouses a sensation when applied with just sufficient pressure to bend it (see Fig. 269).

If a more rigid object, such as a match-stick, is pressed against the skin the sensation aroused is one of pressure. Pressure, though usually classed as a cutaneous sensation, and often confused with touch, is, in reality, due to the stimulation of receptors (Pacinian corpuscles) situated in the subcutaneous tissues. These sense organs are also found in other parts, e.g., in the surface membranes of bones (periosteum), beneath tendons and in the mesentery. If the rigid object is pressed still more firmly into the skin, or if the

skin is pricked with a sharp pointed instrument such as a pin, pain is experienced.

FIG. 269. A von Frey hair (or esthesiometer) for measuring the sensitivity of the skin to touch.

The sensations of touch, pressure, heat and cold are each dependent upon a special type of sense organ in which the nerve fiber terminates after losing its neurilemma and myelin sheath. The sensation of pain, on the other hand, is transmitted by fibers which terminate as bare axis cylinders. That is, the nerve fiber mediating pain loses its neurilemma and myelin sheath, but does not end in a structure of special design. The receptors of touch, pressure and temperature respond, each, to one type of stimulus, but the nerve endings giving rise to pain respond also to any other type of stimulation — mechanical, thermal, electrical or chemical — provided it is intense enough. Thus the sensation of pain is protective in function, serving to signal a threat of injury to the body. The several types of cutaneous receptor are shown in Fig. 270.

The different types of cutaneous sense organ are separated from one another by measurable distances. By applying the appropriate stimulus to points upon the skin, the positions of the receptors can be determined. The small skin

areas mapped out in this way are referred to as "spots."
Thus, when the sensitivity of the skin to touch is investigated
with a von Frey hair, the sensation is elicited only from certain points; these are called touch "spots," while those
which respond to heat or cold or to pain are called, respec-

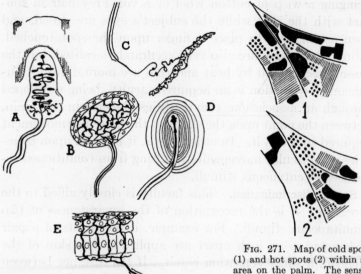

FIG. 270. Cutaneous receptors. A, touch
(Meissner's corpuscle); B, cold (Krause's end
bulb); C, warmth (Ruffini's end organ); D,
deep pressure (Pacinian corpuscle); E, pain
(bare nerve endings in cornea).

FIG. 271. Map of cold spots
(1) and hot spots (2) within an
area on the palm. The sensation in each case was most intense in the black areas, less
so in the lined areas, and mildest
in the dotted areas. In the
blank parts no definite sensation was aroused. (After
Goldscheider.)

tively, hot, cold and pain "spots" (see Fig. 271). The touch
spots are most numerous over the tips of the fingers and in
the mucous membrane of the tip of the tongue. In cutaneous regions covered with hair, i.e., almost the entire skin
surface except the palms of the hands and the soles of the
feet, the touch spots lie on the "windward" side of the hairs
(the hairs slant in one or other direction like grass bent by a
breeze). For this reason, light contact with the hair tips
causes a sensation of touch. The hair when moved acting as
a tiny lever transmits the movement to the skin at its base;

thus the touch end organ is stimulated. Pain fibers form a rich network in the skin; they also ramify within the hair sockets around the hair roots.

The localization of cutaneous sensations is effected with remarkable accuracy. The localization of touch is tested by bringing a wisp of cotton wool or a von Frey hair in contact with the skin while the subject's eyes are closed, and then asking him to place a finger upon the spot touched. Pain and pressure are also very accurately localized, but the sensations aroused by heat and cold are more diffuse. Cutaneous localization is an acquired faculty, being developed through an association, previously established in the brain, between the point upon the skin and the muscular movement required to touch it. In other words, it is based upon memories of muscular movements resulting from conditioned responses to cutaneous stimuli.

Spatial discrimination. This faculty is closely allied to the foregoing; it is the recognition of the separateness of two simultaneous stimuli. For example, if the points of a pair of compasses an inch apart are applied to the skin of the forearm, a single sensation is felt. If the distance between the compass points is increased to one and a half inches or more, and applied as before, two distinct sensations are experienced. Two-point discrimination is a faculty of essential importance. In acquiring information, through the sense of touch, of the size, texture and shape of various objects, it is indispensable. This faculty varies considerably in different regions, being most highly developed in the coverings of the more mobile parts of the body, i.e., parts such as the fingers, lips and tip of the tongue, which have received the most practice in investigating the immediate environment.

In Table 19 several different regions are compared with regard to the minimal distance at which two simultaneous stimuli must be separated in order to arouse a dual sensation.

TABLE 19

Different regions compared as to the minimal distance by which two stimuli must be separated in order to arouse a double sensation

Region	Minimal distance in millimeters
Tip of tongue	1.1
Palm side of finger tip	2.3×
Red part of lips	4.4
Tip of nose	6.6
Palm of hand	11.3
Heel	22.0
Back of hand	31.6
Forearm	39.6
Middle of back, upper arm and thigh×	67.0

CHAPTER XII

THE PHYSIOLOGY OF REPRODUCTION [1]

THE FEMALE REPRODUCTIVE ORGANS

The female sex glands are called the *ovaries,* since they produce the ova or eggs. The human ovaries are two bodies about the size and shape of shelled almonds, lying within the pelvis. The ova are developed from columnar epithelial cells — the *germinal epithelium* — covering the surface of the ovary. In the mature female, groups of epithelial cells migrate into the substance of the ovary and develop into a structure called the *Graafian follicle.* In the formation of a follicle, one cell of the group, which is destined to become an ovum, takes up a central position with the others arranged in a single row around it. This body — an immature Graafian follicle — penetrates deeper into the ovarian substance. As it does so, two more layers of encircling cells develop from the surrounding tissue. The outer one of these layers is fibrous in structure, and called the *theca externa;* the inner one, known as the *theca interna,* is more vascular and cellular in character. The original layer of cells surrounding the ovum multiplies to form a mass several layers thick, which soon becomes partially separated into an inner and an outer zone by the collection of fluid — the *liquor folliculi.* The inner zone in contact with the ovum is called the *discus proligerus* (Fig. 272), the outer zone the *membrana granulosa.* As the follicle matures, it becomes distended by the accumulation of fluid and moves outwards again to the surface of the ovary. From here it projects as a small globular cyst-like swelling, which ultimately ruptures and discharges the ovum. In women the discharge of an ovum, or *ovulation* as it is termed,

[1] The sex hormones are dealt with in Chapter VIII.

occurs at regular intervals of about 28 days (see p. 368). The
cavity of the ruptured follicle becomes filled with a clot of
blood which is soon replaced by a mass of cells filled with a
yellow fat-like material. These are derived from the cells
of the membrana granulosa and theca interna of the follicle.
The yellow mass filling the follicle is called the *corpus luteum*
(yellow body); it elaborates a hormone named *progestin*
(p. 370).

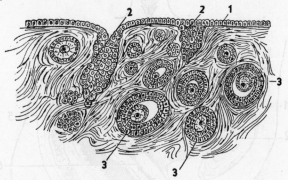

FIG. 272. Section of ovary. 1, germinal epithelium; 2, downgrowth of germinal epithelium; 3, Graafian follicles.

The ovum at the time of its discharge is not mature.
Maturation occurs during its progress along the *Fallopian
tube*. The Fallopian tubes (called *oviducts* in animals) are
two ducts, one on either side, possessing a trumpet-shaped
extremity with a fringed rim which lies in close relation to
the ovary (Fig. 273). This expanded upper end of the Fallopian tube receives the ovum, which is then conveyed along
the duct by the movement of the cilia in its mucosa, as well
as by peristaltic contractions of its wall. The Fallopian tubes
open below into the upper part of the *uterus* (womb). Conjugation of the ovum with the male germ cell (spermatazoon),
or *fertilization* of the ovum, as this event is usually termed, is
thought to take place in the Fallopian tube. In birds, the
oviducts transmit the fertilized ovum to the exterior, but
in the human body, and in the bodies of most other mammals, it is delivered into the uterus. The uterus is a hol-

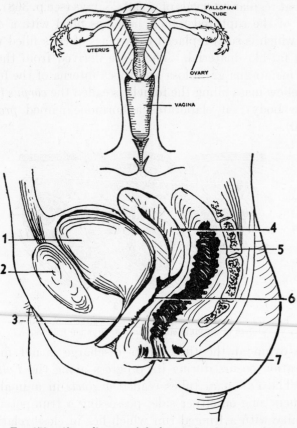

Fig. 273. *Above,* diagram of the human female organs of reproduction. *Below,* a section through the female pelvis to show the
relations of the reproductive organs in neighboring parts. 1, bladder (distended); 2, pubic bone; 3, urethra; 4, uterus; 5, rectum;
6, vagina; 7, sphincter ani. (Redrawn from Cunningham.)

low pear-shaped organ. Its walls are composed of smooth
muscle and lined with mucous membrane. Its smaller end,
directed downward, opens into the *vagina* — a narrow canal
lined with mucous membrane and communicating with the
exterior. The fertilized ovum, upon reaching the cavity of
the uterus, establishes vascular connections with the uterine
mucosa and develops into the embryo (p. 541). As the

dimensions of the embryo increase, corresponding changes take place in the uterus; its cavity enlarges and its walls thicken.

THE MALE REPRODUCTIVE ORGANS

The testes are the sex glands of the male and, therefore, correspond to the ovaries of the female. They are two ovoid bodies which, in such animals as fish, frogs, reptiles and birds, lie within the abdominal cavity. Even in the mammalian fetus they occupy this position. Shortly before, or soon after birth, the testes descend and, leaving the abdomen, become enclosed in a small cutaneous pouch, suspended from the pubic and perineal regions, and called the *scrotum*. In the human fetus the testes enter the scrotum two months before birth.

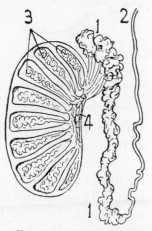

The interior of the testis is a compact mass of narrow and very tortuous tubules — the *convoluted seminiferous tubules*. Fibrous partitions divide the testicular substance into a great number of wedge-shaped lobes, each of which consists of from one to three convoluted tubules.

FIG. 274. Diagram showing the structure of the interior of the testis. 1, epididymis; 2, vas deferens; 3, convoluted tubules; 4, rete testis.

The tubules of neighboring lobes unite to form a series of larger straight ducts which, after a short course, unite in a plexiform manner. This plexus — known as the *rete* testis — leads again into a number of ducts, small and straight at first, but which, after a short course, become enlarged and tortuous (Fig. 274), and ultimately unite into a single large convoluted duct. This is called the *epididymis;* it is applied to the posterior aspect of the testis, its upper part or *head* being considerably larger than the lower part or *tail*. From the tail a straight tube — the *vas deferens* — ascends along the posterior border of the testis, to enter the abdomen, wherein it joins the duct of the seminal vesicle of the corresponding side (Fig. 275).

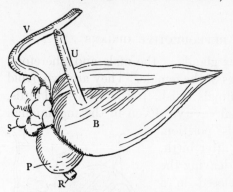

Fig. 275. Showing the relation of the vas deferens (V), seminal vesicles (S) and prostate (P) to the bladder (B). R, urethra; U, ureter. (Redrawn from Cunningham.)

The seminal vesicles are two coiled tubes with sacculated walls, situated between the lower part of the bladder and the rectum. The *ejaculatory ducts* are short tubes formed one on each side by the union of the duct of the seminal vesicle with the vas deferens; they open into the urethra (the canal of the penis) near the outlet from the bladder.

The seminiferous tubules are lined by several layers of cells. Those of the outermost layer, i.e., the layer lying upon the basement membrane, are of two types, (a) cuboidal cells, supported by (b) columnar cells. The latter, which are known as the *cells of Sertoli*, extend inwards (i.e., toward the lumen of the tubule) through the other layers. The former, called the *spermatogenic cells*, give rise through a series of divisions to the male germ cells or *spermatozoa*.

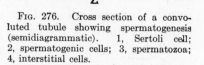

Fig. 276. Cross section of a convoluted tubule showing spermatogenesis (semidiagrammatic). 1, Sertoli cell; 2, spermatogenic cells; 3, spermatozoa; 4, interstitial cells.

The inner cell layers forming the wall of the tubule consist of spermatogenic cells showing various stages in the maturation process, those most advanced in development lying nearer the lumen of the tubule. The cells, as they mature into spermatozoa, become detached from the tubule wall (Fig. 276). The spermatozoon is about 0.1 mm. long; it has an oval flattened head and a long tail-like process (Fig. 277) by which it propels itself. The head is the essential part of the cell, consisting of a large nucleus surrounded by a narrow rim of protoplasm. The connective tissue lying between the convoluted tubules contains scattered cells with yellow granules in their cytoplasm. These are called *interstitial cells* or the *cells of Leydig*. They are believed to furnish the male hormone (testosterone, p. 371).

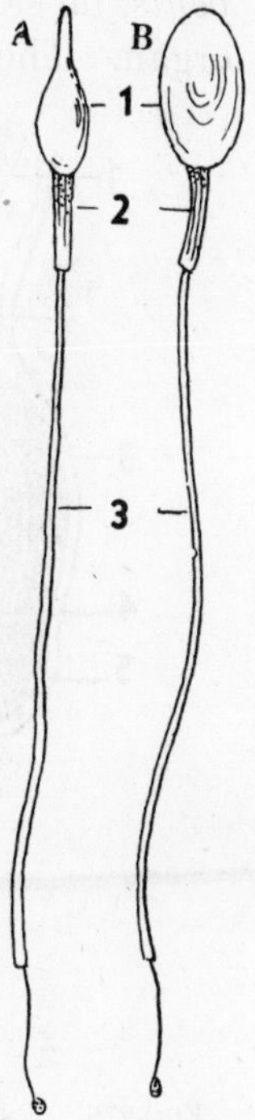

The spermatozoa are conveyed from the convoluted seminiferous tubules along the complex system of canals, just described, to the epididymis. The spermatozoa show no spontaneous movements in the convoluted tubules, but become actively motile in the epididymis. During coitus peristaltic contraction of the walls of the epididymis and vas deferens force the suspension of germ cells along the ejaculatory ducts into the urethra. The seminal vesicles contract at the same time and expel a thick glary fluid. The *semen*, as the material emitted from the ejaculatory ducts is called, is propelled along the urethra by rhythmical contractions of the urethral muscles.

FIG. 277. Human spermatozoa. A, in profile; B, viewed on the flat. 1, head; 2, middle piece; 3, tail. (Redrawn from Retzius.)

The spermatozoa, deposited in the upper part of the vagina during coitus, propel themselves upwards by lashing movements of their tails at the rate of about six inches per hour and, passing through the uterus, enter the Fallopian tube. It is probable that contractions of the uterus during coitus may draw the semen into the uterine cavity.

The penis, the copulatory organ of the male, is composed of *erectile* tissue arranged as three longitudinal cylinders bound together by fibrous tissue, and covered with skin. Two of the cylindrical masses, called the *corpora cavernosa penis*, lie side by side on the upper or anterior aspect of the organ. The third, called the *corpus cavernosum urethrae*, lies

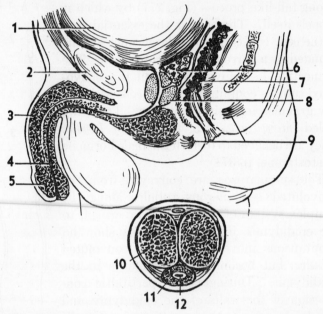

FIG. 278. *Upper drawing*, a section through the lower part of the male pelvis to show the relationship of the reproductive organs. 1, bladder (artificially distended); 2, pubic bone; 3, corpus cavernosum penis; 4, urethra; 5, glans penis; 6, seminal vesicle; 7, rectum; 8, prostate; 9, external sphincter ani. *Below*, a cross section through the terminal part of the penis. 10, corpus cavernosum penis; 11, corpus cavernosum urethrae; 12, urethral canal. (After Cunningham, redrawn and modified.)

beneath the other two and is canalized by the urethra. The urinary bladder is evacuated through the urethra which also transmits the semen during coitus. The extremity of the corpus cavernosum urethrae is expanded into a pyramidal structure called the *glans penis*, which is moulded over the ends of the corpora cavernosa penis (Fig. 278).

Erectile tissue possesses a sponge-like structure, showing

a meshwork of wide blood spaces (cavernous spaces). These are fed by capillaries and arterioles and drained by small veins. Smooth muscle fibers run in the walls of the blood spaces and surround their venous outlets. To this construction of erectile tissue is due its peculiar property, namely, the ability to alter in volume and consistency. Erection of the penis is brought about in the following way. The arterioles feeding the blood spaces dilate, and the muscle fibers in the walls of the latter relax. The muscle guarding the venous outlets contracts, thus impeding the outflow of blood. The spaces are thus expanded, and an increased volume of blood is driven through them at a relatively high pressure. The organ, thus becoming turgid with blood, is rendered tense, hard and erect.

The nerve fibers governing this mechanism are derived from the pelvic (parasympathetic) nerves. The sympathetic sends fibers which exert the reverse effect (contraction of the smooth muscle of the arterioles and in the walls of the blood spaces, accompanied by relaxation of that surrounding the venous outlets) with consequent relaxation of the penis.

The erectile organ of the female corresponding to the penis is called the *clitoris*. It is situated above and just outside the entrance to the vagina. Erectile tissue is also present beneath the mucosa of the vagina.

The prostate is a body about the size of a chestnut and somewhat conical in shape. Its base is directed upwards and lies in contact with the lowest part of the bladder. It embraces the first one and a half inches of the urethra. The ejaculatory ducts pierce its upper and posterior part (see Fig. 278). The prostate is composed of muscular and glandular tissues. It secretes a thin fluid into the urethra. Prostatic enlargement, with consequent interference with the passage of urine, not uncommonly occurs in men past middle age.

Maturation of the sex cells or gametes (sperm and egg cells). The spermatogenic cells lining the seminiferous tubules undergo maturation as follows. First the chromatin within the nucleus loses its net-like arrangement and becomes spun into a long twisted thread, which then breaks up into small sections (the number varying with the species) called *chromosomes* (see Fig. 279, p. 537). Soon fine lines are seen radiating from the centrioles into the surrounding cytoplasm. The star-like bodies thus formed soon separate from one another, and move one to either side of the nucleus. Each chromosome next divides lengthwise into two halves while the rays from each star-body are seen to stretch toward them, the whole nuclear structure, being now referred to as the *spindle*. As the radiating strands of the spindle shorten, the chromosome halves are drawn apart and collect together at opposite sides of the cell to form two separate nuclei. Each half chromosome develops into a complete chromosome, so, obviously, each new nucleus must have the same number of chromosomes as the original one. The protoplasm between the two nuclei then divides to form two separate *daughter cells*. These redivide, and their daughter cells divide in turn. The divisions are repeated through several cell-generations. The above description of cell division is termed *mitosis* and is typical of the division of body cells in general. From now on, the development of the sperm cells takes a characteristic course. For a time the cells of the last division cease to multiply, but they enter a growth period and form large cells called *spermatocytes*. Among these the division process recommences, but the chromatin follows a different course from that pursued in the previous divisions. The chromatin breaks into the same number of sections (chromosomes) as before, but these arrange themselves in pairs, and *do not divide lengthwise*. A spindle forms, the singles of the pairs are drawn apart, and two daughter cells are formed which are converted directly into mature spermatozoa. It is clear that each of these must have just half the number of chromosomes found in the original germ cell. This is spoken of as *reduction division*. The mature eggs are formed after a similar fashion from the germ cells of the female reproductive organ. Multiplication by mitosis occurs for a series of cell-generations, maturation being accompanied by reduction division (see Fig. 279). In the case of the egg, however, some of the cells resulting from the final divisions are small in size and do not develop fully, but are discarded.

Conjugation of the egg and sperm cells. The unfertilized ovum in some unknown way exerts an attractive force upon the spermatozoon which, by means of the lashing movements of its tail, reaches the female gamete. The head of the sperm penetrates the ovum. A change in the boundary wall of the ovum then occurs, which as a rule serves to prevent the entrance of other spermatozoa. The tail of the latter soon disappears, leaving the head within the cytoplasm of the egg. The result is the formation of a single cell, which has a power for growth not possessed by either ovum or spermatozoon alone. The single cell almost at once commences to divide and redivide. In this way are formed great numbers of cells (see *segmentation*, p. 540), which do not separate from one another but are held together. Gradually, as they multiply and develop in various directions, tissues and organs of different structure and functions appear, until finally a new and complete individual is created almost identical with others of its species. Whether plant or worm, fish, bird or man, nearly all forms of life other than the very primitive have developed from a single cell resulting from the union of sperm and egg.

The conjugation of the male and female gametes (ovum and spermatozoon) is termed the *fertilization or impregnation of the ovum*. The cell resulting from the union is then spoken of as the *fertilized ovum, oosperm or zygote*.

Changes in the nuclei of the conjoined cells. Almost im-

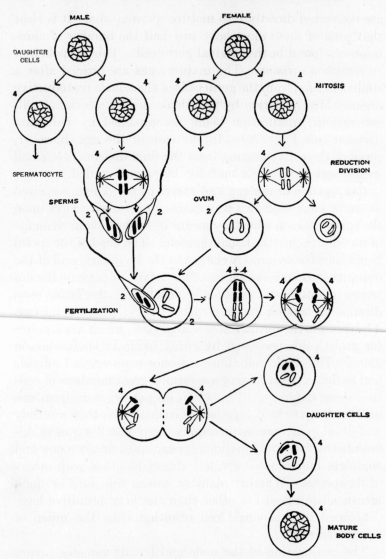

FIG. 279.   The maturation of the germ cells and the fertilization of the ovum.
The numbers refer to the chromosomes.

mediately after fertilization both nuclei commence to enlarge, move toward each other, come together, and finally fuse near the center of the ovum. Fusion is followed by the complicated changes already described as characteristic of mitosis. The chromatin of each nucleus is not broken up into sections at random or in any haphazard fashion, but is always divided into precisely the same number of pieces (chromosomes) as are found in the sperms and ova in the final stage of their maturation. Furthermore, the number of chromosomes in each nucleus, as in each original gamete nucleus, is always the same for a given species and, as a result of the reduction division already described, is precisely half the number of those in the body cells and in the original germ cells of the reproductive organs (see Fig. 279). *The fused nucleus must therefore contain an equal number of maternal and paternal chromosomes and the total number must be equal to that in each body cell of the species.*[1] By the division lengthwise of each chromosome into equal halves the number is straightway doubled. The halves lie in pairs near the center of the ovum and, as in ordinary mitosis, star-bodies appear on either side, form a spindle, and soon draw them apart. The protoplasm separates between and two daughter cells are formed. Each of these has therefore received maternal and paternal chromosomes, and the number is precisely the same as in a body cell but double the number in each original gamete. It is clear then that, though each gamete contains just half the number of chromosomes characteristic of the body cells of the species, the latter number is restored when fertilization of the ovum occurs. This is an important and fundamental fact in the mechanism of reproduction.

[1] In some insects, such as the fruit-fly, the number of chromosomes in the body cells is 8, which are reduced to 4 in the sex cells. In certain species of worms there are 12 in the body cells and 6 in the ova and sperms. The mouse, the trout and the lily have 24 in their body cells and 12 in their sex cells. Other forms of animals and plants have each a characteristic number, which may be as low as 4 or as high as 168. There are 24 chromosomes in the gametes of the human race and 48 in the body cells.

Chromatin, of which the chromosomes are composed, is believed to be the essential procreative substance. Through it hereditary characters are transmitted, and upon its existence the perpetuation of the species depends. Yet it has been stated that the total quantity of chromatin contained in all the ova and sperms from which have been created the two billion-odd persons inhabiting the globe could have been no greater in size than a match head.

Parthenogenesis. In some animal forms, especially certain insects, the females, though themselves produced from a fertilized egg, may for some generations lay eggs which do not become fertilized. These spermless eggs, nevertheless, develop into the young of the species. In other words, the young of these generations have a mother but no father. To this mode of reproduction *parthenogenesis*, a term derived from the Greek word *parthenos*, a virgin, is applied. The drones of the honey-bee, for instance, are developed from unfertilized eggs of the Queen. The female workers of the hive arise from fertilized eggs, which have been laid about the same time as the unfertilized. A frog's egg, though under ordinary circumstances it must receive a spermatozoon before segmentation will ensue, may be induced to develop into a tadpole by artificial means. Pricking the wall of the ovum with a needle will start segmentation, which ultimately results in the production of a fatherless frog.

Segmentation of the fertilized ovum and the development of the embryo. Each daughter cell divides into two and each of the four cells which result likewise divides. In this way groups of 2, 4, 8, 16, 32, 64, etc., are produced successively. So, by a process of division and redivision, large masses of cells are formed, which ultimately produce a new individual. This process whereby the fertilized ovum undergoes repeated divisions is called *segmentation* or *cleavage*. With each cell division the chromatin breaks up into chromosomes; as described above for mitosis, each chromosome splits into half, and an equal number of halves go to each new nucleus. All the cells resulting from the long series of divisions which occur in the development of the offspring must therefore contain the same number of chromosomes as did the original fused nucleus of the fertilized ovum, and each receives chromatin material from both parents.

In the earlier stages of embryonic development of the various mammalian species, cell-multiplication follows a common pattern. At first a rounded, mulberry mass of cells is formed, called the *morula* (L. diminutive of *morus*, a mulberry). The morula soon differentiates into an outer and an

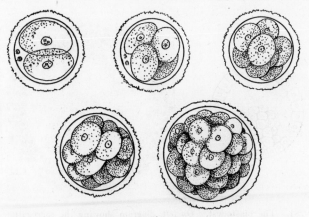

Fig. 280. First stages of segmentation of a mammalian ovum and the formation of the morula (semidiagrammatic). (Redrawn and modified from Allen Thomson.)

inner group of cells (Figs. 280 and 281). The outer group of cells forms a number of fringe-like processes which give the ovum a shaggy appearance. Later, as this outer layer develops it is called the *chorion;* the processes enlarge and become branched and are now known as the *chorionic villi*. The more centrally situated group of cells becomes arranged to form the walls of two sacs — the *amnion* and the *yolk sac* (Pl. 15 A). The cells in the region where the walls of these sacs are in contact multiply to form a plaque-like elevation called the *embryonic shield*, from which the body of the embryo is developed. The ovum at this stage is referred to as the *blastocyst*, and is still in the Fallopian tube. Between the 7th and 8th days after fertilization, it enters the uterine cavity. Owing to the destructive action which the chorionic villi exert upon the uterine mucosa, the ovum is able to embed itself and, like a parasite, derive nourishment from the maternal tissue. The uterine mucosa, in turn, shows increased activity; multiplication of its surface epithelium, enlargement of its glands and dilatation of its vessels result. A specialized type of tissue is thus produced, called the *decidua* because it is shed after the birth of the offspring

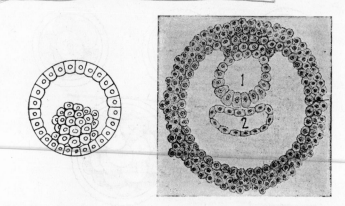

FIG. 281. The blastocyst. *On left,* diagram showing the segregation of cells of the morula into an outer and an inner group. (After Simon.) *On right,* formation of amnion (1) and yolk sac (2). (After Bryce.)

(Pl. 15 B). The changes in the uterine mucosa commence before the ovum reaches the uterus, and even though fertilization does not occur (see p. 367).

The walls of the amnion gradually expand and come into contact with the inner surface of the chorion. Thus a double-layered sac filled with fluid is formed, which comes in time completely to enclose the embryo. The yolk sac shrinks, its contents having been used for the nourishment of the embryo in the earlier stages of its growth (Fig. 282). The chorionic villi disappear, except where the ovum has become attached to the uterine wall. In this situation they increase in size and form numerous branches which become

surrounded by masses of decidual tissue. Thus the maternal
and decidual tissues become interlocked.

When the blood-vascular system develops vessels penetrate the chorionic villi, which project into blood spaces
formed in the decidual tissue. The structure formed by the

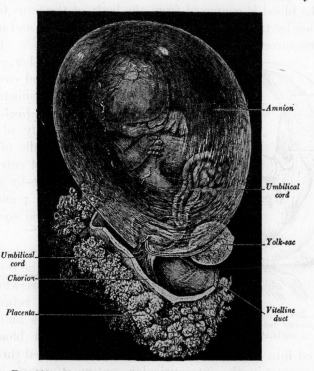

FIG. 282. Showing the fetus at age of about eight weeks enclosed in the amnion, magnified a little over 2 diameters. (After
Thomson from Gray's Anatomy.)

union of the maternal and chorionic tissues is called the
placenta. The latter, when fully developed, is a disc-like
mass which occupies a third or so of the interior of the uterine
wall (Fig. 283). In the placenta the blood vessels of mother
and embryo (or *fetus*, as the developing organism is soon
called) are brought into contact. Yet the two bloods do not
mix, the thin walls of the chorionic vessels being interposed.

Oxygen, food, materials, etc., are transferred from the mother to the fetus, and waste materials from embryo to mother across the walls of the chorionic vessels. The placenta thus serves as a means whereby the respiratory, nutritional and excretory functions of the fetus are carried out.

The blood is conveyed from the body of the fetus to the chorion by two vessels — the *umbilical arteries* — and in the reverse direction, by the *umbilical vein* (see Pl. 15 C). These

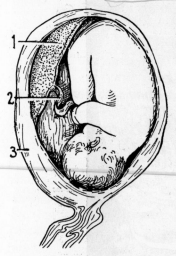

three vessels run together, coiled round one another and covered by a soft jelly-like substance, to constitute the *umbilical cord*. This enters the body of the fetus about the middle of the abdomen; its point of entrance is marked in after life by a circular, depressed and puckered area of skin called the *navel* or *umbilicus*.

The oxygenated blood of the umbilical vein joins the *inferior vena cava* of the fetus wherein it mixes with blood returning from the lower limbs and abdomen. This mixed blood is

Fig. 283. Usual position of the fetus shortly before birth. 1, placenta; 2, umbilical cord; 3, uterus.

poured into the right auricle, whence it is directed through an opening in the interauricular septum (*foramen ovale*) to the left side of the heart. From the left ventricle it is discharged into the aorta, a part being distributed to the fetal tissues; the remainder is returned through the umbilical arteries to the placenta.

The blood returned from the upper part of the body (head and neck, upper limbs and thoracic walls) enters the right auricle through the *superior vena cava*. It is directed into the right ventricle (without mixing, apparently, with the stream of blood directed from the inferior vena cava through the foramen ovale). It is then pumped into the pulmonary artery, but only a small fraction passes through the lungs — a quantity sufficient only for the nourishment of the pulmonary tissue. The greater part of the blood discharged into the pulmonary artery is transferred to the aorta by a vessel called the *ductus arteriosus*. It is evident then, that the great bulk of the blood received by the right side of the fetal heart is "shunted" to the left side through the short cuts provided by the foramen ovale and ductus arteriosus.

With the first few respirations the lungs of the newborn child are expanded, and the course of the circulation becomes altered to meet the requirements of an organism leading an independent existence. The foramen ovale closes and the lumen of the ductus arteriosus becomes obliterated. All the blood from the right side of the heart is, therefore, directed through the pulmonary circuit. The umbilical vessels shrink and become converted into solid cords.

Pregnancy and parturition. Pregnancy is the term used to designate the period in the reproductive cycle occupied by the development of the fetus, that is, from the fertilization of the ovum (conception) to the birth of the young (parturition). In the human race pregnancy has a duration of about 280 days, or from nine to nine and a half months. From about the middle of pregnancy onwards, movements of the fetus occur of which the mother is aware, and which are referred to as *quickening*. Sucking and spasmodic movements of the chest resembling those of respiration, have been observed in the fetuses of animals. The unborn child lies within the amniotic sac, submerged in a fairly large quantity of fluid which serves to protect it from sudden jars or injuries which it might otherwise receive from the outside world. The amniotic sac fills the uterus and is considerably larger than the fetus itself, which is thus permitted a certain freedom of movement. The umbilical cord is sufficiently long not to prevent the fetus from changing its position.

Toward the latter part of pregnancy, the unborn child

usually takes up a position with the head directed downwards, and fitted into the cavity of the pelvis (Fig. 283). The birth of the child is brought about by strong contractions of the muscular walls of the uterus. The uterine contractions, weak at first and of short duration, become stronger and more prolonged in an hour or two. Their effects are moulding of the infant's head and gradual dilatation of the outlet from the uterus, the vagina at the same time becoming softer and more distensible. Later, the membranous sac enclosing the child ruptures, and a part of the amnionic fluid escapes. When the canal from the uterus to the exterior has enlarged sufficiently to allow the passage of the baby's head, the latter is expelled by powerful contractions of the uterus, accompanied usually by contractions of the abdominal muscles. The rest of the child's body follows almost immediately.

For a time the newborn babe still remains attached to the interior of the uterus through the umbilical cord and placenta. The physician ties the cord with tape close to the child's body and divides it on the mother's side of the tape. Not until 15 or 30 minutes later is the placenta, and the attached sac composed of the chorionic and amniotic membranes, expelled. The placenta and membranes are commonly referred to as the *after-birth*. *Labor* or *parturition* is the term used to designate the series of events bringing about the emptying of the uterus and the termination of pregnancy.

INDEX

547

Gravity, effect of on circulation, 105–107
Gray matter, of cerebellum, 458, 459
of cerebrum, 438
of spinal cord, 432
Gray rami communicantes, 463
Gristle (or cartilage), 13
Growth, 2, 289, 362 (see also Giantism)
amino acids essential for, 293, 294
effect of pituitary on, 354
effect of thymus extract on, 378
effect of vitamin B₁ on, 314
retarded (see Dwarfs)
Growth hormone of pituitary (see Hormone)
Guanine, 295
Gullet, 221
Gum acacia, in blood transfusion, 42
Gyri of cerebral cortex, 440

Hair cells (see Cell)
Haldane, J. S., 192
Hales, Rev. Stephen, 91
Harvey, William, 76
Hassall's corpuscles (see Corpuscle)
Haversian canals, 16
Headache, due to constipation, 275
Hearing, physiology of, 503
resonance theory of, 506, 507
resonance-volley theory of, 509
telephone theory of, 507, 508
thresholds of, 509
volley theory of, 508
Heart, action of, 122 et seq.
action of atropine and other drugs on, 144
of calcium and potassium on, 117
of CO₂ on, 146
of vagus on, 140
anatomy of, 72–75
athletics and, 148, 414
blood supply of, 158
compensatory pause of (see extrasystoles of)
delayed conduction in, 136
denervated, 344, 346, 347
dilatation of, 414
disease of (see Heart disease)
electrical changes in, 129–131
extrasystoles of, 114, 116, 136, 137
fetal, 544
hypertrophy of, 129, 148, 414
inhibition of, 141
junctional tissues of (see specialized tissues of)
movements of, 135

murmurs in, 128
muscle of (see Cardiac muscle)
nerves of, 139 et seq., 465
output of, 88, 89
pacemaker of, 119, 120
pain in, 143
perfusion of, 115, 116
rate of (see Heart rate)
reflex control of, 153–155
regulation of, 138 et seq.
rhythmicity of, 114
specialized tissues of, 119 et seq.
stroke volume of, 88
vagal "escape" of, 141
valves of, 72, 126, 127
work of, 87
Heart beat, 118
disorders of, 135 et seq.
Heart block, 122, 135, 136
Heart disease, athletes and, 199
dyspnea in, 199
valvular, 128
Heart murmurs, 128
Heart rate, 138, 139, 140
Heart sounds, 128
Heart valves, 72, 126, 127
Heat, latent, 306
loss from body, 307
production, 305, 410
Heat balance, 305
Heat rigor, 405
Helmholtz, resonance theory of, 506, 507
Hematin, 29
Hematinic principle, 35
Hematocrit, 19, 26
Heme, 29
Hemeralopia, 312 (see Night blindness)
Hemianopia, 481
Hemiplegia, 445
Hemispheres, cerebral, 438
cerebellar, 457, 458
Hemoconia, 32
Hemodynamics, 82 et seq.
Hemoglobin, 22, 29, 30
affinity of for carbon monoxide, 201
bile pigment from, 261
concentration of, 30
iron in, 29
oxygen capacity of, 30
oxygen dissociation curve of, 188, 189, 190
oxygenated, 29, 188
reduced, 30, 188
cause of cyanosis, 202
respiratory function of, 187, 190
Hemolysins, 43